THE CHEMISTRY OF FREE RADICALS

THE CHEMISTRY OF FREE RADICALS

BY

W. A. WATERS
FELLOW OF BALLIOL COLLEGE, OXFORD

SECOND EDITION

OXFORD
AT THE CLARENDON PRESS

Oxford University Press, Amen House, London E.C. 4
GLASGOW NEW YORK TORONTO MELBOURNE WELLINGTON
BOMBAY CALCUTTA MADRAS CAPE TOWN
Geoffrey Cumberlege, Publisher to the University

FIRST EDITION 1946
SECOND EDITION 1948
Reprinted lithographically in Great Britain
at the UNIVERSITY PRESS, OXFORD, 1950
from sheets of the second edition

PREFACE

THE author's attempts, in an earlier book on *Physical Aspects of Organic Chemistry*,† to develop rational explanations of the mechanisms of organic reactions, led him to the conclusion that the original ionic activation theories of Lapworth, Robinson, and Ingold, though cogent for the vast majority of reactions in solution, were inapplicable to a few decomposition processes, which had many features akin to those of gas-phase reactions in which free neutral atoms and active neutral radicals had been shown to participate. At about this time (1934) Dr. D. H. Hey, in Manchester, suggested tentatively that one of these 'abnormal' liquid-phase reactions—the decomposition of aromatic diazo-compounds in non-aqueous solvents—involved the production of free neutral aryl radicals of short life. Correspondence on this subject led to experimental collaboration, which substantiated this hypothesis, and to the publication, in 1937, of a joint review‡ which indicated that transient free neutral radicals might be involved in quite a number of liquid-phase reactions.

Since a more comprehensive consideration of this novel subject was obviously desirable the author, in 1938, planned the present volume, which describes experimental evidence showing that free neutral atoms of elements such as hydrogen, chlorine, and oxygen can exist at normal temperatures, and that active free organic radicals, with atomic properties, can participate in both gas-phase and liquid-phase reactions.

The completion of the book has been delayed by the much more important duties of the war years, during which time, however, the 'New Organic Chemistry' of free radicals has developed at an astonishing rate, and has proved to be of value in elucidating the mechanisms of several industrially important processes, such as polymerizations and autoxidations. In addition it has given chemists a much clearer picture of at least one general mechanism of catalysis. In order to put the theoretical basis of this new chemistry of free radicals into due prominence, it has, therefore, been necessary to amend the scope of the original book, so as to make it a general survey of relevant reactions rather than a detailed monograph dealing with but a few of them, but it is hoped that this change will make the book a volume of more lasting value.

Professor D. H. Hey, who has been interested in the work throughout, has very kindly assisted in reading the proofs. For constructive and

† Routledge, London, 1935.

‡ *Chemical Reviews*, 1937. **21**, 169–208.

helpful criticism of several of the more physico-chemical sections, the author is deeply indebted to his present colleague, Mr. R. P. Bell. Valuable help in the revision of the chapter on Photochemical Decomposition (Chapter VI) has been given by Mr. E. J. Bowen, whilst Professor A. R. Todd has made many helpful suggestions which have been incorporated into the final chapter (Chapter XII) dealing with Biochemical Processes. Other portions of the book have been read by Professors H. W. Melville and M. G. Evans. To all these friends and colleagues the author expresses his thanks.

Thanks are also due to the staff of the Clarendon Press, who have been helpful on all occasions in speeding publication in these difficult times.

W. A. W.

OXFORD, 1946

CONTENTS

I. THE DISCOVERY OF FREE RADICALS . . . 1–19

Early Theories : Triphenylmethyl : Structure of Free Radicals : Discovery of Atomic Hydrogen : Discovery of Free Alkyl Radicals : Characterization of Free Alkyl Radicals : General Methods of Preparation : Characteristics of Reactions involving Free Radicals.

II. PHYSICAL PROPERTIES OF FREE RADICALS 20–34

Theoretical : Atomic Magnetism : Magnetic Susceptibility—Paramagnetism : Magnetic Interconversion of *Ortho-* and *Para*-Hydrogen.

III. TRIPHENYLMETHYL AND ITS ANALOGUES . . . 35–61

Dissociation of Hexaphenylethane : Mesomerism of the Ions of Triphenylmethyl : The Neutral Ph_3C Radical : Preparation of Compounds of the Triarylmethyl Series : Reactions of Free Triarylmethyl Radicals : Molecular Dissociation and the Stability of Radicals—Measurements and Theories : Bi-radicals.

IV. FREE RADICALS CONTAINING ELEMENTS OTHER THAN CARBON 62–79

Nitrogen Compounds—Oxides of Nitrogen—Diphenyl Nitrogen—Aminium Salts—Hydrazyl radicals—Diphenyl Nitric Oxide : Oxygen and Sulphur Compounds : Semi-quinones : Organo-metallic Radicals.

V. FREE ATOMS AND THEIR GAS REACTIONS . . . 80–105

Electrical Dissociation and Spectral Analysis : Atomic Hydrogen and its Reactions : Atomic Oxygen : Atomic Chlorine : Reactions of Atomic Sodium.

VI. PHOTOCHEMICAL DECOMPOSITIONS 106–126

General Theory : Photo-sensitization : Chemical Nature of Photochemical Decomposition : Photolysis of Inorganic Molecules—Halogens, Water and other Hydrides, Oxides : Photolysis of Organic Molecules—Alkyl Halides, Aldehydes and Ketones, Carboxylic Acids, Alcohols, Amines, Organo-metallic Compounds.

VII. REACTIONS OF FREE ALKYL RADICALS . . . 127–145

Average Life of Free Methyl : Gas Reactions of Free Alkyl Radicals : Catalysis and Anti-catalysis of Thermal Decomposition : Reactions involving Free Alkyls in Solution—Decompositions of Lead Tetra-ethyl, Diacyl Peroxides, Lead Tetra-acetate, the Kolbe Reaction, Electrolysis of Organo-metallic Compounds.

VIII. FREE ARYL RADICALS AND THEIR REACTIONS IN SOLUTION . 146–173

Decompositions of Azo and Diazo-compounds—Aryl-azo-triarylmethanes—Diazo-acetates, Diazo-hydroxides, Diazo-cyanides, Diazonium Chlorides : the Sandmeyer Reaction : Decompositions of Diaroyl Peroxides : Decompositions of Organo-metallic Compounds : Other Thermal Decompositions : Electrolyses of Grignard Reagents.

IX. REACTIONS CATALYSED BY FREE RADICALS . . 174–200

Reactions initiated by Halogen Atoms—Halogen Substitution and Addition : Peroxide Catalysed Reactions—Addition of Hydrogen Bromide to Olefines—Reactions of Sulphuryl Chloride—Additions of Bisulphites and of Thiols to Olefines—Carboxylation with Oxalyl Chloride—The Cannizzaro Reaction : Chain Polymerization of Olefines—Perspex and Analogues—Emulsion Polymerization—Structural Features.

X. Reactions involving Metals . 201–225

The Chemical Character of Metals : Reactions of Alkali Metals—Metallic Ketyls—the Wurtz-Fittig and Ullmann Reactions—Abnormal Reactions of Grignard Reagents : Surface Catalysis by Metals—Catalytic Hydrogenation : Electrode Reactions—Over-voltage—Cathodic Reduction.

XI. Some Oxidation Mechanisms 226–258

Theoretical Introduction : Oxidations with Lead Tetra-acetate : Autoxidation—Sulphites—Aldehydes—Olefines : Reactions of Hydrogen Peroxide and the Per-acids—Fenton's Reagent : Positive Halogen Compounds : Other Oxidizing Agents.

XII. Some Possible Mechanisms for Biochemical Processes . 259–284

Nature of Biological Oxidation : Role of Oxygen in Metabolism : Wieland's Dehydrogenation Theory : Co-enzymes : Free Radical Theories of Enzyme Action—Criticisms--Alternative Considerations : Reaction Promoters in Enzymes : Inhibition of Enzyme Action.

Index of Names 285–289

Index 290–295

I

THE DISCOVERY OF FREE RADICALS

Early Theories

CHEMISTRY is very largely concerned with the way in which the chemical elements combine together to form compounds, and, since the days of Lavoisier, the term *radical* has been used to denote a component from which a chemical compound may be built up.

Lavoisier recognized that the component radicals of inorganic compounds were very frequently the chemical elements, whilst in organic substances there existed *compound radicals* or *groups of atoms which together behave as a single atom.* This distinction between inorganic and organic substances was realized more clearly by Berzelius, who, in 1817, concluded that 'in inorganic nature all oxidized bodies contain a simple radical, while all organic substances are oxides of compound radicals'. Organic chemistry was therefore regarded as the chemistry of the compound radicals.

The earliest of these compound radicals to be recognized were the ammonium radical, investigated in 1808 both by Davy and by Berzelius, and the cyanogen radical, characterized by Gay Lussac in 1815. The quasi-metallic nature of the ammonium radical was demonstrated by Berzelius and Pontin† who prepared 'ammonium amalgam' by electrolysing an ammonium salt solution using a mercury cathode, whilst the same product was obtained by Davy‡ by treating an ammonium salt with sodium or potassium amalgam. Gay Lussac showed conclusively that the cyanogen radical, CN, behaved like a halogen element, and, by heating mercuric cyanide, prepared cyanogen gas, $(CN)_2$.§ Not realizing that even the halogen elements formed gaseous diatomic molecules, e.g. Cl_2, he regarded cyanogen gas as a 'free' compound radical.

As knowledge of organic chemistry developed during the first half of the nineteenth century, several of these compound radicals were characterized, and many of them were thought to have been prepared by methods similar to those applicable for the isolation of metals from their compounds. Thus Bunsen in 1842‖ completed a study of the cacodyl radical, $\cdot As(CH_3)_2$, by preparing cacodyl itself by treating cacodyl chloride with metallic zinc, and in 1849 Frankland¶ claimed to

† Gilbert's *Annalen*, 1810, **6**, 247.
‡ *Works*, v. 122.
§ *Ann. de Chimie*, 1815, **95**, 172.
‖ Liebig's *Ann. Chem. Pharm.* 1842, **42**, 27.
¶ *Annalen*, 1849, **71**, 171; 1850, **74**, 41.

have prepared the ethyl radical by heating ethyl iodide with zinc in a sealed glass tube.

In 1854 Wurtz† showed that though sodium reacted with methyl iodide to give a gas of the empirical composition of methyl (CH_3) and with ethyl iodide to give a gas of the empirical composition of ethyl (C_2H_5), yet when a mixture of these two iodides was used there was also formed a product of composition $CH_3+C_2H_5 = C_3H_8$, which was regarded as a 'mixed' radical. Though this discovery supported the alternative view, first propounded by Gerhardt and Laurent—that the 'methyl' of Frankland was in reality a radical twin, $CH_3—CH_3$, and identical with the hydride of ethyl, $C_2H_5—H$,—it was not until 1863 that it was demonstrated conclusively by Schorlemmer‡ that the radical twin of methyl and the hydride of ethyl were identical and not isomeric.

Before that date, however, Cannizzaro had explained the method of determining molecular weights by measuring vapour density, and it had been realized that elements such as hydrogen, oxygen, and chlorine did not exist as free atoms but as the diatomic molecules H_2, O_2, and Cl_2. The paraffin hydrocarbons were recognized as being substances of the hydrogen type and hence it was concluded that, when liberated from combination with other elements, e.g. by the action of a metal, the compound radical would *immediately* unite to form a double molecule: $2CH_3 \rightarrow C_2H_6$. Similarly, since attempts to prepare the methylene radical invariably resulted in the formation of ethylene, $CH_2{=}CH_2$, it was considered that divalent carbon compounds, with the sole exception of carbon monoxide, were incapable of separate existence.

With the development of the *theory of types*, and thence of Kekulé's doctrine of the quadrivalency of carbon, structural organic chemistry progressed so successfully during the second half of the nineteenth century that the idea of the *constant* valency of carbon rapidly became an accepted dogma. So fruitful were the investigations of practical organic chemists during this period that the theoretical possibility of isolating any compound radical in its 'atomic' form did not receive any experimental study. Nevertheless, by using the same decisive vapour-density method of Cannizzaro, which had shown that gases such as hydrogen and oxygen possessed diatomic molecules, it was proved without doubt that free atoms could exist as such, for metallic elements such as sodium, zinc, and mercury formed monatomic vapours. Moreover Victor Meyer,§ by making vapour-density measurements at high tem-

† *Compt. rend.* 1854, **40,** 1285.
‡ *J.* 1863, **16,** 425; 1864, **17,** 262.
§ *Ber.* 1880, **13,** 394.

peratures, proved that the diatomic molecule of iodine could dissociate reversibly into free iodine atoms: $I_2 \rightleftharpoons 2\,I$.

In reality, during the latter half of the nineteenth century the organic chemists' concept of valency was little more than a method of interpretation of molecular geometry. Van 't Hoff, and the majority of organic chemists of his time, postulated that the carbon atom had four definite valency bonds, localized in the directions of the four corners of a tetrahedron, and that all *had* to be utilized in chemical combination. Though Baeyer had been quite unable to deduce the steric location of all four valencies of carbon in benzene derivatives, few chemists would have agreed with Claus† that 'the hypothesis that valency in multivalent atoms is a pre-existing force acting in definite units of affinity is as unfounded as it is unnatural', for the graphic formulae of Couper and Kekulé interpreted successfully the chemical behaviours of a vast number of natural organic products and synthetic substances of ever-growing complexity.

TRIPHENYLMETHYL

Great interest, mingled with no small degree of incredulity, was aroused in 1900 by Gomberg's wholly unexpected discovery that the hydrocarbon hexaphenylethane, $Ph_3C—CPh_3$, dissociates into the *free radical* triphenylmethyl, $Ph_3C\cdot$ which possesses a *trivalent* carbon atom.‡

It had been anticipated that hexaphenylethane would be quite a stable, unreactive compound, but Gomberg was able to isolate it only by treating triphenylmethyl bromide with silver powder, or with zinc dust, *in the complete absence of air*. The hexaphenylethane was found to be a colourless crystalline solid, which, however, dissolved in a number of solvents yielding yellow solutions. It reacted instantly with a number of reagents, such as atmospheric oxygen, iodine and nitric oxide, giving derivatives of triphenylmethyl:

$$\text{(colourless)}\quad Ph_3C—CPh_3 \rightleftharpoons 2Ph_3C\cdot \quad \text{(yellow)}$$
$$2Ph_3C\cdot + O_2 \longrightarrow Ph_3C—O—O—CPh_3$$
$$2Ph_3C\cdot + I_2 \longrightarrow 2Ph_3C—I$$
$$Ph_3C\cdot + NO \longrightarrow Ph_3C—NO$$

and none of these reactions was typical of normal hydrocarbon molecules.

A whole range of analogous compounds was prepared soon afterwards, and the inference that hexaphenylethane dissociated into two

† *Ber.* 1881, **14**, 432. ‡ Ibid. 1900, **33**, 3150; *J.A.C.S.* 1900, **22**, 757.

free radicals was substantiated by carrying out molecular weight determinations.†

The properties of these free radicals are considered in greater detail in a later chapter (Chapter III), but it may be stated here that the following definition, due to Wieland,‡ adequately summarizes their nature:

Free radicals are complexes of abnormal valency, which possess additive properties, but do not carry an electrical charge and are not free ions.

The Structure of Free Radicals

In the early years of the present century many attempts were made to account for the existence of free radicals by utilizing the theories of Werner, who, like Claus, had suggested that the carbon atom had a general 'combining affinity' which could be divided irregularly between two, three, or four groups according to their natures. Thus three phenyl groups were supposed to have such large 'affinity demands' that the central carbon atom in triphenylmethyl was considered to have only a small 'residual affinity' available for union with other groups.

With the development of the electronic theory of valency these ideas of combining affinity had to be abandoned. In 1920 G. N. Lewis pointed out that since stable molecules, and ions, all possess an even number of electrons, the normal non-ionizing valency bond, or *covalence*, is evidently formed by the sharing of a pair of electrons between two atomic nuclei. Unpaired or *odd electrons* are present in active free atoms, such as sodium or iodine, and, as will be explained in Chapter II, can be detected magnetically. Free organic radicals, such as triphenylmethyl, also contain an odd number of electrons. They too have proved to be paramagnetic substances, and indeed the measurement of the magnetic susceptibility of any compound can be used to determine the extent of its dissociation into free radicals.

Whilst the majority of these paramagnetic free radicals are, in accordance with Wieland's definition, electrically neutral substances, complex *radical ions* are not unknown, particularly amongst aromatic nitrogen compounds and heterocyclic dyestuffs (see pp. 66–7, 73–7).

The great chemical reactivity of the free radicals is to be associated with the available combining energy of the odd electron, and their reactions, whenever possible, result in the completion of electron pairs.

The reason for the comparative stability of triphenylmethyl and its

† Gomberg and Cone, *Ber.* 1904, **37**, 2037; 1906, **39**, 3274.
‡ Compare Wieland, ibid. 1915, **48**, 1098.

analogues has not been an easy problem for theoretical chemists to solve. However, the application of wave-mechanics to organic chemistry has led to an extended conception of *resonance* within complicated molecules, and it has been realized that the domain of the odd electron of triphenylmethyl, like that of the aromatic sextet of benzene, may extend over a large region of intramolecular space. In consequence much less intrinsic energy is to be associated with the free valency electron in the complex molecule triphenylmethyl than in a simple atom such as hydrogen.

The Discovery of Atomic Hydrogen

Although measurements of the vapour densities of gases at high temperatures had indicated that diatomic molecules could dissociate into free atoms, the possibility of the independent existence, at normal temperatures, of free atoms such as hydrogen, oxygen, or chlorine, received scarcely any consideration until 1913, when Niels Bohr showed that the spectrum emitted from a hydrogen discharge tube could be interpreted exactly as an emission spectrum of an atomic and not of a molecular form of hydrogen.

In 1922 R. W. Wood† separated atomic hydrogen from an electrical discharge tube by pumping. He investigated its properties and found with surprise that free atoms of hydrogen, $H\cdot$, did not recombine instantly to give molecular hydrogen (Chapter V).

Other free atoms, such as chlorine and oxygen, have been made in similar ways and there is now abundant experimental evidence to substantiate the theory that the combination of two atoms requires the presence also of a third body capable of removing the quantized energy liberated by the chemical change.

The Discovery of Free Alkyl Radicals

Though there had been many suggestions of the transient existence of free alkyl radicals,‡ it was not until 1929 that the free neutral radical *methyl*, $\cdot CH_3$, was first prepared by Paneth and Hofeditz,§ who decomposed lead tetramethyl by heat, and, by an ingenious adaptation of the system used by Bonhoeffer in 1924 for studying atomic hydrogen (p. 82), showed that there was produced thereby an active product with chemical properties very similar to those of atomic hydrogen.

$$Pb(CH_3)_4 \xrightleftharpoons{\text{heat}} Pb + 4\cdot CH_3.$$

† R. W. Wood, *Phil. Mag.* 1922, vi, **44**, 538.
‡ Bone and Coward, *J.* 1908, **93**, 1197.
§ Paneth and Hofeditz, *Ber.* 1929, **62**, 1335.

The following method was used.

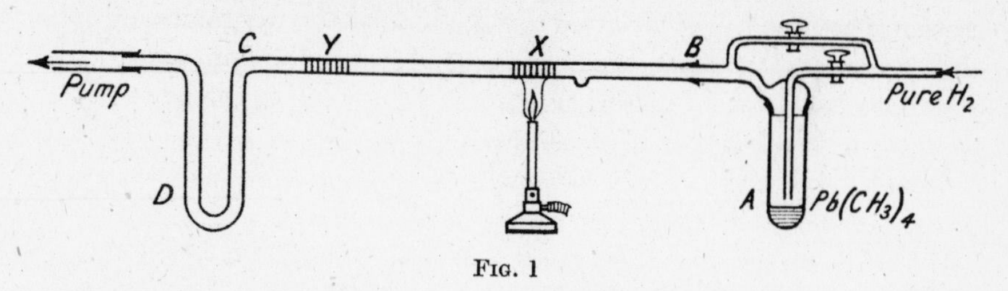

Fig. 1

A rapid current of pure hydrogen, or nitrogen, at 1–2 mm. pressure was charged with lead tetramethyl vapour by passage through a tube, *A*, containing lead tetramethyl cooled in solid carbon dioxide, and then was allowed to stream through a long quartz tube, *BC*. The gases then passed through a trap, *D*, which could be immersed in liquid air, to a high-speed mercury pump, by means of which a gas velocity of 10–15 metres per second could be maintained in *BC*.

A mirror of pure lead was first deposited at a point *Y* by heating the tube locally and thereby decomposing the lead tetramethyl vapour. When the tube was heated subsequently at a second point, *X*, nearer the inflow of gases, but kept cold at *Y*, it was found that whilst a fresh mirror deposited near *X*, simultaneously the original mirror at *Y* disappeared, provided that the distance between the points *X* and *Y* did not exceed about 30 cm. Hence one of the products of thermal decomposition of lead tetramethyl at *X* must be a gas capable of reacting with cold metallic lead at *Y*. This can be nothing else than the free radical methyl, $\cdot CH_3$, since it was verified experimentally that all other possible gaseous decomposition products, such as hydrogen, methane, or ethylene were quite without action upon the lead mirror.

By cooling the trap *D* in liquid air it was possible to isolate the volatile product obtained by the chemical attack on the mirror *Y* and it was found to be none other than lead tetramethyl. By heating fragments of zinc or of antimony in the stream of hydrogen clean mirrors of these metals could be deposited at *Y* in the place of the lead. They too were removed at room temperature. When zinc was used, zinc dimethyl collected in *D*, and when antimony was used two products were formed which were subsequently identified as antimony trimethyl, $Sb(CH_3)_3$ of m.p. $-20°$ and the antimony analogue of cacodyl,

$$(CH_3)_2Sb—Sb(CH_3)_2,$$

of m.p. $+13°$.

An attempt was made to isolate the free radical by cooling the initial decomposition products in liquid air, but the freezing led to a complete loss of chemical reactivity and nothing else than a mixture of stable hydrocarbons, including methane, ethane, and ethylene was obtained.

In 1931 Paneth and Lautsch† prepared the free radical ethyl, $\cdot C_2H_5$, from lead tetra-ethyl by a similar procedure, but they were unable to obtain any higher alkyl radicals, such as propyl or butyl, for these apparently broke down to methyl or ethyl radicals (see p. 129). They obtained free benzyl, $C_6H_5—CH_2\cdot$, by decomposing tetrabenzyl-tin,‡ but found no definite evidence for the existence of the free phenyl radical, $C_6H_5\cdot$.

Characterization of Free Alkyl Radicals

The study of the thermal decomposition of organic compounds was greatly stimulated by this important work of Paneth and Hofeditz, and their *mirror technique* has been adopted generally for detecting the presence of free atoms or radicals of very short life. Other elements, such as arsenic, mercury, and tellurium have been used for identification purposes, and a large number of microchemical methods have been developed for the characterization of the reaction products, which, of course, are definite organo-metallic compounds. Thus F. O. Rice§ showed that reaction with mercury and conversion of the initial products to alkyl mercuric bromides, which could easily be identified by means of their X-ray diffraction photographs, was a very convenient way of characterizing the simple alkyl radicals:

$$2R\cdot + Hg \longrightarrow HgR_2, \qquad HgR_2 + HgBr_2 \longrightarrow 2R—Hg—Br;$$

whilst Pearson and Purcell|| have made use of the highly crystalline trialkylarsine mercuri-chlorides, $R_3As,HgCl_2$, for identification purposes.

The most sensitive method for detecting, but not characterizing, free hydrocarbon radicals is to place in the gas stream, in front of a liquid air trap, a lead mirror containing a proportion of the radioactive isotope, Radium-D.¶ If the resultant condensate in the liquid-air trap becomes radioactive then some attack on the lead mirror must have occurred, though it well may be invisibly minute.

Another valuable development in technique is the *guard mirror method*, originally due to Pearson, Robinson, and Stoddart.†† They confirmed Paneth's work in detail, and showed that it was possible to

† Paneth and Lautsch, *Ber.* 1931, **64**, 2702.
‡ Paneth and Lautsch, *J.* 1935, p. 380.
§ Rice, *The Aliphatic Free Radicals*, Baltimore, 1935.
|| *J.* 1935, p. 1151.
¶ Leighton and Mortensen, *J.A.C.S.* 1936, **58**, 448; Burton, Ricci, and Davis, *J.A.C.S.* 1940, **62**, 265.
†† *Proc. Roy. Soc.* 1933, A **142**, 275.

differentiate between atomic hydrogen and free alkyl radicals. Whereas both hydrogen atoms and alkyl radicals will react with either antimony or tellurium, free alkyl radicals attack metallic lead, but atomic hydrogen does not do so, since lead hydride does not exist. The presence of atomic hydrogen in an active gas mixture can thus be established by passing the gas stream first over a heavy lead mirror and then over a thin antimony mirror. Only if atomic hydrogen is present will the second mirror be attacked. The presence of a trace of a free alkyl in admixture with atomic hydrogen may be revealed by placing a thin lead mirror before a thick antimony mirror (compare p. 122).

General Methods of preparing Free Radicals

1. Thermal decomposition of organic compounds. The discovery of free methyl, or more especially Paneth's invention of the mirror technique, proved to be a stimulus to the study of gas reactions which led, in a very few years, to notable developments in both experimental and theoretical knowledge of molecular decomposition.

In 1933 Leermakers† showed that free methyl could easily be obtained in quantity by heating azomethane to about 400° C.,

$$CH_3—N{=}N—CH_3 \longrightarrow N_2 + 2CH_3\cdot,$$

whilst in 1934 F. O. Rice and his colleagues showed that, at temperatures of 800° C. or over, the thermal decompositions (*pyrolyses*) of the vapours of a whole range of stable organic compounds, such as paraffin hydrocarbons, ethers, alcohols, aldehydes, ketones, and amines yield the simple alkyl radicals methyl and ethyl. More complex radicals are obtained less easily, since they break down rapidly, yielding olefines and simpler radicals (p. 129).

From pyrolyses of several types of organic compounds Rice and Johnston‡ estimated the average activation energy of the decomposition processes by comparing the rates of removal of standard antimony mirrors, in fixed positions, by the radicals generated by the passage of gas streams at known constant pressure through electrically heated zones at a series of measured temperatures. They assumed that the rate of production of radicals must vary with temperature according to the statistical equation $dn/dt = CN_0 e^{-E/RT}$, from which it follows that

$$\log_e \frac{t_1}{t_2} = \frac{E}{R}\left(\frac{1}{T_1} - \frac{1}{T_2}\right),$$

† Leermakers, *J.A.C.S.* 1933, **55**, 3499.
‡ Rice and Johnston, ibid. 1934, **56**, 214.

where t_1 and t_2 are the times of removal of the standard mirrors, T_1 and T_2 are the absolute temperatures at the points of decomposition, and E is the activation energy. Since activation energies thus obtained were very concordant with estimates of bond energies, as calculated from heats of combustion, Rice and his colleagues suggested that fission into two free neutral radicals was one of the simplest modes of decomposition of any covalent bond:

$$\text{A—B} + \text{Energy} \longrightarrow \text{A}\cdot + \cdot\text{B}.$$

Subsequent investigations however have now made it evident that, in thermal decompositions of organic molecules, free radical formation often comprises only a small proportion of the total reaction, and that simple molecular products, such as methane and water, can be formed directly (compare pp. 132–6). In many ways Rice's picture of thermal decomposition over-simplifies the true state of affairs.

Since the role of the aliphatic free radicals in high-temperature decomposition processes has been described in detail in a monograph by F. O. and K. K. Rice† it need not be dealt with *in extenso* in this book, and will therefore only receive discussion in connexion with points of theoretical significance. The application of a similar procedure to the study of thermal decompositions in solution is described in Chapter VIII.

2. Photochemical decomposition. Between 1931 and 1934 Norrish and his colleagues, as a result of a detailed study of the photochemical decomposition of aldehydes and ketones concluded that although the main process which occurs when acetone vapour is exposed to ultraviolet light can be represented by the equation

$$CH_3\text{—}CO\text{—}CH_3 = CH_3\text{—}CH_3 + CO,$$

the reaction involved an initial decomposition to methyl radicals, and this conclusion was substantiated in 1934 by Pearson,‡ who, by using the mirror technique of Paneth, was able to isolate characteristic organo-metallic compounds from this decomposition.

There is now abundant evidence that the photochemical decomposition of molecules of all types, both in the gaseous and in the liquid phase, leads to the formation of active free radicals of short life. This subject receives more detailed treatment in Chapter VI.

3. Discharge tube reactions. There can be no doubt that, just as atomic hydrogen is formed by the passage of an electrical discharge through molecular hydrogen gas, so free alkyl radicals are formed when

† F. O. and K. K. Rice, *The Aliphatic Free Radicals*, Baltimore, 1935.
‡ *J.* 1934, p. 1718.

electrical discharges are passed through gases such as methane. It has frequently been shown that the active products thereby obtained will attack metallic mirrors, but since reactions with metals might also be ascribed to gaseous positive ions, such as CH_3^+ (see Chapter X), mirror removal is not a diagnostic test for the production of free *neutral* radicals in electrical discharges.

Moreover the features of the explosive combustion of gaseous hydrocarbons brought about by an electrical discharge resemble so closely those of the chain reaction between hydrogen and oxygen (pp. 88, 95) that one can scarcely doubt that free neutral atoms, or radicals, are involved in both cases. Both α- and X-rays can excite gas reactions of this atomic type.†

Many chemical reactions can be brought about by irradiating solutions with X-rays, or with α-particles.‡ It has been shown that in the main these changes are due to an initial decomposition of the solvent, and can be explained by the supposition that the radiation causes electrons to be ejected singly from solvent molecules. Thus

$$H_2O + \text{Energy} \longrightarrow (H_2O)^+ + e.$$

Thereupon the resulting ionized molecule dissociates to give a neutral radical and a stable positive ion,

$$(H_2O)^+ \longrightarrow H^+ + (\cdot OH),$$

whilst the ejected electron, when slowed down sufficiently by multiple collisions, reacts with another solvent molecule to give a neutral radical and a negative ion

$$e + H_2O \longrightarrow H\cdot + (:OH)^-.$$

The free radicals (H· and ·OH from water), produced at a distance from one another, do not all recombine in pairs. Some persist for a sufficiently long time to react with solute molecules, causing oxidation or reduction. It is probable that many of the chemical processes involved in radiotherapy are explicable along these lines.§

4. Use of metals. It has already been stated that Gomberg used the action between metals and organic halogen compounds for preparing free radicals

$$Ph_3C\text{—}Cl + Ag\cdot \longrightarrow Ph_3C\cdot + Ag^+Cl^-.$$

The decomposition of a molecule by an atom of a univalent metal is in fact a general method of preparing free radicals, and as long ago as

† Eyring, Hirschfelder, and Taylor, *J. Chem. Phys.* 1936, **4**, 479.

‡ Allsopp, *Trans. Faraday Soc.* 1944, **40**, 79; Weiss, *Nature*, 1944, **153**, 748.

§ See D. E. Lea, *Actions of Radiation on Living Cells*, Cambridge, 1946.

1911 Schlenk showed that reactive substances analogous to triphenylmethyl could be obtained by allowing metallic sodium to react, in inert solvents such as benzene or ether, with aromatic ketones, olefines, and nitriles. The products, which are both sodium salts and free radicals, are all to be formulated as substances in which one electron has added on to a double bond, e.g.

$$(C_6H_5)_2C{=}\ddot{\underset{..}{O}} + Na\cdot \longrightarrow (C_6H_5)_2\dot{C}{-}\ddot{\underset{..}{O}}\!:{-}Na^+.$$

A number of well-known reactions of metals in organic chemistry may involve the transient formation of neutral radicals (Chapter X), but since a solid metal is a conductor its precise mode of electron donation, i.e. whether singly or in pairs, is indeterminate. In contrast, there can be no doubt of the exact mechanism of reactions in which a metallic vapour is used, since elements such as sodium yield monatomic gases. Kinetic studies of reactions between sodium vapour and the vapours of organic substances, such as the alkyl and aryl halides, have been made by Polanyi and his colleagues since 1930 (see pp. 100–105) and it has been proved conclusively that neutral hydrocarbon radicals are formed thereby. Thus in the initial reaction between sodium atoms and methyl chloride vapour the sodium atom loses its unpaired electron and the carbon-to-chlorine covalent bond is broken with the formation of a chloride anion and a neutral methyl radical, i.e.

$$H_3C^{\cdot}.\ddot{\underset{..}{Cl}}\!: + \cdot Na \longrightarrow H_3C\cdot + (:\ddot{\underset{..}{Cl}}\!:)^- + Na^+.$$

It has been possible to give a direct experimental proof of the formation of free methyl radicals in this reaction by showing that the gaseous reaction products will, even when freed from sodium vapour, react with molecular iodine to yield methyl iodide and attack mirrors of antimony or tellurium (p. 104).

Di-radicals, such as trimethylene $\cdot CH_2{-}CH_2{-}CH_2\cdot$ have also been prepared by this method.†

5. Electrode reactions. A neutral radical must obviously be produced whenever a univalent ion is discharged at an electrode, but the liberated radicals usually react, either with each other or with adjacent substances, so quickly that they can scarcely be termed *free*.

The production of neutral organic radicals by the cathodic reduction of organic dyestuffs of quinonoid type can often be deduced from a

† Bawn and Milsted, *Trans. Faraday Soc.* 1939, **35**, 889.

careful analysis of electrode potentials,† since the discharge potential at a reversible electrode may be expressed by the formula

$$E = E_0 + \frac{RT}{nF}\log_e\frac{[\mathrm{Ox}]}{[\mathrm{Red}]},$$

where [Ox] and [Red] are the concentration of the oxidized and reduced forms of the substance in the solution and n is the number of electrons required in the chemical change. It follows therefore that the form of the *reduction potential/composition* curve for the reduction of an organic substance depends upon the exact mechanism of the reduction process (p. 77).

Clear evidence of the occurrence of single electron changes can often be obtained by the use of *polarographic* technique, in which *current/voltage* curves for reduction at a dropping mercury electrode are measured.‡ Thus Ilkovič has shown that the average diffusion current, I_d produced by the reduction of any substance at concentration C in the electrolyte is $I_d = KnD^{\frac{1}{2}}C$, where K is constant for any one fixed electrode, D is the measurable diffusion coefficient of the reduced substance, and n the number of electrons involved in the reduction stage.

In these ways it has been shown that a large number of heterocyclic bases, of the quinoline, acridine, and phenazine series can give products of radical type, such as (I) on reduction.

ĊH

NH

(I)

Frequently, however, these radicals dimerize to products of quinhydrone type, and this dimerization is apt to obscure the evidence adducible from electrode potential measurement.

Chemical reactions at electrodes are dealt with in some detail in Chapter X, but attention may be drawn here to the facts that organometallic compounds of lead or mercury may easily be obtained by the reduction of ketones at cathodes of these metals, whilst the ethyl derivatives of lead and antimony have been obtained at anodes by the electrolysis of a zinc-ethyl solution of sodium ethyl.§ Thus there is abundant evidence to show that when liberated at electrodes neutral hydrocarbon radicals behave in an exactly similar way to the gaseous free radicals. Again many of the molecular reaction products formed both at cathodes and at anodes by electrolysis can best be accounted

† Michaelis, *Chemical Reviews*, 1935, **16**, 243; Michaelis and Schubert, ibid., 1938, **22**, 437.

‡ Kolthoff and Lingane, *Polarography*, New York, 1941.

§ F. Hein and collaborators, *Z. anorg. Chem.* 1924, **141**, 161; 1926, **158**, 153.

for as interaction products of highly active neutral radicals and vicinal solvent molecules.

6. Use of neutrons. In 1939 Lu and Sugden† indicated a further method of production of neutral radicals that may be applicable for the initiation of chain reactions. When an organic halide, such as ethylene dibromide, bromobenzene, or chlorobenzene is irradiated with neutrons the carbon-to-halogen bond is broken and the halogen element is set free as a radioactive *atom*. It was shown that the radioactive product reacted with vicinal organic molecules preferentially by attacking hydrogen atoms, giving an ionizable product (compare pp. 98–100, 174–6),

i.e. $Br^* + H—C_nH_m \longrightarrow H—Br^*$ (*ionizable*)

not $Br^* + H—C_nH_m \longrightarrow Br^*—C_nH_m$ (*not ionized*),

and thereby the radioactive halogen could be separated from the unaffected organic halide and the induced radioactivity concentrated as much as 30,000-fold. This method of concentration of radioactive halogens was particularly effective when substances such as aniline or phenol, which rapidly react with free halogens, were added to the halide to be irradiated with neutrons.

Previously Glückauf and Fay‡ had shown that the radioactive halogen obtained by irradiating with neutrons substances such as methyl iodide, carbon tetrachloride, and carbon tetrabromide would substitute hydrogen in benzene, but had not fully realized that these results indicated that free radioactive halogen *atoms* had been produced.

Concomitantly with the production of radioactive halogen atoms, free alkyl or aryl radicals must be produced, but as yet no one has established their independent existence in these systems.

7. Radical catalysed reactions. Certain free atoms, such as atomic chlorine, and several thermally unstable substances, as for example dibenzoyl peroxide, have proved to be potent catalysts of reactions which, from kinetic evidence (see pp. 180–200), undoubtedly involve free neutral radicals of short life. Again a number of simple inorganic reactions involving the transference of one electron from one substance to another, e.g.

$$Fe^{++} \rightleftharpoons Fe^{+++} + e,$$

are capable of catalysing further chemical changes of this same kinetic type, and often the net result is to bring about a chemical change which can be effected by no other means.

Catalyses of these types are discussed in Chapters IX–XII. They

† *J.* 1939, p. 1273. ‡ Ibid. 1936, p. 390.

include the technically important processes for synthesizing long-chain polymers, such as polystyrene and 'perspex', oxidation by atmospheric oxygen, and probably a number of important biochemical oxidation processes. The elucidation of the detailed mechanisms of these complex catalysed reactions is as yet by no means complete, but much progress can now be made by studying the chemical reactions of such free organic radicals as have already been characterized.

Characteristics of Reactions involving Free Neutral Radicals

Even when one cannot diagnose the presence of a free neutral radical by the formation of an organo-metallic compound, as described on p. 7, it is often possible to decide that transient neutral radicals must have taken part in a reaction process by examining carefully its kinetics and the conditions under which it has been carried out. Reaction velocity measurement often gives the surest guide to the mechanism of a chemical change, and it is possible to make a clear-cut differentiation between an ionic and an electrically neutral reaction process by this means, although without detailed search one may not be able to decide the exact natures of the essential reactive particles.

The nature of covalent bond fission. A covalent bond may be broken *either* to give two neutral radicals, each of which retains one electron of the bonding pair

$$\mathrm{A{:}B} \xrightarrow[\text{Homolysis}]{} \mathrm{A\cdot + \cdot B}\,; \qquad \text{(i)}$$

or alternatively to yield two ions, one of which separates with both the electrons

$$\mathrm{A{:}B} \xrightarrow[\text{Heterolysis}]{} \mathrm{(A)^+ + ({:}B)^-}. \qquad \text{(ii)}$$

If one considers a single molecule, e.g. a gas particle, then in most cases more energy is required to effect ionic or *heterolytic* fission (ii), than neutral or *homolytic* fission (i), since process (ii) yields two electrically charged particles which can only be separated if work is done against electrostatic forces, which, at molecular distances, are quite large.

No such energy is needed to separate two uncharged particles. Though some energy is often gained by transferring an electron from an atom A to an atom B, (iii), or vice versa,

$$\mathrm{A\cdot + \cdot B \longrightarrow A^+ + ({:}B)^-}, \qquad \text{(iii)}$$

this is usually less than the electrostatic work of separating to a distance the charged ions A^+ and B^-. For this reason gas reactions are almost exclusively of the atomic, or homolytic, type (i).

In solution, however, where molecules are always in such close proximity that mutual electrostatic interactions have to be taken into account, neutral bond fission is not usually favoured. The high dielectric constants of the solvents most frequently used for carrying out chemical reactions greatly decrease the electrostatic work of ion separation. Moreover, prior to actual bond fission, the electrical polarization of a dissociable bond A—B may be greatly enhanced by the formation of a closed chain of polar molecules. Thus

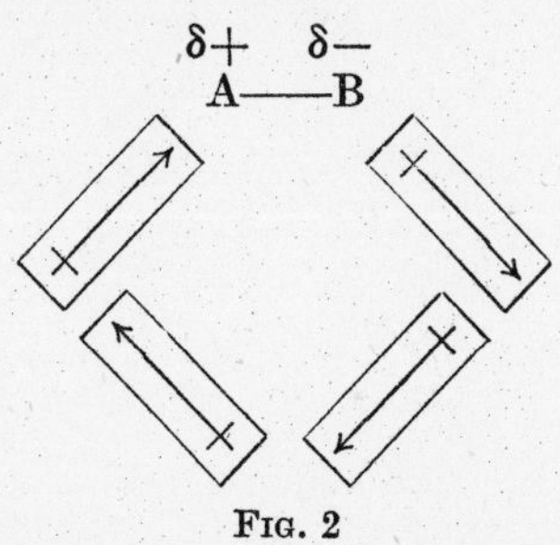

FIG. 2

Consequently the energy for the heterolytic fission of a covalent bond in a dissolved substance may easily become much less than that required for homolytic fission, and, indeed, in the case of the great majority of organic reactions in solution it can be demonstrated that ions must intervene.†

The greater the electrical dissymmetry of a covalent bond (i.e. the greater its dipole moment) the greater is the probability that it will dissociate into charged ions and not into neutral radicals. To a first, very rough, approximation one can gauge the limiting criterion for the neutral fission of an unsymmetrical covalent bond, $\overset{+\longrightarrow}{\mathrm{A—B}}$, from the equation‡

$$E_{\mathrm{ions}} \gtreqless 2E_{\mathrm{dipole}},$$

where E_{ions} is the coulombic energy associated with the separated ions A and B, i.e.

$$\frac{e^2}{2D}\left(\frac{1}{r_A}+\frac{1}{r_B}\right),$$

and E_{dipole} is the electrostatic energy of the original dipolar bond, i.e. $\frac{1}{2}\mu^2/\alpha$, where μ is the dipole moment and α the bond polarizability. It will be seen that the dependence of E_{ions} upon the dielectric constant of the environment makes the latter the controlling factor, and Table I gives critical data for the dissociation of the commoner reactive bonds of organic compounds.

† See Waters, *Physical Aspects of Organic Chemistry*, London, 1935; Hammett, *Physical Organic Chemistry*, New York, 1940.

‡ Waters, *J.* 1942, p. 153.

TABLE I

Electrostatic Properties of Covalent Bonds

Bond	*Bond length*	*Dipole moment*	*Polarizability*	*Limiting dielectric constant*
C—F	1·41 Å	$1{\cdot}4\times10^{-18}$ e.s.u.	$0{\cdot}63\times10^{-24}$ c.c.	5
C—Cl	1·76 ,,	1·5 ,,	2·6 ,,	15
C—Br	1·88 ,,	1·4 ,,	3·7 ,,	22
C—I	2·05 ,,	1·2 ,,	5·7 ,,	44
C—OH	1·43 ,,	0·8 ,,	0·58 ,,	18
C—N	1·47 ,,	0·4 ,,	0·57 ,,	55
C—H	1·09 ,,	0·4 ,,	0·67 ,,	64
O—H	0·97 ,,	1·5 ,,	0·74 ,,	6
N—H	1·01 ,,	1·3 ,,	0·74 ,,	7
S—H	1·35 ,,	0·7 ,,	1·88 ,,	20

TABLE II

Dielectric Constants of Common Solvents

Cyclo-hexane	2·0	Benzene	2·3	*Favour radical formation*
Carbon tetrachloride	2·2	Chloroform	4·7	
Carbon disulphide	2·6	Ether	4·3	
Ethyl acetate	6·4	Acetic acid	7·1	
Pyridine	12·5	Acetone	19·6	*Favour ionization*
Methyl alcohol	32·4	Ethyl alcohol	25·0	
Nitrobenzene	36	Formic acid	48	
Water	80	Hydrogen cyanide	95	

From Tables I and II it will be seen that the formation of neutral radicals by dissociation of covalent bonds is to be expected only in a relatively small group of common solvents of low dielectric constant. It may be looked for when the reacting bonds are weakly polar, like C—C, C—N, and even C—I, but not when they have strong polar characteristics, as for example O—H, N—H, or C—Cl.

Chain reactions. Many free monovalent atoms, such as hydrogen or chlorine, and free neutral radicals, such as methyl, have such high energy contents that they readily react, upon collision, with normal molecules. By the resulting chemical change the original 'odd electron' of the initial radical, R·, becomes part of a stable electron pair, but since normal molecules contain an even number of electrons a fresh radical, ·B, must thereby be formed

$$R\cdot + A{:}B \longrightarrow R{:}A + \cdot B. \quad \text{(iv)}$$

The new radical, ·B, necessarily has similar chemical properties to ·R, since it has the same type of electronic structure, and hence the displacement process (iv) may be followed by another similar one (v) and so on (vi):

$$\mathrm{B}\cdot + \mathrm{C{-}D} \longrightarrow \mathrm{B{-}C} + \cdot\mathrm{D} \qquad \text{(v)}$$

$$\mathrm{D}\cdot + \mathrm{A{-}B} \longrightarrow \mathrm{D{-}A} + \cdot\mathrm{B}; \qquad \text{(vi)}$$

with the net result that the active radicals continue to effect the overall chemical change

$$\mathrm{A{-}B} + \mathrm{C{-}D} = \mathrm{A{-}D} + \mathrm{B{-}C},$$

until eventually two active radicals meet and combine, giving up their available energy to other molecules, e.g.

$$\mathrm{B}\cdot + \cdot\mathrm{D} \longrightarrow \mathrm{B{-}D} + \text{Energy}, \qquad \text{(vii)}$$

or alternatively are firmly adsorbed on the walls of the reaction vessel. Self-perpetuating reactions, such as the sequence (v)–(vi) are known as *chain reactions*, and are characteristic of the displacement reactions of free neutral radicals.

The kinetic characteristics of processes involving consecutive reactions are quite distinct. Thus (*a*) the reaction is initiated by the formation of active particles (e.g. free radicals) and accelerates with time until their rate of generation equals their rate of destruction by processes such as (vii). (*b*) When this steady state has been reached the reaction velocity becomes constant, and independent of the bulk concentrations of the main reactants (AB and CD); (*c*) finally the reaction velocity drops as one of the displacement processes (v) or (vi) becomes less frequent on account of the exhaustion of the supply of a reactant.

It is rare for a chain reaction to proceed quantitatively, since the active participants can easily be destroyed in pairs by mutual collisions, or by side reactions with other molecules.

In accordance with the conclusions of the preceding section it has been found that the majority of homogeneous gas reactions are chain processes, whereas most reactions in solution proceed at rates proportional to the bulk concentrations of the molecular reactants in accordance with simple unimolecular or bimolecular equations. The occurrence of a chain reaction in a solution can be taken as diagnostic evidence for the transient existence of active, electrically neutral, radicals.

Inhibitors of chain reactions. The less the available combining energy of a free radical the greater will be the activation energy needed to effect a displacement reaction such as (iv). Hence the less will be the rate of destruction of this radical by collision with molecules and the longer its free life. Consequently one can say that the more stable a free radical is the more specific will its reactions become. For instance, atomic chlorine (p. 97) attacks all organic molecules without distinction, whereas atomic iodine, when generated, usually persists until it encounters a similar atom and then gives molecular iodine, I_2. Again, free radicals such as $CH_3\cdot$ react promptly with all organic solvents, whereas stable solutions containing free triphenylmethyl can easily be prepared.

Since chain processes can be perpetuated only so long as *all* the displacement reactions of the participating radicals can occur easily, it follows that any displacement reaction

$$R\cdot + X\text{—}Y \longrightarrow R\text{—}X + \cdot Y,$$

which leads to the replacement of an active radical, R·, by one of low energy content, ·Y, will soon bring about the cessation of the whole chain process, even though the molecule of the *inhibitor*, i.e. X—Y, may be present only in very low concentration in the reacting system.

The possibility of effecting the inhibition, or anti-catalysis, of a reaction process is therefore a further characteristic of a system involving free radicals. It will usually be found that inhibitors, or *stabilizers*, are either molecules which can yield stabilized resonance systems, as for example the radicals of quinonoid dyestuffs and similar heterocyclic compounds, or else free atoms, such as iodine, of very low energy content.

Free radicals in solutions.† Active free radicals are often generated in pairs by such reactions as thermal or photochemical decompositions, but within liquids, as within gases, they can usually persist sufficiently long for them to migrate apart. In 1934 Franck and Rabinowitch‡ pointed out that in solution each individual particle is surrounded by a 'cage' of solvent molecules which, by their impacts, prevent vicinal particles from rapidly moving apart. Consequently there is a much greater probability of impact, and chemical reaction, between an active radical and each of its surrounding molecules than one could calculate proportionally from the bulk composition of the liquid. Hence *primary recombination* of active radicals tends to lower the initial yield of radical formation in solution in comparison with radical formation in the vapour phase.

However, when once a free radical has been formed, the surrounding sheath of solvent molecules will tend to prevent its recombination with

† Waters, *Trans. Faraday Soc.* 1941, **37**, 770.

‡ Ibid. 1934, **30**, 120. Compare Norrish, ibid. 1937, **33**, 1504.

a second radical, and will favour the occurrence of a displacement reaction between the radical and a solvent molecule. Thus displacement reactions with solvent molecules are to be expected of all active free radicals. They will, as a rule, not be chemically specific, since the point of attack on the solvent is almost invariably the nearest available group, or, in other words the outermost atoms of the solvent molecules. Radicals can thus be expected to dehydrogenate hydrocarbons, alcohols ketones, and similar molecules, and to remove halogen atoms from solvents such as carbon tetrachloride (compare Chapters VII and VIII).

It will be obvious from the foregoing sections that chain reactions initiated by free radicals in solution can very soon become reactions essentially characteristic of the solvent, rather than of particular dissolved substances in low concentration. For instance free halogen atoms in water will promptly yield hydroxyl radicals, $\cdot OH$, and they will therefore act as hydroxylating agents rather than as halogenating agents. By a proper choice of solvent, however, it is possible to arrange that the free atom or radical is continually regenerated in type, but not of course in identity, by a solvent collision. Thus carbon tetrachloride will favour the persistence of atomic chlorine

$$Cl\cdot + CCl_4 \rightleftharpoons Cl_2 + \cdot CCl_3,$$

whilst similarly hydroxyl groups can persist in water,

$$\underline{HO}\cdot + HOH \longrightarrow H\underline{OH} + \cdot OH,$$

and acetate radicals in glacial acetic acid,

$$\underline{CH_3COO\cdot} + H—OCOCH_3 \longrightarrow \underline{CH_3—COOH} + \cdot OCOCH_3.$$

One can in this way obtain high yields in specific reactions of certain free radicals in solutions, and, as the following chapters will show, great practical advantage has been taken of this fact.

II

PHYSICAL PROPERTIES OF FREE RADICALS

BOTH the physical and the chemical properties of an atom, or of a molecule, depend upon its electronic state, and satisfactory theories of chemical combination can be developed from the primary postulate that minima of energy content, with consequent maxima of stability, can be assigned to structures composed of electron pairs, and still more definitely of electron octets. Thus the ionization of atoms by processes of electron transfer, leads to the formation of stable electron octets, whilst covalent bond formation is a process of electron sharing which leads to the production of stable electron pairs.

The significance of the stability of the electron pair can best be comprehended from the aspect of the quantum theory. Two atoms can be expected to combine together to form a stable molecule only if the total energy of their separate electronic systems can be decreased, and in 1927 Heitler and London deduced that two electrons possess less total energy in conjunction than when separated if their *spin quantum numbers* **s** have opposite signs. When two electrons couple together to form a bonding pair they comprise one covalence, which can be depicted mathematically as one combined wave system in which all marks of individuality of the electrons have disappeared.

The liberation of a definite amount of exchange energy is one essential characteristic of covalent bond formation. Since in complicated molecules the wave systems of different electron pairs interact, particularly when resonance between different groups of electrons occurs, energies of covalent bond formation can be computed approximately only for the very simplest of molecules, though they can be assessed experimentally from thermochemical data.

Another characteristic of covalent bond formation between atoms is an abrupt change in magnetic properties. Each planetary electron contributes to an atom, or molecule, a magnetic moment. This can be associated with its quantized angular momentum, and is therefore limited to values which depend upon its subsidiary (**l**) and spin (**s**) quantum numbers. An atom or molecule can only have a resultant magnetic moment, beyond the minute amount due to nuclear spin (p. 25), if it is a system possessing a resultant electron momentum, and this does not occur in any structure in which all the electronic shells have their complete quota of electrons. Moreover each bonding pair of electrons, in which the spin quantum numbers **s** are of opposite signs ($+\frac{1}{2}$ and $-\frac{1}{2}$), has no resultant electron spin, and thus no magnetic moment due to spin momentum.

The s electrons of atoms, and the corresponding σ electrons of molecules, for which the subsidiary quantum number $\mathbf{l} = 0$, possess spin momentum only. Hence a pair of s, or of σ, electrons have no resultant magnetic moment. This system, which is described as the spectroscopic state $^1S_0$, occurs in the divalent elements of the alkaline earth series, and also in the elements zinc, cadmium, and mercury.

On the other hand, the p electrons of atoms, and the corresponding π electrons of molecules, which have the quantum number $\mathbf{l} = 1$, have both orbital and spin momentum. One finds, however, that not only does the system of two s and six p electrons, which forms the normal stable octet of the rare gas structure, have no resultant magnetic moment, but also that the system of two s and two p electrons, described as the spectroscopic state $^3P_0$, has no resultant magnetic moment. This system occurs in the element carbon, and in the metals tin and lead. However, systems containing four p electrons, as present in the elements oxygen and sulphur, can have a resultant momentum. One of the normal spectroscopic states of the oxygen atom, the $^3P_2$ state, does correspond to an atom which may possess a magnetic moment.

From the chemical point of view, it is significant that those atoms and molecules which have an odd number of electrons have an unbalanced electron spin, and therefore *must* have resultant magnetic moments. The magnitude of the magnetic moment of any such molecule is strictly limited in accordance with quantum laws, and is not affected by resonance interactions between electron groups in the same way as is the exchange energy of bond formation. As will be explained on pp. 25–31, only those substances which possess permanent magnetic moments have paramagnetic properties. *Paramagnetism can therefore be regarded as a physical property diagnostic of free radicals, for all organic compounds and for other derivatives of the lighter elements.* This generalization is not valid, however, for derivatives of the transition elements, such as iron, cobalt, and nickel, or for the metals of the rare earths, for these heavy atoms can possess stable electron systems in which the simple octet rule does not hold.

Atomic Magnetism

Any particle which has a permanent magnetic moment will behave like a small bar magnet: if placed in a magnetic field of constant intensity it will tend to orient itself in the direction of the field, and if placed in a field of varying intensity it will tend to move from the weaker field to the stronger field.

If the field, H, is varying in intensity, then the force acting on the magnet in any direction (x) is $F = \mu_i \partial H/\partial x$, where μ_i is the resolved part of the moment of the magnet in the direction of the field.

In 1921 Stern† pointed out that if the magnetic particle is a single molecule, then the value of μ_i must be restricted to certain quantum values, such that

$$\mu_i = \mathbf{m} g \mu_B.$$

In this equation **m** is a possible *magnetic quantum number* for a valency electron. It is related to the values of the quantum numbers **l** and **s**, and represents the quantized energy level of an electron in a magnetic field. It is sufficiently a vector quantity to have no meaning in the absence of a magnetic field, but is not dependent upon the field strength. g is the *Landé factor*, by means of which can be evaluated the coupling together of the spin and orbital momenta of the different constituent electrons in the atom or molecule. μ_B is the *Bohr magneton*, which has the value

$$\mu_B = eh/4\pi mc = 9{\cdot}174 \times 10^{-21} \text{ erg/gauss}$$

(where m is the *mass* of the electron). This is the magnetic moment associated with a single uncoupled electron in its most stable state ($\mathbf{l} = 0$, $\mathbf{s} = \frac{1}{2}$) and is the convenient quantum unit for the measurement of atomic or molecular magnetism.

It will be seen, from Stern's equation, that the force acting on a molecular magnet is not a function of the spatial orientation of the molecule in the magnetic field.

On the earlier, classical, theory of magnetism the force acting on any particle of moment μ would be $\mu \cos\theta \, \partial H/\partial x$ where θ, the angle between the magnetic axis and the direction of the field, H, might have any value, but in accordance with the quantum theory θ is restricted to particular values such that $\mu \cos\theta = \mu_i = \mu_B \mathbf{m} g$. This phenomenon is termed *space quantization*.

To verify the quantum theory of magnetism, Stern and Gerlach passed narrow beams of vaporized atoms, or molecules, through a magnetic field of varying intensity, using apparatus shown schematically in Fig. 3.

The substance under investigation was vaporized in an electrically

† Stern, *Zeit. für Physik*, 1921, **7**, 249; **8**, 110.

heated oven, O, and a fine stream of particles at a very low pressure then issued, in a narrow beam defined by the slits, S, into the evacuated chamber AB. The beam passed between the two poles of an electromagnet E, which were shaped as shown in Fig. 4, so as to produce a magnetic field of very high intensity in the proximity of the knife edge

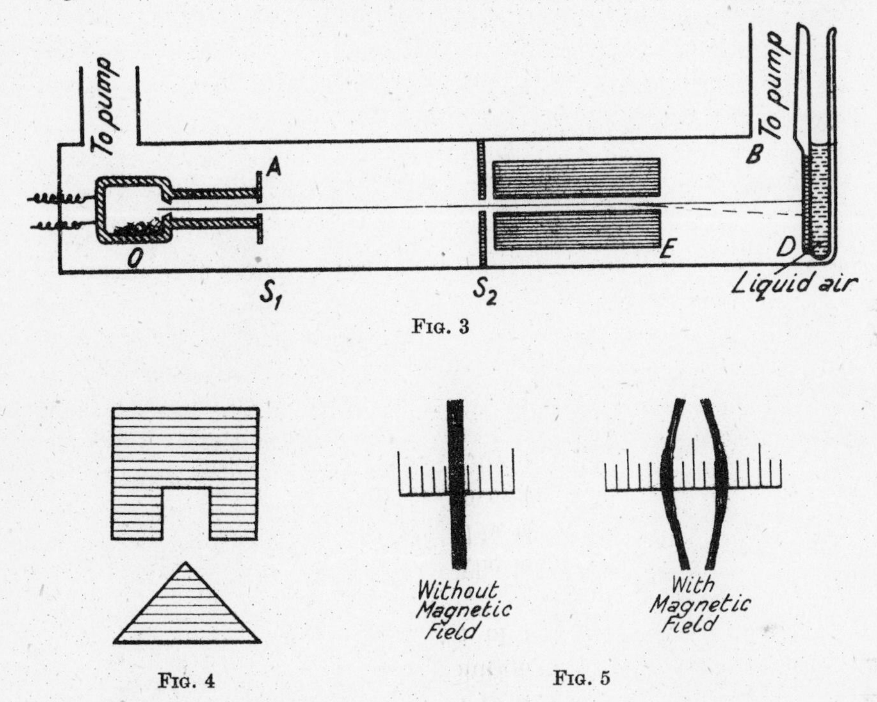

FIG. 3

FIG. 4

FIG. 5

and of much lower intensity in the direction of the slot. Consequently particles having permanent magnetic moments were deflected by the electromagnet, and the extent of their deviation was measured by allowing the beam to impinge upon a detecting plate D, upon which they condensed or reacted chemically. From the amount of deviation of the particles from the rectilinear path traversed in the absence of any applied magnetic field the magnetic moment of the molecule could be computed.

The results of the first experiments fully substantiated the quantum theory of magnetism. A beam of silver atoms was deflected as shown in Fig. 5. Some atoms were deflected towards the stronger magnetic field, acquiring a position of less energy, whilst others were deflected away from it, but *no atoms were undeflected*. Silver is an atom containing *one* valency electron, and it can therefore have only two values of m*g*, corresponding to spin quantum values of $+\frac{1}{2}$ and $-\frac{1}{2}$, and a resolved magnetic moment μ_i of one Bohr magneton.

The apparatus of Stern and Gerlach can be used for examining many simple atoms and molecules. The simplest form of detector, D, is a glass plate cooled in liquid air. Though it is difficult to pass a molecular beam for a sufficient time to leave an easily visible deposit of condensed atoms, it is not hard to 'develop' thinly deposited films, since metallic atoms, such as silver or copper form sensitized areas for catalysing the reduction of silver nitrate by a photographic developer such as quinol, and thereby a photographic picture can be obtained. Atomic hydrogen may be detected by using a target covered with white molybdenum trioxide, which yields the blue dioxide by reduction. For oxygen a target covered with yellow litharge has been used; brown lead peroxide is formed where the oxygen molecules impinge.

A still more sensitive method of detecting the position of a molecular beam is to use a hot-wire manometer. The rate of cooling of a thin wire depends upon the thermal conductivity of its environment, and this depends essentially upon the local pressure of the gas in which it is situated. So sensitive is this method that pressure changes of as little as 10^{-8} mm. of mercury can be detected in vacuum systems.

Investigations by this molecular ray method have shown that atomic hydrogen (p. 81), the alkali-metals lithium, sodium, and potassium, and also the metals copper, silver, and gold give deflexions corresponding to one Bohr magneton. These elements of the first group of the periodic system are described as possessing the $^2S_{\frac{1}{2}}$ state, since they contain only one s electron to which the resultant magnetic field is due.

Atoms of the divalent elements zinc, cadmium, and mercury, and also of the quadrivalent elements tin and lead, were found to have no resultant magnetic moments. Their spectroscopic states are described as $^1S_0$ and $^3P_0$ respectively.

Thallium, which has three valency electrons, and the spectroscopic state $^2P_{\frac{1}{2}}$, gave a deflexion corresponding to 0·33 magnetons, whilst atomic bismuth gave a deflexion of 0·72 magnetons. These low values are due to the coupling together of the quantized orbits of the valency electrons, but correspond to calculable values of the Landé factor, g.†

Atomic oxygen, which possesses six valency electrons, was shown by Kurt and Phipps‡ to contain both magnetic and non-magnetic particles.

† For a discussion of the above see E. C. Stoner's *Magnetism and Matter*, Methuen, London, 1934.

‡ Kurt and Phipps, *Phys. Rev.* 1929, **34**, 1357.

It has an atomic structure in which there is but little energy difference between several possible electronic states, some of which have magnetic moments due to the presence of one electron in a high quantum orbit.

The presence of an unpaired electron, and a consequent magnetic moment, in the 'odd molecule' nitric oxide has been confirmed by the molecular beam method.†

Molecular oxygen, O_2 which in the stable spectroscopic state, $^3\Sigma$ possesses two electrons with unneutralized spins, is remarkable amongst normal molecules in having a resolved moment of *two* Bohr magnetons,‡ for all other normal molecules which have as yet been investigated by the molecular-ray method, as for example hydrogen and water, have resultant moments of the order of $\frac{1}{1840}$ of a Bohr magneton.§ This minute magnetic moment is not an electronic moment, but is due to the spin of the positive nucleus of the atoms. With the easily deflected hydrogen molecule, the difference between the *ortho* and *para* states is just detectable.

Magnetic Susceptibility

Whilst the direct molecular-ray method of determining magnetic moments has such obvious experimental limitations that it is applicable to only a few substances, it is possible to estimate the resultant magnetic moment of any compound by determining its magnetic susceptibility.

The *magnetic susceptibility per unit volume*, K_v, of any substance is defined as the ratio:

$$K_v = \frac{\text{intensity of magnetization inside substance}}{\text{intensity of applied magnetic field}} = \frac{I}{H}.$$

From this can be calculated the *susceptibility per unit mass*, $\chi_m = K_v/\rho$, where ρ is the density, and also the *molecular susceptibility* $\chi_M = \chi_m M$, where M is its molecular weight.

These quantities can be measured by determining the force which acts on a specimen of the substance when it is brought near to the poles of a magnet.

Since the potential energy of any particle of volume δv and susceptibility K_v in a field of intensity H is

$$\delta E = -\int_0^H I\,dH\,\delta v = -\int_0^H K_v H\,dH\,\delta v = -\tfrac{1}{2}K_v H^2\,\delta v.$$

† Schnurmann, *J. Phys. Radium*, 1935 [vii], **6**, 99.

‡ Schnurmann, *Zeit. für Physik*, 1933, **85**, 212 (and note † above).

§ Estermann, Stern, and Frisch, ibid. 1933, **85**, **4**, **17**; **86**, 132.

The force F_x acting on the particle in the direction x is

$$F_x = -\frac{\partial E}{\partial x} = +\tfrac{1}{2}\mathrm{K}_v\,\delta v\frac{\partial H^2}{\partial x}.$$

This is obviously zero if the magnetic field is of uniform intensity, but in an inhomogeneous magnetic field the resultant force in any direction x on a particle of susceptibility K surrounded by a medium of susceptibility K_0 is

$$F_x = \tfrac{1}{2}(\mathrm{K}-\mathrm{K}_0)\,\delta v\,\partial H^2/\partial x.$$

If $\mathrm{K} > \mathrm{K}_0$, the resultant force tends to move the particle from the weak field to the strong field ($\partial H/\partial x$ positive), and vice versa. In a vacuum K must obviously be *unity* for then I is always equal to H. Substances which have $\mathrm{K} > 1$ are termed *paramagnetic*; they are attracted by magnets: substances having $\mathrm{K} < 1$ are termed *diamagnetic*; they are repelled by magnets.

Methods of measurement. The simplest method of measuring the magnetic susceptibility of a solid, first used by Gouy in 1889, and

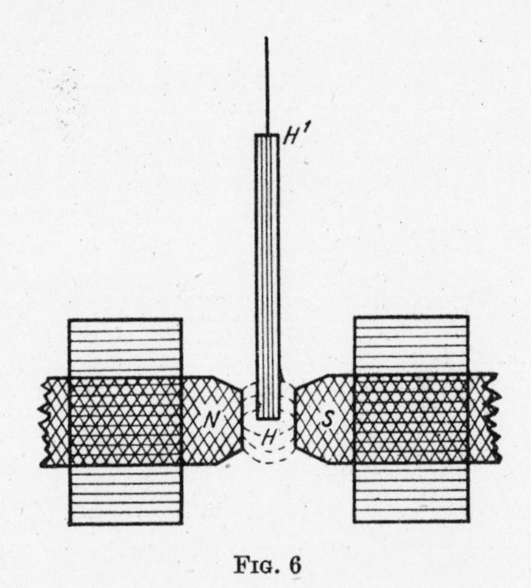

FIG. 6

improved by later workers,† is to place it, in the form of a rod, near the poles of a powerful electromagnet, as indicated in Fig. 6.

If H and H' are the magnetic intensities at the two ends of the rod, and A is its cross-section, then the force on the rod

$$F = \tfrac{1}{2}(\mathrm{K}-\mathrm{K}_0)A(H^2-H'^2).$$

† For examples see Stoner, *Magnetism and Matter*, Methuen, London, 1934; Sugden, *J.* 1932, p. 167; 1943, p. 328; Angus and Hill, *Trans. Faraday Soc.* 1943, **39**, 185.

H and H' can be determined once and for all by the use of search coils, and H' is negligible if a long rod is used. The force F can easily be measured by suspending the specimen under examination from one arm of a sensitive balance. Liquids can, of course, be placed inside a thin glass tube.

For the examination of liquids and solutions it is, however, much

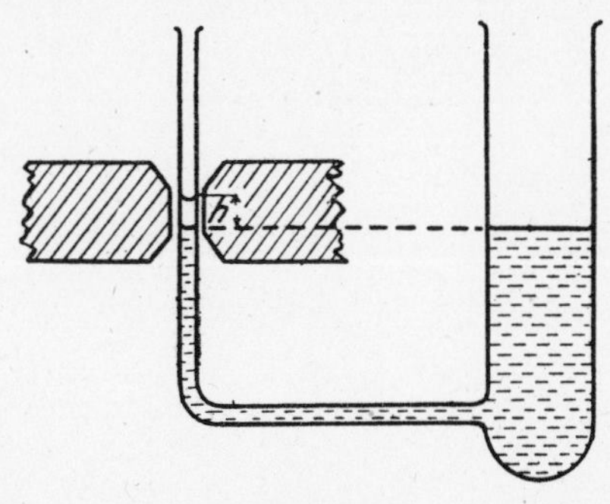

FIG. 7

simpler to use a fixed U-tube, of the design shown in Fig. 7. The wide limb is kept away from the magnetic field, whilst the narrow limb, which can be examined by means of a reading microscope, passes between the poles of a powerful electromagnet, and the liquid level is adjusted to reach the locality of most intense magnetization. When the magnetic field is applied the meniscus level of the liquid moves. If the total change in level is h and the density of the liquid is ρ, then the pressure change balances the magnetic force on the liquid when

$$h\rho g = \tfrac{1}{2}(\mathrm{K}-\mathrm{K}_0)(H^2-H'^2).$$

In practice only very small movements of the liquid level occur, and extreme care has to be taken to avoid relatively large systematic errors due to the residual magnetism of the pole pieces of the electromagnet, and to the occurrence of slight temperature, and consequent density, changes in the liquid. The U-tube method can, however, be used for the investigation of substances such as triphenylmethyl which react with the air, and for studying the course of magnetic changes during slow chemical reactions. Fig. 8 illustrates the principle of typical all-glass apparatus designed for this purpose.† The reactants are mixed in vessel A, and, after reaction has occurred inside a sealed, evacuated, system, the resulting solution is filtered through the sintered plate P into the U-tube section, which is then fitted between the poles of an

† Compare Roy and Marvel, *J.A.C.S.* 1937, **59**, 2622.

electromagnet. When the susceptibility measurements have been completed, samples of the solution can be withdrawn for analysis.

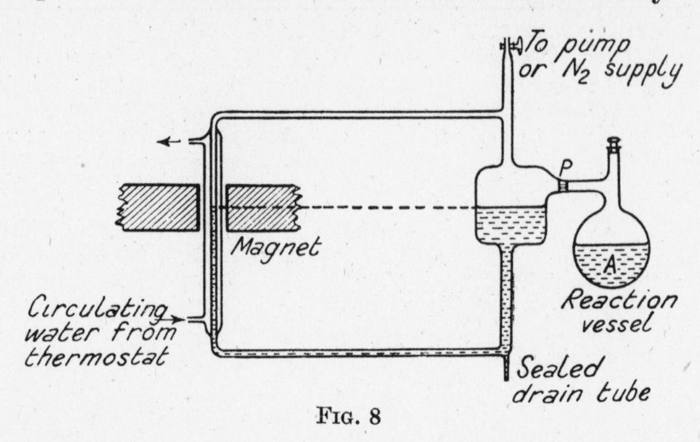

FIG. 8

Diamagnetism. Just as a coil of wire carrying an electric current tends to move into the position of least potential energy in a magnetic field, so, for the same reason, the planetary electrons of any molecular system will, when placed in a magnetic field, take up new orbits in which their resultant potential energy has, so far as is possible, been reduced to a minimum. Since it can be shown that any substance not possessing a permanent moment gains potential energy when it is placed in a magnetic field, the induced magnetization resulting from this redistribution of electronic orbits will tend to decrease the applied field, H. In other words, I tends to become less than H and consequently K becomes less than unity, a state of affairs corresponding to diamagnetism.

This readjustment of electronic orbits, which confers diamagnetic properties, is common to *all* molecules. For very simple atoms and molecules it can be calculated† that

$$\chi_d = -\frac{Ne^2}{6mc^2}\sum \bar{r}^2,$$

where e and m are the charge and mass of the electron and $\sum \bar{r}^2$ is the time average of the distance of the electron from the nucleus, summed up for all circumnuclear electrons, a factor which can be assessed by methods of quantum mechanics.‡ The experimental researches of Pascal in 1909–11 showed that the diamagnetic contribution, χ_d, to the molecular susceptibility of compounds was very closely an additive property of the component atoms. However, as in the case of most other additive properties of molecules, structural factors cannot

† Langevin, *Ann. Chim. Phys.* 1905, **5**, 70.

‡ Angus, *Annual Reports of the Chemical Society*, 1941, **38**, 27–46.

entirely be neglected. Whilst the diamagnetism of a salt is very closely the sum of the diamagnetic susceptibilities of the component ions, covalent bond formation causes a definite depression of diamagnetism.†

Atomic diamagnetic susceptibilities, χ_d, are quantities of the order of 10^{-6} electromagnetic units, and it is extremely difficult to measure them to more than 1 per cent. accuracy. Since systematic errors are prone to occur in all methods of magnetic susceptibility measurement, it is difficult to correlate the experimental results of different workers, and it is, as yet, somewhat premature to use diamagnetic susceptibility measurements for the elucidation of fine details of molecular structure.

Paramagnetism. As stated in earlier pages, some molecules have permanent magnetic moments, and such molecules will therefore tend to orient themselves in the direction of any applied magnetic field so as to reduce their potential energies. By reason of thermal collisions, this orientation of magnetic molecules in the direction of an applied magnetic field is never completely attained in either a gaseous or a liquid system. Langevin calculated that in a fluid the resultant mean moment $\bar{\mu}$ of any pure substance, was

$$\bar{\mu} = \mu^2 H/3kT,$$

where μ is its permanent molecular magnetic moment and k is Boltzmann's gas constant.

This resultant magnetic moment $\bar{\mu}$ in the direction of the applied field H, tends to increase the magnetic intensity, and consequently K is greater than unity.

Since the intensity of magnetization, I, of a substance can be expressed as the magnetic moment per unit volume, it follows that the magnetic susceptibility of a paramagnetic substance

$$\mathrm{K} = I/H = n_v \mu^2/3kT,$$

where n_v is the number of molecules per unit volume.

Hence the Molecular paramagnetic susceptibility can be written

$$\chi_\mu = \mathbf{N}\mu^2/3kT,$$

where **N** is Avogadro's number.

These equations of Langevin show that whilst diamagnetic susceptibility should be independent of temperature, paramagnetic susceptibilities should vary inversely with absolute temperature, and this had been shown to hold experimentally by Curie in 1895.

† For discussion of this see Angus, *Annual Reports of the Chemical Society*, 1941, **38**, 27–40; Trew, *Trans. Faraday Soc.* 1941, **37**, 476; Angus and Hill, ibid. 1943, **39**, 190, 197.

The expression of Langevin does not take into account the mutual interaction between magnetic particles. When this is done the Curie relationship becomes

$$\chi_{\mu} = \text{const.}/(T-\theta),$$

where θ is a second constant.

The molecular susceptibility χ_{μ} of any paramagnetic substance can be expressed in terms of its molecular magnetic moment by the equation

$$p_B = 2{\cdot}84\sqrt{\{\chi_{\mu}(T-\theta)\}},$$

p_B being measured in Bohr magnetons.

The measurable magnetic susceptibility of any substance χ_M, can be represented as the algebraic sum of its diamagnetic and paramagnetic contributions, χ_d and χ_{μ}, together with a small resonance term χ_R which is usually negligibly small. Whereas χ_d is of the order of 10^{-6} e.m.u., χ_{μ} for molecules which have permanent magnetic moments is of the order of 10^{-3} e.m.u. and thus completely outweighs the diamagnetic term in the equation

$$\chi_M = \chi_d + \chi_{\mu} + \chi_R.$$

As explained on p. 20 the magnetic moment of a molecule depends on the resultant angular momentum of its electrons. To a first approximation† the magnetic moment of a molecule can be calculated from the simple formula

$$p_B = \sqrt{\{4\mathbf{S}(\mathbf{S}+1)\}}, \quad \text{whence } \chi_{\mu} = \frac{4\mathbf{S}(\mathbf{S}+1)}{8{\cdot}06T},$$

where **S** is the net spin of the uncompleted electronic shells.

It must be noticed that the resultant magnetic moment of a molecule p_B is not equal to μ_i, the resolved (quantized) moment in the direction of an applied field (p. 22), for the resultant magnetic moment of a molecule containing one uncoupled electron ($\mathbf{S} = \frac{1}{2}$) is $\sqrt{3}$ Bohr magnetons.

Paramagnetic substances, in which the resultant magnetic moment is due merely to the resultant angular momentum of unpaired valency electrons, must be differentiated from *ferromagnetic* substances which have susceptibilities several thousand times as great. It has been suggested that ferromagnetic substances, which are invariably solids, have structures composed of atoms possessing electrons with parallel spins and not neutralizing spins.

Table III gives representative values for the magnetic susceptibilities of a few normal molecules, and of some simple free radicals, from which

† For a discussion of this, see Sugden, *J.* 1943, p. 328.

it can be seen that less than 0·5 per cent. of a free radical can be detected amongst normal diamagnetic substances.

TABLE III

Molecular Susceptibilities, in 10^{-6} e.m.u. at 20° C.†

Substance	χ_M measured	χ_d calculated	χ_μ	χ_μ theoretical
Helium	−1·88	−1·88	0·0	0
Water	−13	−13	..	0
Benzene	−56	−56	..	0
$CuCl_2$	+1252	−40	+1292	+1270
NO	+1465	−10	+1475	+1270
NO_2	+1392	−15	+1407	+1270
ClO_2	+1341	−25	+1366	+1270
O_2	+3388	−10	+3398	+3390
$(KSO_3)_2NO$	+1100	−40	+1140	+1270
$(NO_2C_6H_4)_3C$ Solid	+651	..	+792	..
$Ph_2C^{\cdot}—O^-K^+$ (15% solution in dioxane)	+1050	..	..	..

Further results of magnetic susceptibility measurements are discussed in later chapters of this book.

MAGNETIC INTERCONVERSION OF ORTHO- AND PARA-HYDROGEN

Free radicals can often be detected by means of their catalytic properties. These catalyses are usually due to chemical reactions of the radicals themselves whereby there can be initiated, or terminated, chain processes involving other molecules. In one reaction, however—the interconversion of the *ortho* and *para* forms of hydrogen—the catalysis may be purely physical in nature and brought about by the molecular magnetic fields of free radicals. This reaction can therefore be used for the diagnosis and measurement of free radicals.

Molecular hydrogen has two ground states, which have different heat capacities, and exhibit different rotation spectra.‡ In *para-hydrogen* the two atoms have antisymmetrical nuclear spins, and in *ortho-hydrogen* they have symmetrical nuclear spins. At normal temperatures the *ortho* and *para* forms of hydrogen do not tend to change, of themselves, into one another even upon mutual collision, and it has been shown that pure *para* hydrogen can be preserved for several weeks in glass at room temperature without being converted into the equilibrium

† Collected from Sugden, *Trans. Faraday Soc.* 1934, **30**, 22; Sugden and Allen, *J.* 1936, p. 440.

‡ For a review see A. Farkas, *Ortho-hydrogen, Para-hydrogen and Heavy Hydrogen*, Cambridge, 1935.

mixture (25 per cent. *para* H_2 to 75 per cent. *ortho* H_2) which is normal hydrogen gas. In 1933, Wigner† calculated that very strong magnetic fields might perturb molecular hydrogen sufficiently to bring about the interconversion of the *ortho* and *para* states without actually causing any molecular dissociation, and estimated that an atom or radical possessing a magnetic moment of one Bohr magneton could bring about this change provided that it came as close as an Angstrom unit (10^{-8} cm.) to a hydrogen molecule. He showed that the rate of interconversion should be proportional to the square of the magnetic moment of the catalyst, and inversely proportional to the sixth power of its distance away.

This theory has been abundantly confirmed, for both oxygen and nitric oxide are effective catalysts for the *ortho-para* hydrogen interconversion, whilst nitrogen, nitrous oxide, ammonia, and other diamagnetic gases are not catalysts. Nitrogen peroxide acts as a catalyst to an extent proportional to the degree of dissociation of diamagnetic N_2O_4 into paramagnetic NO_2.

Again, *para*-hydrogen can be changed to the equilibrium mixture by bubbling it through solutions containing paramagnetic atoms or radicals, or by adsorbing it on surfaces which have local foci of strong magnetization, and it can therefore be used to investigate molecular paramagnetism.

For example, whilst the rate of interconversion of hydrogen in water is only of the order of 10^{-5} of that induced by free radicals, and therefore ascribable to the minute magnetic moments of the atomic nuclei of the solvent molecules,‡ dissolved oxygen is quite as powerful a catalyst in water as in the gas phase. Paramagnetic cations in solution are powerful catalysts, whereas diamagnetic ions are not catalysts. This is shown by the following table.

TABLE IV

Rate of Conversion of Para-hydrogen by Metallic Sulphates

Ion	*Magnetic moment (Bohr magnetons)*	*Relative rate of interconversion due to ion catalysis*
Zn^{++}	0·0	0·0
Cu^{++}	3·53	1·15
Ni^{++}	5·56	1·95
Co^{++}	6·56	5·56
Fe^{++}	6·54	6·05
Mn^{++}	5·92	8·05

† *Zeit. phys. Chem.* 1933, B **23**, 28.

‡ L. Farkas and Sandler, *Trans. Faraday Soc.* 1939, **35**, 337.

Moreover Schwab and Agallides† have shown that solutions containing free triphenylmethyl bring about the interconversion of *ortho-* and *para*-hydrogen at a rate equal to that calculable for a free radical of moment 1·73 Bohr magnetons, which is the value deduced from magnetic susceptibility relationships (p. 30).

Though many surfaces can effect the *ortho–para* interconversion of adsorbed molecular hydrogen, it is often a difficult problem to decide whether the surface catalysis is a physical process, brought about by local magnetic fields, or a chemical reaction involving dissociated, but chemi-sorbed, hydrogen atoms which interchange with molecular hydrogen at a surface by the same reaction process,

$$H\cdot + H_2(\text{para}) \rightleftharpoons H_2(\text{ortho}) + \cdot H,$$

as that which occurs in the gas phase at high temperatures (p. 86) whenever free atomic hydrogen is present, or can be made by displacement reactions of active free radicals, such as $CH_3\cdot + H_2 = CH_4 + H\cdot$ (compare p. 91).

However, it seems clear that the normal process of making pure *para*-hydrogen, by cooling hydrogen adsorbed on activated charcoal to as low a temperature as possible by means of an external bath of liquid hydrogen, does not involve the momentary production of hydrogen atoms, because under these conditions the interchange reaction between hydrogen and deuterium, $H_2 + D_2 \rightleftharpoons 2H—D$ does not take place.‡ Low temperature surface catalysis of this interconversion by charcoal, unlike the interconversion brought about on platinum or nickel surfaces (pp. 217–18), must therefore be attributed to the presence of uncoupled electrons which would produce intense local electrical fields, and this conclusion substantiates the view that solid carbon has essentially the crystal structure of graphite, built up of sheets of tercovalent carbon atoms, each of which is linked to other ring structures as in hydrocarbons of the triphenylmethyl type.§

Magnetic surface catalysis undoubtedly occurs on paramagnetic compounds of iron and of copper, such as haematin and copper phthalocyanine,|| since the metal-free analogues are devoid of catalytic activity. Catalysis by chromic oxide, Cr_2O_3, vanadium trioxide, V_2O_3,

† *Zeit. phys. Chem.* 1938, B **41**, 59.
‡ Gould, Bleakney, and Taylor, *J. Chem. Phys.* 1934, **2**, 362.
§ Riley *et al.*, *J.* 1936, p. 456; 1937, p. 1305; *J. Inst. Fuel*, 1937, **10**, 149.
|| Eley, *Trans. Faraday Soc.* 1940, **36**, 500.

and the oxides of the rare earths can possibly be explained in the same way.†

The surface of the solid nitrogenous free radical αα-diphenyl-β-picryl hydrazyl (III of Chapter IV, see p. 68) is also an active catalyst for bringing about this interconversion of hydrogen.‡

† Taylor and Diamond, *J.A.C.S.* 1935, **57**, 1251.
‡ Turkevitch and Selwood, ibid. 1941, **63**, 1277.

III

TRIPHENYLMETHYL AND ITS ANALOGUES

GOMBERG'S discovery of triphenylmethyl, and his evidence for the reversible dissociation of the parent hydrocarbon hexaphenylethane, have been described in Chapter I. Later work has greatly extended practical knowledge of aromatic compounds of this type, but only in comparatively recent years has it been shown that one can prepare a whole range of substances from the easily dissociable type

$$(Aryl)_3C—C(Aryl)_3$$

to compounds such as $Ph_2C(CH_3)—C(CH_3)Ph_2$ with which one may infer the occurrence of thermal dissociation in solution only from the reactions which they undergo.

Whilst it has been a comparatively easy matter to obtain conclusive experimental evidence of the dissociation of these aryl-substituted ethanes, it has been a difficult problem to assign correct structural formulae to the trivalent dissociation products. Not for many years was it realized clearly that a covalent bond could be broken *either* to give ions *or* neutral radicals, and that hexaphenylethane could dissociate in both ways. Moreover, though it was at once pointed out that the production of colour upon dissociation was indicative of the production of a quinonoid ring system, it has been only with the development of the conception of resonance that it has been realized that the possible formulation of triphenylmethyl in both benzenoid and quinonoid states contributes to its inherent stability.

IONIC DISSOCIATION OF HEXAPHENYLETHANE

The disruption of the carbon to carbon linkage of hexaphenylethane frequently results from the ionization $Ph_3C—CPh_3 \rightleftharpoons Ph_3C^+ + CPh_3^-$,

TABLE V

Molecular dilution (litres)	*Molecular conductivity*
24	8·24
43	11·97
66	17·14
98	22·15
137	26·79
165	28·89
230	31·27
461	32·50
2138	39·59

the occurrence of which was first established by Walden, who in 1903† showed that solutions of hexaphenylethane in liquid sulphur dioxide had a high molecular conductivity which increased upon dilution (compare Table V).

Solvation plays an important part in the stabilization of the cation formed by the ionic dissociation of hexaphenylethane, since coloured addition compounds can be obtained from solutions in ethers, esters, ketones, and nitriles, amongst other substances. These addition products must be given the formulae of oxonium or ammonium salts, e.g. (I) or (II):

$$\left[\begin{matrix} C_2H_5 & & CPh_3 \\ & O & \\ C_2H_5 & & \end{matrix}\right]^+ (CPh_3)^- \qquad (CH_3{-}C{\equiv}N{-}CPh_3)^+(CPh_3)^-$$

(I) (II)

in which the triphenylmethyl cation is stabilized by the formation of a dative bond with the available electron pair of an oxygen or nitrogen atom.‡

Sidgwick has suggested that sulphur dioxide reacts in a similar way, yielding a product in which each atom has its complete octet of electrons:

$$Ph_3C^+ + \overset{-}{O}{-}\overset{++}{S}{-}\overset{-}{O} \rightleftharpoons Ph_3C{-}O{-}\overset{++}{S}{-}\overset{-}{O}.$$

The anion of triphenylmethyl, $(Ph_3C:)^-$, cannot be further stabilized in this manner, since no common solvents are electron acceptors. As one would anticipate, therefore, it is a much more reactive substance than is the cation. It is present in solutions of sodium triphenylmethyl in ether, pyridine, or liquid ammonia, all of which are good conductors of electricity.§

Mesomerism of the Ions of Triphenylmethyl

Both the cation and the anion of triphenylmethyl are mesomeric. Thus one can assign to the cation, Ph_3C^+, which is present in the deep orange-yellow solutions of triphenylcarbinol in strong mineral acids, a benzenoid state (III) and also two quinonoid states (IV and V), in which any one of the three aromatic rings may be involved. Analogous structures may be assigned to the canonical states of the red triphenylmethyl anion.

† Walden, *Zeit. phys. Chem.* 1903, **43**, 385; compare Walden, *Chemie der Freien Radikale*, Leipzig, 1924.

‡ Cf. Bowden, *J.* 1939, p. 35.

§ Schlenk and Ochs, *Ber.* 1916, **49**, 614; Kraus and Rosen, *J.A.C.S.* 1925, **47**, 2739.

```
Ph   +   Ph          Ph       Ph          Ph       Ph
   \ C /                \ C /                \ C /
     |                    ‖                    ‖
     C                    C                    C
   /   ⫽                /   \  +             /   \
 CH     CH            CH     CH            CH     CH
 ‖      |             ‖      |             ‖      ‖
 CH     CH            CH     CH            CH     CH
   \   ⫽                \   ⫽                \ +  /
     CH                   CH                   CH
   (III)                (IV)                  (V)
```

Definite chemical evidence for the participation of quinonoid states in the structure of the cation has been supplied by Gomberg and Cone,† who showed that when tri-*p*-bromophenylmethyl chloride is dissolved in liquid sulphur dioxide it is, in part, transformed into chloro-dibromo-triphenylmethyl bromide. Moreover, tri-*p*-bromophenylmethyl chloride on treatment with silver powder yields some chloro-dibromo-triphenylmethyl. This interchange of halogen elements is due to the occurrence of the equilibria,

$$(BrC_6H_4)_2\overset{+}{C}{-}C\begin{matrix}\diagup CH{-}CH \diagdown\\ \diagdown CH{=}CH \diagup\end{matrix}C{-}Br \quad \underset{\text{with}}{\text{mesomeric}} \quad (BrC_6H_4)_2C{=}C\begin{matrix}\diagup CH{=}CH \diagdown\\ \diagdown CH{=}CH \diagup\end{matrix}\overset{+}{C}{-}Br$$

$$\downarrow Cl^-$$

$$(BrC_6H_4)_2C{=}C\begin{matrix}\diagup CH{=}CH \diagdown\\ \diagdown CH{=}CH \diagup\end{matrix}\overset{+}{C}{-}Cl \quad \underset{-Br^-}{\overset{+Br^-}{\rightleftharpoons}} \quad (BrC_6H_4)_2C{=}C\begin{matrix}\diagup CH{=}CH \diagdown\\ \diagdown CH{=}CH \diagup\end{matrix}C\begin{matrix}\diagup Cl\\ \diagdown Br\end{matrix}$$

and is favoured by the fact that silver bromide has a smaller solubility than silver chloride.

The facts that although triphenylmethyl fluoride does not (in common with most other organic fluorides) react with silver,‡ it is possible to displace fluorine from tri-*p*-fluorophenylmethyl chloride $(FC_6H_4)_3CCl$, by dissolving it in liquid sulphur dioxide,§ or by shaking it with molecular silver in benzene solution|| indicate that all halogen atoms in quinonoid structures such as (VI)

$$R_2C{=}\langle\bigcirc\rangle{=}C\begin{matrix}\diagup F\\ \diagdown Hal\end{matrix} \qquad \text{(VI)}$$

are particularly labile.

The presumption that the above changes follow an ionic course is substantiated by the fact that one can, by use of silver sulphate, replace

† *Annalen*, 1910, **376**, 183. ‡ Blicke, *J.A.C.S.* 1924, **46**, 1515.
§ Bacon and Gardner, *J. Org. Chem.* 1938, **3**, 281.
|| Bowden and Watkins, *J.* 1940, p. 1249.

halogen atoms by sulphate radicals and obtain products which, on subsequent hydrolysis yield hydroxy compounds,† e.g.

$$Ph_2C(Cl)-C_6H_4-F \xrightarrow[\text{followed by water}]{Ag_2SO_4 \text{ in } PhNO_2} Ph_2C(OH)-C_6H_4-OH$$

Neutral Triphenylmethyl Radicals

The dissociation of hexaphenylethane occurs not only in ionizing solvents such as sulphur dioxide but also in non-ionizing solvents such as benzene and naphthalene. The solutions of this latter type are paramagnetic, and therefore must contain the free *neutral* radical, $Ph_3C\cdot$, having an unpaired electron (Chapter II). This again must be regarded as a resonance hybrid, considerably more stable than is the free methyl radical (see pp. 57–60), and in its solutions it may be further stabilized by solvation, since it has been shown that hexaphenylethane forms easily dissociated addition complexes with solvents such as chloroform, benzene, cyclohexane, and heptane.‡

Gomberg and Sullivan§ regarded the colours of solutions of hexaphenylethane in ionizing and in non-ionizing solvents as being qualitatively different, and considered that in this way they could differentiate between the charged ions and the radicals of triphenylmethyl. The more exact measurements of Ziegler and Ewald,‖ however, have shown that the differences between the absorption spectra of solutions of hexaphenylethane in different solvents are but slight, particularly when one takes into account the fact that many of these solutions are decomposed by light. It would seem that the relationship between colour and constitution in such complicated resonance systems as that of triphenylmethyl is far too involved for one to be able to arrive at any definite conclusions regarding molecular structure in solution in this way.

Preparation of Compounds of the Triarylmethyl Series

1. Gomberg's method.

$$(Aryl)_3C{-}Cl + \text{Metal} \longrightarrow (Aryl)_3C\cdot + \text{Metallic chloride.}$$

The metals silver, zinc, copper, and mercury have been most used for the preparation of the triarylmethyls, though many others will react

† Bowden and Watkins, loc. cit. Cf. Gomberg, *Ber.* 1907, **40**, 1852.

‡ Gomberg, *Chemical Reviews*, 1924, **1**, 91; 1925, **2**, 310.

§ *J.A.C.S.* 1922, **44**, 1811.

‖ *Annalen*, 1929, **473**, 163; compare Gomberg and Forrester, *J.A.C.S.* 1925, **47**, 2373; Marvel, Mueller, and Ginsberg, ibid. 1939, **61**, 2008; Anderson, ibid. 1935, **57**, 1673.

successfully.† Silver powder and mercury are the most suitable reagents to choose, since they react quite readily at room temperature and give halides which are easily removed by filtration. A large number of solvents such as ether, benzene, petrol, carbon disulphide, and ethyl acetate have been used, according to the solubility of the starting

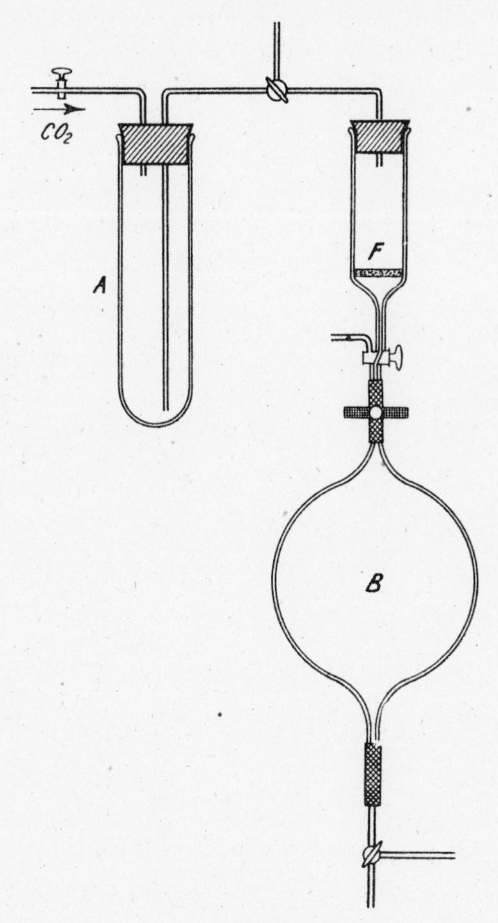

FIG. 9

product. The solvent, however, must be quite free from moisture, dissolved oxygen, or traces of acids. Light tends to bring about the decomposition of many of the free radicals and should therefore be excluded as much as possible.

For handling the free radicals it is necessary to shake together the reactants and then filter off the inorganic halide in a vessel from which

† Compare Thomas, Bowden, and Jones, *J.* 1930, p. 473.

all air has been excluded. A simple type of apparatus for this purpose is illustrated in Fig. 9.

A solution of the halide and silver powder can be shaken together in tube *A*, which is completely filled with liquid, and when the reaction is complete the clear liquid can be siphoned over into the bulb *B* through a filter *F* by passing pure dry carbon dioxide into *A*. The solution in *B* can then be evaporated in a stream of carbon dioxide or, alternatively, other reactants can be added without there being any access of air.

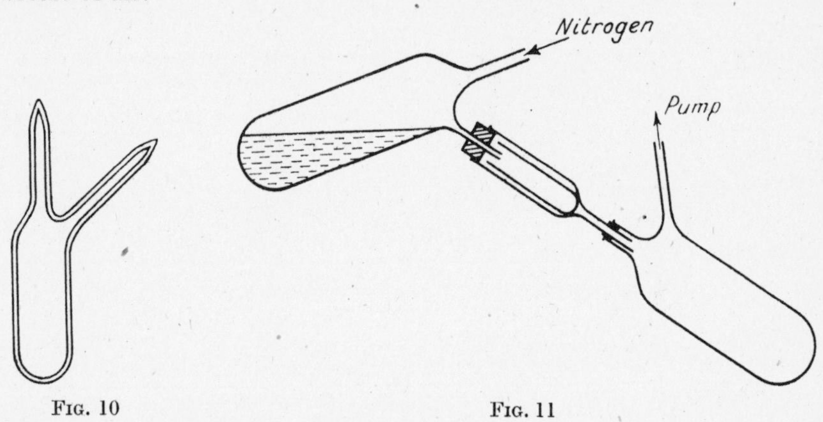

Fig. 10 Fig. 11

For keeping solutions of free radicals, Schlenk made use of tubes of the shape of Fig. 10. With these, filtration in an inert atmosphere can easily be carried out through a Soxhlet thimble as illustrated in Fig. 11. Ground glass joints and sintered filter plates can of course be used in modern refinements of apparatus of this type, but it must be borne in mind that the design should be such as to allow cleaning and drying to be carried out with ease.

For making physical measurements with solutions of free radicals it has often been found necessary to prepare the solution to be used in a section of the apparatus and then to filter off a part through a sintered glass plate attached directly to the reaction vessel. In this case it is necessary either to assume that the preparative reaction has been quantitative, or else to withdraw another portion of the filtered solution for analysis. Quantitative reaction with gaseous oxygen, and collection of the resultant peroxide, has frequently been used for this latter purpose.

Descriptions of special apparatus of this type have been published by Ziegler, Bent, Marvel, and others† (compare Fig. 8).

† Ziegler and Ewald, *Annalen*, 1929, **473**, 163; Bent and Keevil, *J.A.C.S.* 1936, **58**, 1228; Roy and Marvel, ibid. 1937, **59**, 2622.

2. Use of Grignard reagents. The halogen atom, or other acid radical of a carbonium salt, may be removed by interaction with a Grignard reagent, or with a metallic alkyl. In simple cases, stable hydrocarbons are thereby formed, but occasionally a free radical results and its production is evidenced by the appearance of a colour, or better by the formation of a peroxide when the resultant solutions are exposed to the air. For example, in the xanthene series Ziegler and Ochs found that both the following reactions occurred:†

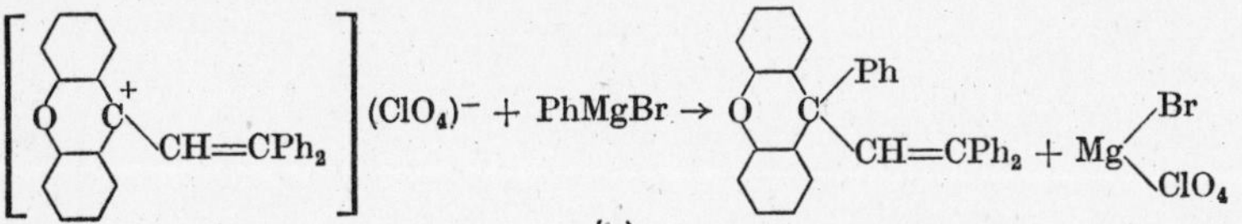

[O C$^+$—CH=CPh$_2$] $(ClO_4)^-$ + PhMgBr → O C(Ph)—CH=CPh$_2$ + Mg(Br)(ClO$_4$)

(a)

2[O C$^+$—CH=CPh$_2$] $(ClO_4)^-$ + 2PhMgBr → 2[O C—CH=CPh$_2$] + Ph$_2$ + 2Mg(Br)(ClO$_4$)

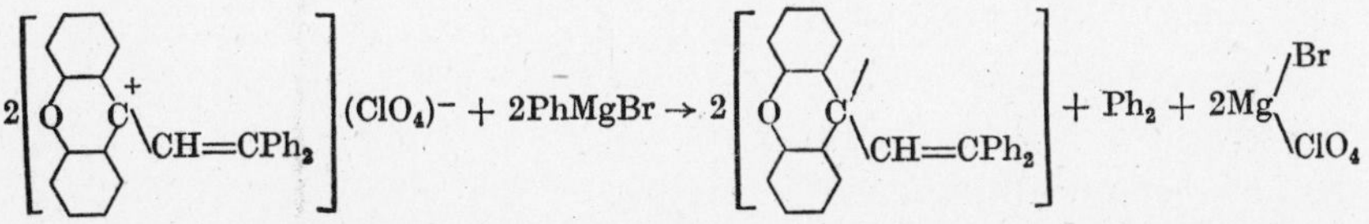

(b)

The reaction between triphenylmethyl chloride and phenyl magnesium bromide is complex, for the products include tetraphenylmethane, triphenylmethane, and also the diphenyl derivatives (VII) and (VIII).‡

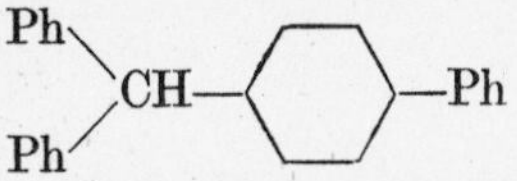

$Ph_2CH—C_6H_4—Ph$ (VII) $Ph—CH(C_6H_4Ph)_2$ (VIII)

Schoepfle§ ascribed the formation of the hydrocarbons (VII) and (VIII) to a reaction of triphenylmethyl chloride in the quinonoid form

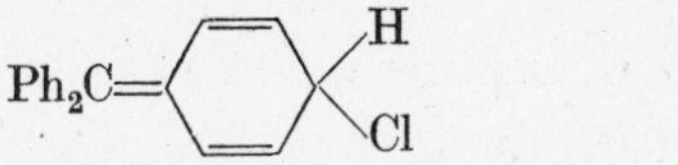

$Ph_2C{=}C_6H_4(H)(Cl)$ (IX)

followed by molecular rearrangement of (IX) to give (VII) (compare p. 37).

It is evident, therefore, that either the free mesomeric cation $(Aryl)_3C^+$ or else the free mesomeric radical $(Aryl)_3C\cdot$ must be present during the course of the reaction. Since the anomalous products can be formed in solvents such as benzene, which do not favour ion formation, it would appear that Grignard reagents can react with halides in two consecutive stages:

(i) $Ph_3C—Cl + PhMgBr \longrightarrow Ph_3C\cdot + Ph\cdot + MgClBr$

(ii) $Ph_3C\cdot + \cdot Ph \longrightarrow Ph_4C$ (or isomerides)

† *Ber.* 1922, **55**, 2257. ‡ Gilman and Jones, *J.A.C.S.* 1929, **51**, 2840.
§ *J.A.C.S.* 1936, **58**, 791; 1937, **59**, 372.

and that as alternatives to stage (ii) other reactions of the phenyl radical may also occur (compare pp. 49–52). This mechanism will account for the formation of triphenylmethane in this reaction.

Triphenylmethyl chloride, and its analogues, react with magnesium metal in dry ether to give Grignard reagents of the type $Ph_3C—MgHal$. Solutions of these Grignard reagents react very rapidly and quantitatively with a further molecule of the original halide, yielding hexaphenylethane, and of course some triphenylmethyl.†

3. Other reducing agents. Conant has shown that solutions of triarylmethyl chlorides, or of triaryl carbinols in concentrated hydrochloric or sulphuric acids, can be reduced to the free radicals by powerful reducing agents such as vanadous chloride, titanous chloride, and chromous chloride, which undergo a unit valency change:‡

$$Ph_3C^+ + Ti^{+++} \longrightarrow Ph_3C\cdot + Ti^{++++}.$$

The reactions have to be carried out in an inert atmosphere. By this method Conant and Bigelow§ have shown that strongly acid solutions of triphenylmethane dyes can yield free radicals (X), as reduction products intermediate between the colour base and the leuco base.

$$Ph_2C\begin{matrix}\diagup C_6H_4—NMe_2\\ \diagdown Cl\end{matrix} \longrightarrow Ph_2C\cdot\diagup C_6H_4—NMe_2 \longrightarrow Ph_2C\begin{matrix}\diagup C_6H_4—NMe_2\\ \diagdown H\end{matrix}$$

(X)

The intermediate free radicals are very highly coloured substances which can form peroxides and alkali metal derivatives.

Sodium diethyl phosphite is another reducing agent of this type.||

Reactions of Free Triarylmethyl Radicals

1. Addition of alkali metals. Solutions of triphenylmethyl react with sodium and potassium metals to form brick-red solids, Ph_3CNa, Ph_3CK, solutions of which conduct electricity, and, therefore, contain the anion Ph_3C^-.¶ The analogous Grignard reagent, Ph_3CMgBr, may be made either by treating an ether solution of triphenylmethyl bromide with an excess of magnesium or by shaking triphenylmethyl in ether with a mixture of magnesium metal and magnesium bromide (which behaves as the system $Mg + MgBr_2 = 2\cdot MgBr$).††

† Schmidlin, *Ber.* 1908, **41**, 423; Gomberg and Bachmann, *J.A.C.S.* 1930, **52**, 2455.
‡ *J.A.C.S.* 1923, **45**, 2466; 1925, **47**, 1959.
§ Ibid. 1931, **53**, 677.
|| Arbusov and Arbusov, *J. Russ. Phys. Chem. Soc.* 1929, **61**, 1923.
¶ Schlenk and Marcus, *Ber.* 1914, **47**, 1664.
†† Gomberg and Bachmann, *J.A.C.S.* 1930, **52**, 2455.

Sodium triphenylmethyl is in reality a salt, of similar nature, and with similar chemical properties, to other sodium alkyls and aryls, e.g. sodium phenyl Ph^-Na^+ (compare Chapter X, pp. 203–9). Thus it can be used for metallation of organic compounds, i.e. for preparing the sodium salts of very weak acids. A good estimate of the extent to which this interchange of alkali metal atoms may occur is given by the fact that solutions of sodium triphenylmethyl in liquid ammonia yield an equilibrium mixture

$$Ph_3CNa + NH_3 \rightleftharpoons Ph_3C{-}H + NaNH_2.\dagger$$

The red colour of sodium triphenylmethyl is undoubtedly due to the fact that the anion is a resonance hybrid, since sodium phenyl is colourless. Similar coloured alkali-metal compounds are obtained by the addition of two molecules of an alkali metal to olefines containing aromatic groups.‡

The reaction $(Ph_3C\cdot)+Na\cdot \rightleftharpoons (Ph_3C:)^-Na^+$ is reversible, for when a solution of sodium triphenylmethyl in ether is shaken with metallic mercury some sodium amalgam is formed. The same is true of the analogous potassium and lithium derivatives.

By analysing the sodium amalgam produced by reactions of this type, Bent and his colleagues§ have determined the equilibrium constants and free energy changes of the ionization processes. Bent and Keevil‖ have also determined these equilibrium constants by the use of electrolytic cells of the type

Na amalgam | triphenylmethyl solution | platinum.

They have used their results for computing the bond strengths of hexa-arylethane derivatives and of analogous dissociable compounds of the dixanthyl series.¶

In ether solution the free energy change $Ph_3C\cdot + e \rightarrow (Ph_3C:)^-$ was found to be 17·9 k.cals. per mol.

2. Addition of halogens. The halogens react very rapidly with solutions of hexaphenylethane giving triphenylmethyl halides, which, though colourless in the solid state, dissolve in ionizing solvents yielding conducting solutions containing the yellow carbonium cation. This

† Kraus and Rosen, *J.A.C.S.* 1925, **47**, 2739; Kraus and Kawamura, ibid. 1923, **45**, 2756.

‡ Schlenk and Bergmann, *Annalen*, 1928, **463**, 1; 1930, **479**, 58.

§ Bent, *J.A.C.S.* 1930, **52**, 1499; 1931, **53**, 1789; Bent and Dorfman, ibid. 1932, **54**, 1393; Bent, Dorfman, and Bruce, ibid., p. 3250.

‖ Bent and Keevil, *J.A.C.S.* 1936, **58**, 1228; Keevil, ibid. 1937, **59**, 2104.

¶ Bent and Ebers, *J.A.C.S.* 1935, **57**, 1242. Compare Conant, *J. Chem. Phys.* 1935, **1**, 427.

dissociation is favoured by solvation (p. 36) and also by double salt formation with other halides, such as $AlCl_3$, $SbCl_5$, and $SnCl_4$: e.g.

$$Ph_3C—Cl + AlCl_3 \longrightarrow (Ph_3C)^+(AlCl_4)^-.$$

In the case of iodine, the reaction $2Ph_3C\cdot + I_2 \rightleftharpoons 2Ph_3C—I$ is reversible, since the triphenylmethyl iodide dissociates to the extent of 20–40 per cent. even in non-ionizing solvents.† This dissociation may also be brought about photochemically.

Iodine does not appear to react with undissociated hexaphenylethane, but the combination of the free triphenylmethyl radical and molecular iodine seems to require scarcely any activation energy. This reaction has been used by Ziegler, Ewald, and Orth‡ to determine the rate of dissociation of hexaphenylethane into triphenylmethyl. In a specially designed apparatus, iodine solution was added to a chloroform solution of hexaphenylethane, containing also both ethyl alcohol and pyridine, and the rate of disappearance of the iodine, which is independent of its concentration, was determined colorimetrically by recording photographically, at short intervals, the optical extinction coefficient of the reaction mixture. The alcohol and pyridine served to prevent the dissociation of any triphenylmethyl iodide by reacting with it immediately to form the stable colourless products, ethoxytriphenylmethane and pyridine hydriodide:

$$Ph_3C—I + HOEt \rightarrow Ph_3C—OEt + HI; \qquad HI + C_5H_5N \rightarrow C_5H_5N,HI.$$

Bachmann and Osborn§ have measured the rates of dissociation of pentaphenylethane, and of several of its derivatives, by the same method.

The reaction between hexaphenylethane and bromine solutions was found by Ziegler to be practically instantaneous, and it was therefore concluded that bromine, unlike iodine, can react with the undissociated hexa-arylethane molecule. However, a rapid chain reaction may well be involved (see below—reaction of oxygen)

$$Ph_6C_2 \rightleftharpoons 2Ph_3C\cdot \qquad Ph_3C\cdot + Br_2 \longrightarrow Ph_3C—Br + Br\cdot$$

$$Ph_6C_2 + \cdot Br \longrightarrow Ph_3C—Br\cdot + Ph_3C\cdot.$$

3. Addition of nitric oxide and of nitrogen peroxide. Schlenk and Mair‖ found that addition occurs when nitric oxide is passed into solutions of triphenylmethyl, and that there is formed a bluish-green

† Gomberg, *Chemical Reviews*, 1924, **1**, 116.
‡ *Annalen*, 1930, **479**, 277.
§ Bachmann and Osborn, *J. Org. Chem.* 1940, **5**, 29.
‖ *Ber.* 1911, **44**, 1170.

product, nitroso-triphenylmethane, $Ph_3C—NO$, which rapidly polymerizes to a colourless product, believed to be $(Ph_3C—NO)_2$. Ziegler, Orth, and Weber† showed that this reaction was unimolecular and that, in a large number of solvents, it proceeds at a rate which is independent both of the pressure and of the solubility of the nitric oxide provided that the initial solutions were saturated with nitric oxide gas at a partial pressure of not less than one atmosphere. They therefore concluded that the reaction sequence was:

$$\text{(i)} \quad Ph_3C—CPh_3 \longrightarrow 2Ph_3C\cdot \qquad \text{(slow)}$$

$$\text{(ii)} \quad Ph_3C\cdot + \cdot NO \longrightarrow Ph_3C—NO \qquad \text{(instantaneous)}$$

and, by measuring the rate of absorption of nitric oxide, they determined the rate of dissociation of hexaphenylethane, and of some of its analogues, in a large number of solvents. The combination of triphenylmethyl and nitric oxide seems to be slightly reversible, but the forward reaction could be favoured by adding about 5 per cent. of aniline to the solvent mixture. This reacts immediately with the nitroso compound, though under these conditions rapid secondary reactions occur, in which three molecules of nitric oxide in all are absorbed for each molecule of triphenylmethyl. No very great accuracy can be obtained by this technique, since the time of half dissociation of dilute solutions of hexaphenylethane is of the order of 2–5 minutes.

A very similar reaction seems to occur between triphenylmethyl and nitrogen peroxide, but this has not, as yet, been studied kinetically. The reaction product is a mixture of the nitro compound $Ph_3C—NO_2$ and the nitrite, $Ph_3C—O—NO$. It would seem, therefore, that nitrogen peroxide has a mesomeric structure in which the odd electron is capable of association with both the nitrogen and the oxygen atom, i.e.

$$:\ddot{\underset{\cdot\cdot}{O}}:\dot{\underset{\cdot}{N}}::\ddot{O}: \quad \text{and} \quad \cdot\ddot{\underset{\cdot\cdot}{O}}:\ddot{N}::\ddot{O}:$$

though a three-electron bonded structure can also be used, viz.

$$:\underset{\cdot\cdot}{O}\overset{\cdot\cdot\cdot}{—}N{=}\underset{\cdot\cdot}{\ddot{O}} \quad \text{(compare p. 63).}$$

4. Addition of oxygen. Gomberg‡ showed that oxygen gas reacts quantitatively with solutions containing triphenylmethyl to give the colourless peroxide, $Ph_3C—O—O—CPh_3$, which can also be obtained by treating triphenylmethyl chloride with sodium peroxide.§

† *Annalen*, 1933, **504**, 131.

‡ *Ber.* 1900, **33**, 3150.

§ Wieland, *Ber.* 1911, **44**, 2550.

On heating, this peroxide undergoes a molecular rearrangement to tetraphenyl-diphenoxy-ethane, the phenyl ether of a pinacone. This change may be interpreted as occurring by a dissociation of the peroxide, followed by a rearrangement of the free oxygen radical so produced.

$$Ph_3C—O—O—CPh_3 \rightarrow 2Ph_3C—O\cdot \rightarrow 2Ph_2\dot{C}—O—Ph \rightarrow \begin{array}{l} Ph_2C—O—Ph \\ \quad | \\ Ph_2C—O—Ph \end{array}$$

The resulting product can itself dissociate into free radicals of $Ph_2\dot{C}—O—Ph$, but this occurs only to a very slight extent.† Further decomposition to a mixture of $Ph_2C(OPh)_2$ and $Ph_2C{=}CPh_2$ occurs at high temperatures.

The reaction between triphenylmethyl and oxygen is, however, much more complicated than the termolecular equation

$$2Ph_3C\cdot + O_2 = Ph_3C—O—O—CPh_3$$

would indicate.‡ Solutions of hexaphenylethane absorb oxygen much more rapidly than they do nitric oxide, and the initial product is evidently an active peroxide free radical, $Ph_3C—O—O\cdot$, which can attack undissociated hexaphenylethane, and be regenerated by a chain reaction process as follows:

(i) $Ph_3C—CPh_3 \longrightarrow 2Ph_3C\cdot$ *chain initiation*

(ii) $Ph_3C\cdot + O_2 \longrightarrow Ph_3C—O—O\cdot$ *chain reaction*

(iii) $Ph_3C—O—O\cdot + Ph_3C—CPh_3 \rightarrow Ph_3C—O—O—CPh_3 + Ph_3C\cdot$

(iv) $2Ph_3C—O—O\cdot \longrightarrow Ph_3C—O—O—CPh_3 + O_2$ *chain breaking.*

If pyrogallol in excess is added to the reaction mixture then one molecular proportion of oxygen is absorbed per triphenylmethyl group and the initial peroxide is stabilized as the hydroperoxide, $Ph_3C—O—O—H$.§ Under these circumstances the rate of uptake of oxygen by hexaphenylethane is unimolecular, independent of the partial pressure of the oxygen, and equal to the rate of uptake of nitric oxide.||

The reaction between triphenylmethyl and oxygen under these conditions has been used by Ziegler and his colleagues for measuring the rates of dissociation of hexaphenylethane derivatives and thence deducing their energies of activation.¶ The results so obtained are illustrated in

† Bowden, *J.* 1939, p. 26.

‡ Mithoff and Branch, *J.A.C.S.* 1930, **52**, 255; Ziegler and Ewald, *Annalen*, 1933, **504**, 162.

§ Wieland and Maier, *Ber.* 1931, **64**, 1207; Ziegler and Herte, *Annalen*, 1942, **551**, 206.

|| Ziegler, Ewald, and Seib, *Annalen*, 1933, **504**, 182; Ziegler and Luttringhaus, ibid., p. 189.

¶ Ziegler, Seib, Knoevenagel, Herte, and Andreas, *Annalen*, 1942, **551**, 150.

Table VI. The much less readily dissociable analogous compounds of the dixanthyl series (XI)

(XI)

have been investigated similarly by Conant and Evans.† These substances which are only half oxidized in an hour at 25°, absorb oxygen unimolecularly at a rate independent of the partial pressure of the gas above the solvent even in the absence of pyrogallol.

Bachmann and Wiselogle‡ have used the same technique for studying the oxidation of pentaphenylethane and its analogues, $Ar_3C—Ar_2CH$. At 100° pentaphenylethane reacts with oxygen by the same mechanism as does hexaphenylethane, but the reaction requires more activation energy.

TABLE VI

Velocity of Dissociation of Hexaphenylethane at 0° C.

Solvent	*Velocity constant = 10k*		*Time of half dissociation (minutes)*
	Nitric oxide method§	*Oxygen method‖*	
Carbon tetrachloride	2·27–2·43	..	2·86–3·03
Chloroform	2·09	2·19	3·30
Ethylene dibromide	1·93–1·99	..	3·57–3·47
Aniline	1·85–1·96	..	3·73–3·53
Ethyl alcohol	1·66–1·79	1·59	4·15–3·85
Toluene	1·48	1·50	4·67
Nitrobenzene	1·40–1·59	1·71	4·87–4·50
Dimethylaniline	1·38–1·41	..	4·98–4·91
Ethylene chlorohydrin	1·31–1·37	..	5·25–5·02
Ethyl malonate	1·34–1·37	1·34	5·15–5·12
Ethyl cyanoacetate	0·93–1·15	1·17	7·30–5·97
Methyl salicylate	1·24	1·25	5·58
Mesityl oxide	1·02–1·46	1·24	6·67–4·72
Pyridine	1·23–1·39	..	5·61–4·96
Acetonitrile	..	0·65	..
Carbon disulphide	..	2·52	..

Ziegler and his colleagues¶ have shown that the initial peroxide radical, $Ph_3C—O—O\cdot$, is a very effective catalyst for bringing about

† Conant and Evans, *J.A.C.S.* 1929, **51**, 1920. ‡ *J. Org. Chem.* 1936, **1**, 354.

§ Results of Ziegler, Orth, and Weber, *Annalen*, 1933, **504**, 131.

‖ Results of Ziegler, Seib, Knoevenagel, and Andreas, *Annalen*, 1942, **551**, 153. (The velocity of dissociation of hexaphenylethane as determined by the iodine method (p. 44) is about 20 per cent. larger than the above values. It is now thought by Ziegler that it is complicated by a side reaction which simultaneously uses up iodine.)

¶ Ziegler and Ewald, *Annalen*, 1933, **504**, 182; Ziegler and Gänicke, ibid. 1942, **551**, 213.

the auto-oxidation of aldehydes and olefines. Thus one molecule of triphenylmethyl is sufficient to effect the oxidation of about 40 molecules of anisaldehyde, 50 molecules of indene, or 2,000–5,000 molecules of dimethylbenzofulvene. This work throws a valuable light on the mechanism of oxygenation processes which are discussed in greater detail in Chapter XI.

A particularly interesting example of addition of oxygen to a substance of the triphenylmethyl type has been afforded by the study of the fluorescent red hydrocarbon *rubrene* (XIII) first prepared by Moureu and Dufraisse† in 1926 by heating the acetylene derivative (XII):

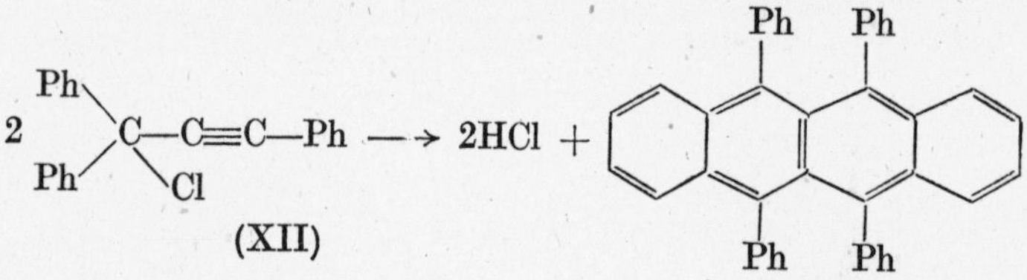

$$2\ Ph_2C(Cl)\text{—}C{\equiv}C\text{—}Ph \longrightarrow 2HCl + \text{(XIII)}$$

(XII) (XIII)

Solutions of this very reactive substance, and of many of its analogues, absorb a molecule of oxygen on irradiation, and form colourless peroxides which, when heated, give up the oxygen and regenerate the parent hydrocarbon with emission of light: i.e.

$$\text{rubrene} + O_2 + \text{light} \rightleftharpoons \text{oxy-rubrene.}$$

Considerable interest has been taken in this reaction in view of its apparent similarity to the Haemoglobin ⇌ Oxyhaemoglobin reaction.

It is evident now, however, that peroxide formation in polycyclic hydrocarbons such as rubrene can be associated with their possible existence in radical forms, or *R states*, such as (XIV) which Clar‡ has associated with their visible colour and enhanced chemical reactivity. It must be noted, however, that neither Clar's hydrocarbons, such as (XIV), nor rubrene itself are paramagnetic,§ and thus are not free radicals in their normal forms.

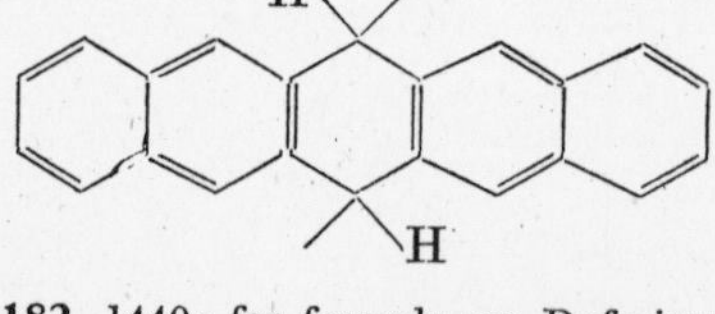

(XIV)

† *Compt. rend.* 1926, **182**, 1440; for formula see Dufraisse, *Bull. Soc. Chim.* 1935, **2**, 1546; 1936, **3**, 1847, 1934; Dufraisse and Velluz, *Compt. rend.* 1935, **201**, 1394.

‡ Clar, *Ber.* 1932, **65**, 503. Compare *Annual Reports of the Chemical Society*, 1932, pp. 163–73.

§ Müller and Müller-Rodloff, *Annalen*, 1935, **517**, 134.

Like triphenylmethyl, rubrene can act as the sensitizer for initiating other oxidations†; its own reaction with oxygen is easily inhibited by the presence of traces of substances such as aniline, quinol, or nitrobenzene.‡

5. Other addition reactions. The reaction between triphenylmethyl and *p*-benzoquinone seems to be very similar to its reaction with oxygen, for it yields thereby the di-triphenylmethyl ether of hydroquinone

$$2Ph_3C\cdot + O{=}C_4H_4{=}O \longrightarrow Ph_3C{-}O{-}C_6H_4{-}O{-}CPh_3.$$

Many olefinic compounds also add on two triphenylmethyl groups to their double bonds. Thus isoprene yields (XV) and maleic acid yields (XVI)§

$$Ph_3C{-}CH_2{-}CMe{=}CH{-}CH_2{-}CPh_3 \quad \text{(XV)}$$

$$\begin{array}{l} Ph_3C{-}CH{-}COOH \\ \qquad\quad | \\ Ph_3C{-}CH{-}COOH \end{array} \quad \text{(XVI)}$$

Other free neutral radicals react instantly with triphenylmethyl, and this type of addition process has been used as a diagnostic test for a free valency. The following reactions may be cited as examples of this:

$$Ph_3C\cdot + \cdot NPh_2 \longrightarrow Ph_3C{-}NPh_2,$$

$$2Ph_3C\cdot + Me_2N{-}C_6H_4{-}S{-}S{-}C_6H_4NMe_2 \longrightarrow 2Me_2N{-}C_6H_4{-}S{-}CPh_3.$$

Another reaction which may be of this type is the reaction between triphenylmethyl and diazomethane, which may simply be explained as being an addition reaction between triphenylmethyl and the methylene diradical:

$$CH_2N_2 + 2Ph_3C\cdot \longrightarrow Ph_3C{-}CH_2{-}CPh_3 + N_2.$$

6. Photochemical decomposition and disproportionation. Gomberg and Cone, in 1904|| noticed that yellow solutions of triphenylmethyl were slowly decolorized on exposure to sunlight, and that triphenylmethane was thereby produced. The other reaction product was shown by Schmidlin and Garcia-Banus¶ to be diphenyl-*bis*-diphenylene-ethane (XVII):

(XVII)

† Schumacher, *Zeit. für Elektrochem.* 1936, **42**, 522.
‡ Bowen and Steadman, *J.* 1934, p. 1098.
§ Conant and Scherp, *J.A.C.S.* 1931, **53**, 1941.
|| Gomberg and Cone, *Ber.* 1904, **37**, 3545.
¶ Schmidlin and Garcia-Banus, *Ber.* 1912, **45**, 1344.

a substance which also dissociates into free radicals, though to a much smaller extent than does hexaphenylethane.†

Bowden and Jones† have shown that this intermolecular hydrogenation is promoted by light of the wave-lengths most strongly absorbed by solutions of triphenylmethyl, and therefore is a reaction of the free radical triphenylmethyl and not of molecular hexaphenylethane. It is significant that this photochemical decomposition only takes place in solvents such as benzene, hexane, and carbon tetrachloride in which hexaphenylethane dissociates in the form of neutral radicals. Solutions in the ionizing solvent sulphur dioxide are photochemically stable.

The photochemical decomposition of hexaphenylethane is essentially a *disproportionation reaction* in which a triphenylmethyl radical hydrogenates itself to triphenylmethane at the expense of the phenyl group of another molecule. Many similar reactions occur between triphenylmethyl and substances containing chemically active hydrogen atoms. For instance, dry hydrogen chloride reacts with solutions of triphenylmethyl to give a mixture

$$2Ph_3C\cdot + HCl \underset{\text{dark}}{\overset{\text{light}}{\rightleftharpoons}} Ph_3C{-}Cl + Ph_3C{-}H,$$

of which the equilibrium may be altered photochemically.‡

These initial reaction products can further interact to give the hydrocarbon (XVIII) which was first obtained by Ullmann and Borsum in 1902§ and which was, at one time, confused with hexaphenylethane.||

The formation of (XVIII), involves the substitution of an aromatic ring by the Ph_3C— group. This may easily be brought about in reactive

$$Ph_3C{-}C_6H_4{-}CHPh_2 \qquad \text{(XVIII)}$$

aromatic compounds such as phenol, which can be substituted directly both by triphenylmethyl chloride and by triphenylmethyl itself, e.g.

$$2Ph_3C\cdot + C_6H_5OH \longrightarrow Ph_3C{-}H + Ph_3C{-}C_6H_4{-}OH.$$

These disproportionation reactions do not occur so easily with more complex aryl derivatives of triphenylmethyl, and when alkyl groups are present the reaction takes a somewhat different course.

† Bowden and Jones, *J.* 1928, p. 1149; Bowden, ibid. 1939, p. 26; Bent and Cline, *J.A.C.S.* 1936, **58**, 1624.

‡ Schlenk and Herzenstein, *Ber.* 1910, **43**, 3545.

§ Ullmann and Borsum, *Ber.* 1902, **35**, 2877.

|| Compare Gomberg, *Ber.* 1902, **35**, p. 3918; 1903, **36**, 376.

Thus tri-*p*-tolylmethyl spontaneously undergoes a disproportionation reaction in which the hydrogen atoms from the side-chain methyl groups are the initial points of attack:

$$2(p\cdot CH_3{-}C_6H_4)_3C\cdot$$
$$\longrightarrow (p\cdot CH_3{-}C_6H_4)_3CH + (p\cdot CH_3{-}C_6H_4)_2C{=}\langle\ \rangle{=}CH_2. \qquad (XIX)$$

The decomposition is a first order reaction and a quinonoid hydrocarbon (XIX) is formed.†

Other *para*-substituted derivatives, $(Alk{-}C_6H_4)_3C\cdot$, of triphenylmethyl react similarly, though the rate of reaction decreases with increase in the size of the alkyl group whilst tri-*meta*-tolylmethyl, which cannot form a quinonoid compound, undergoes no disproportionation. Moreover *p*·*tert*-butylphenyl-diphenylmethyl (XX)

$$(CH_3)_3C{-}\langle\ \rangle{-}\dot{C}Ph_2 \qquad (XX)$$

which also cannot form a quinonoid hydrocarbon by loss of hydrogen is also stable.

Ziegler and his colleagues‡ have investigated in detail the mechanism of a very similar disproportionation reaction in the tetraphenyldialkylethane series (XXI) in which spontaneous decomposition gives a mixture of a saturated and an unsaturated hydrocarbon.

$$\underset{CH_3\quad\ \ CH_3}{Ph_2C{-}CPh_2} \longrightarrow Ph_2C{=}CH_2 + Ph_2CH{-}CH_3 \qquad (XXI)$$

In this series of compounds the occurrence of dissociation to neutral radicals is too slight for detection except from their slow reactions with oxygen, and it is not surprising therefore that the hydrogen abstraction is highly selective.

In all compounds of this type the disproportionation reaction is much slower than the reaction with oxygen in presence of pyrogallol, which yields the hydroperoxide (XXII), and by careful kinetic measurements

$$\underset{CH_3}{Ph_2C}{-}O{-}O{-}H \qquad (XXII)$$

Ziegler and his colleagues were able to show that the mechanism of the disproportionation was:

(i) reversible dissociation

$$\underset{Me\ \ Me}{Ph_2C{-}CPh_2} \rightleftharpoons 2\underset{Me}{Ph_2C\cdot}$$

† Marvel, Rieger, and Mueller, *J.A.C.S.* 1939, **61**, 2769; Marvel, Mueller, Himel, and Kaplan, ibid., p. 2771. ‡ Ziegler, Whitney, and Herte, *Annalen*, 1942, **551**, 187.

followed by

(ii) hydrogen transfer between the two radicals

$$\underset{\displaystyle CH_3}{Ph_2\overset{}{C}\cdot} + H_3C\text{——}CPh_2 \longrightarrow \underset{\displaystyle CH_3}{Ph_2CH} + H_2C{=}CPh_2$$

and not a reaction between one free radical and a molecule of (XXI).

7. Reduction by triphenylmethyl. From the ease with which triphenylmethyl can abstract hydrogen from other molecules one could classify it as a powerful oxidizing agent, but this reactivity only arises on account of the great tendency of triphenylmethyl to acquire, or share, an extra electron and so complete its octet structure.

Triphenylmethyl can equally well act as a powerful reducing agent by abstracting an electron from another molecule. Thus triphenylmethyl will reduce salts of heavy metals such as silver, mercury, and gold, and will reduce ferric salts to ferrous salts.

The reaction $Ph_3C\cdot + FeCl_3 \rightarrow Ph_3C\text{—}Cl + FeCl_2$ has been applied by Conant in providing a diagnostic test for the occurrence of free neutral radicals of organic substances.

If a solution containing both ferric chloride and potassium ferricyanide is mixed with a substance capable of dissociating to a free neutral radical, then reduction of the ferric salt occurs, and, as a result a precipitate of Prussian blue is formed.

The dyestuff methylene blue may be used in a similar manner. Both these colour reactions may be applied for determining the rate at which the dissociation of organic molecules to free radicals can occur.

Molecular Dissociation and the Stability of Free Radicals

During the past forty years very many analogues of hexaphenylethane have been prepared with the object of finding those structural features which permit of the easy thermal dissociation of the carbon—carbon link. With these compounds measurements both of the degree of dissociation in solution, and of the energy changes involved, have been made, but unfortunately the results obtained by different experimenters cannot be collated systematically, since a whole host of different solvent and temperature conditions have been chosen. Moreover, the different experimental methods which have been employed are not strictly comparable and much early work is of a very low degree of accuracy. The theoretical significance of available data is discussed in the following paragraphs, which do not attempt to summarize *all* the experimental work which has been carried out in this field.

Molecular weight determinations. The first method to be employed for finding the approximate extent of dissociation in solution of derivatives of hexaphenylethane was that of determining cryoscopically their apparent molecular weights in solvents such as benzene and naphthalene. By this method measurements can only be made at a very restricted number of temperatures and over a limited range of concentrations, but the recorded data are qualitatively of great significance, for although the accuracy of the experimental results is low (the probable error in the stated figure being about 10 per cent.), the method is one that can be used safely for comparing the dissociability of different compounds under the same experimental conditions. In this way the earlier workers on the subject were able to show that as molecules of the type $R_3C—CR_3$ were further loaded with aromatic nuclei their degree of dissociation into radicals $R_3C\cdot$ increased. This can be illustrated from the following table.

TABLE VII

Dissociation of Compounds $R_3C—CR_3$

Substance	*Per cent. dissociation in benzene at 5° C. (concentration 2–3 per cent.)*	*Observer*
$(CH_3)_3C—C(CH_3)_3$	0	..
$(PhC—(C_6H_{11})_2)_2$	(gives a peroxide)	Marvel
$(Ph_2C—C_6H_{11})_2$	(gives a peroxide)	Ziegler
$(Ph_2C—CMe_3)_2$	(gives a peroxide)	Conant
$(Ph_3C—)_2$	2–3	..
$(Ph—C_6H_4—CPh_2)_2$	15	Schlenk
$((Ph—C_6H_4)_2C—Ph)_2$	79	Schlenk
$((Ph—C_6H_4)_3C—)_2$	100	Schlenk†
$(Ph_3C—CPh_2—)_2$	100	Schlenk
$((NO_2—C_6H_4)_3C—)_2$	100	Ziegler
$(Ph_2C—CH{=}CPh_2)_2$	80	Ziegler
$((Ph—C_6H_4)_2C—CMe_3)_2$	74	Conant
(α-Naphthyl—$CPh_2)_2$	60	..
(β-Naphthyl—$CPh_2)_2$	33	..
(β-Naphthyl$_3$C—$)_2$	24	Marvel

† See, however, Bachmann and Kloetzel, *J. Org. Chem.* 1937, **2**, 362; Marvel and colleagues, *J.A.C.S.* 1942, **64**, 1824.

Colorimetric measurements. Piccard in 1911† showed that the extent to which colourless hexaphenylethane dissociated to yellow triphenylmethyl could be estimated colorimetrically, and he demonstrated the fact that the degree of dissociation increased upon dilution. Ziegler and Ewald‡ have elaborated this method, and have been able to determine, to an accuracy of 5 per cent., both the dissociation constant and the heat of dissociation of hexaphenylethane and of some of its derivatives. They devised an apparatus for preparing and diluting solutions of hexaphenylethane in the complete absence of air and measured spectrographically their optical extinction coefficients for light of wave-lengths corresponding to characteristic absorption bands of the free radical. Thus for hexaphenylethane in benzene they obtained concordant values of the dissociation constant

$$K = (2\alpha)^2/(1-\alpha)v,$$

where α = degree of dissociation, v = dilution, for solutions ranging from M/10 to $M/10^6$. By measuring this dissociation constant at more than one temperature they also calculated, from the van't Hoff isochore $d\log K/dT = Q/RT^2$, the heat of dissociation, Q. The following results were obtained in a series of solvents.

TABLE VIII

Dissociation of Hexaphenylethane

Solvent	*Dissociation constant* $K\times 10^4$ *at 20° C.*	*Heat of dissociation* Q *in k.cals.*
Propionitrile	1·2	11·1
Ethyl benzoate	1·67	12·0
Acetophenone	1·70	11·5
Dioxan	2·5	11·6
Bromobenzene	3·7	11·5
Ethylene dibromide	3·9	11·4
Benzene	4·1	11·3
Chloroform	6·9	10·5
Carbon disulphide	19·2	11·0

Attention was called to the fact that the heat of dissociation of hexaphenylethane appeared to be constant at $11{\cdot}3\pm 1$ k.cals. per gram molecule in all solvents, although the actual dissociation constants varied noticeably.

Measurement of magnetic susceptibility. The measurement of the magnetic susceptibility of solutions (pp. 25–8) affords the most

† *Annalen*, 1911, **381**, 347. ‡ ibid. 1929, **473**, 163.

direct method of determining the extent to which a substance dissociates into free neutral radicals, and has an advantage over the photometric method in that it can be applied to deeply coloured solutions. It is, moreover, the only method by which one can differentiate indubitably between dissociation into neutral radicals and dissociation into ions or disproportionation into simpler molecules (p. 50).

In this way Müller and Müller-Rodloff,† who used the manometric method of measurement (p. 27) obtained the following values for the dissociation of hexaphenylethane in M/10 solution in benzene:

TABLE IX

Temperature	$100 \times \alpha$	*Dissociation const. K*	*Heat of dissociation*
23° C.	2·4	$1{\cdot}5 \times 10^{-4}$	11·6 ±1·7 k.cals.
75° C.	8·9	53×10^{-4}	

Their value of K is definitely less than that found by Ziegler (p. 54) but the value for the heat of dissociation is the same to within the limits of experimental error.

By this same method Roy and Marvel, in 1937,‡ gave the following figures for the percentage dissociation ($= 100\alpha$) of *para*-substituted derivatives of hexaphenylethane $(RC_6H_4)_3C—C(C_6H_4R)_3$, and claimed that the accuracy of their measurements was within 2 per cent.:

TABLE X

Dissociation of para-$(RC_6H_4)_3C—C(C_6H_4R)_3$ in M/10 solution in Benzene at 20° C.

Group R	H	C_2H_5	nC_3H_7	iC_3H_7	nC_4H_9	iC_4H_9	$terC_4H_9$
100α	2·1	3·5	4·2	4·5	4·9	6·7	5·9

but later had to correct their values to take into account the slow disproportionation reaction (p. 51) which destroys the hexa-arylethane without any apparent colour change. It was found to be necessary to measure the magnetic susceptibility over a period of time and to plot back the results to zero time, taking into account also the speed of the dissociation process, which they had to measure by the oxygen absorption method. From their final results it would appear that the degree of dissociation of simple homologues of hexaphenylethane is much greater than had previously been supposed.

† *Annalen*, 1935, **520**, 235; 1936, **521**, 89.
‡ *J.A.C.S.* 1937, **59**, 2622.

TABLE XI

Dissociation of para-$(RC_6H_4)_3C$—$C(C_6H_4R)_3$ in M/10 solution in Benzene at 29° C.†

Group R	C_2H_5	nC_3H_7	$isoC_3H_7$	$isoC_4H_9$	$secC_4H_9$	$cycloC_6H_{11}$
α	0·17	0·21	0·26	0·27	0·33	0·22

† Marvel, Mueller, Himel, and Kaplan, *J.A.C.S.* 1939, **61**, 2775.

Many more complex compounds have also been investigated by Marvel and his colleagues.‡

Measurements of activation energies. The experimental methods for determining the rates of dissociation of hexaphenylethane and its derivatives by means of their reactions with iodine, nitric oxide, or oxygen have been described in previous pages. By carrying out these reactions at a series of temperatures, and making use of the equation $k = PZe^{-E/RT}$, Ziegler and his colleagues§ have been able to amass valuable data concerning both the Activation Energies (E) and Reaction Constants (PZ) of these dissociation processes.

By both the oxygen and the nitric oxide methods it was found that the activation energy for the dissociation of hexaphenylethane was 19 k.cals. (± 1), and Ziegler‖ drew attention to the fact that the activation energy required to break the central C—C link of hexaphenylethane was definitely greater than the Heat of Dissociation (ΔH) which was only 11 k.cals. (± 1). He pointed out that one should regard the *free* radical triphenylmethyl when in solution as possessing 3–4 k.cals. less energy than at the moment of formation. Calculations by Conant¶ indicate that there is also this difference between Energy of Activation (E) and Heat of Dissociation (H) in compounds of the dixanthyl series, but unfortunately his values of ΔH depend upon theoretical assumptions which are open to grave doubt.††

This experimental result is in accord with modern theory, since the unpaired electron in triphenylmethyl will undoubtedly assume a new location, stabilized by resonance, in the free radical. Moreover, the latter probably has a planar structure‡‡ of three phenyl groups equilaterally spaced about the central carbon atom, whereas in hexaphenyl-

‡ Marvel and colleagues, *J.A.C.S.* 1940, **62**, 1551; 1941, **63**, 1892; 1942, **64**, 1824.

§ Ziegler, *Annalen*, 1930, **479**, 277; 1933, **504**, 131; 1942, **551**, 155.

‖ Ziegler, *Trans. Faraday Soc.* 1934, **30**, 13.

¶ Conant, *J. Chem. Phys.* 1933, **1**, 427; Conant and Evans, *J.A.C.S.* 1929, **51**, 1920. Compare Ziegler, *Annalen*, 1942, **551**, 164.

†† Wooster, *J.A.C.S.* 1936, **58**, 2156; Keevil, ibid. 1937, **59**, 2104.

‡‡ Wallis and Adams, *J.A.C.S.* 1933, **55**, 3838; see, however, Karagunis and Drikos, *Zeit. phys. Chem.* 1934, B **26**, 428.

ethane the structure is probably tetrahedral. Free triphenylmethyl will only be able to assume its most stable configuration when separated by some appreciable distance from its fellow group in the dissociating molecule.

The Activation Energies and Reaction Constants for a number of analogues of hexaphenylethane are given below. It will be seen that the reaction constants can vary over a very wide range.

TABLE XII

Activation Energies for Hexaphenylethane Analogues in Bromobenzene†

Compound	*Time of half-dissociation*	*Activation energy, E*	*Reaction constant, PZ (time in sec.)*
$(Ph_3C)_2$	0·4 min.	19 k.cals.	5×10^{12}
$(Ph_2MeC)_2$	19·5 days	30 ,,	$1{\cdot}9\times10^{16}$
$(Ph_2EtC)_2$	6 min.	27·2 ,,	$4{\cdot}4\times10^{17}$
$(Ph_2nPrC)_2$	1·3 ,,	26·7 ,,	$9{\cdot}3\times10^{17}$
$(Ph_2isoPrC)_2$	128 ,,	25·0 ,,	$4{\cdot}2\times10^{14}$
$(Ph_2C_6H_{11}C)_2$	70 ,,	25 ,,	$9{\cdot}0\times10^{14}$
$(Ph(C_6H_{11})_2C)_2$	85 ,,	21 ,,	$8{\cdot}3\times10^{11}$

† Ziegler, *Annalen*, 1942, **551**, 161.

Theoretical. The investigations of the dissociability of analogues of hexaphenylethane have had as their aim the solution of *two* distinct but interrelated theoretical problems:

(i) why can the central bond of hexaphenylethane be broken much more easily than the corresponding bond in ethane?

(ii) why are the dissociation products reasonably stable?

In general terms both these questions have been answered by stating that only with a complex resonance system can carbon to carbon links be broken to give stable products. It must be remembered, however, that the activation energy needed to break a covalent linkage need not be related to the stability of the resulting fragments.

The modern theory of resonance provides a reasonably satisfactory answer to question (ii) above, for it is not difficult to realize that in a complex radical, such as triphenylmethyl, the odd electron can be distributed between several carbon atoms, and will, therefore, have a wave-function of low energy content.

Thus Pauling and Wheland‡ have pointed out that whereas the methyl radical has only one structure, $CH_3\cdot$ (apart from very highly

‡ Pauling and Wheland, *J. Chem. Phys.* 1933, **1**, 362.

activated states), the benzyl radical has five possible structures, in three of which the odd electron is located in the benzenoid ring:

$-CH_2\cdot$ $-CH_2\cdot$ $=CH_2$ $=CH_2$ $\cdot$ $=CH_2$

Resonance between these canonical structures stabilizes the benzyl radical to the extent of 15 k.cals. in comparison with methyl. Similarly triphenylmethyl has a structure in which there is resonance between forty-four canonical states, for the odd electron can take up any one of nine different positions in benzene rings, which are themselves resonance structures.

The following values for this stabilization energy in aromatic systems have been selected from data given by Pauling and Wheland.

TABLE XIII

Resonance Energies of Hydrocarbon Radicals

Radical	*No. of canonical structures*	*Resonance energy*
$CH_3\cdot$	1	0 k.cals.
$C_6H_5—CH_2\cdot$	5	15 ,,
$(C_6H_5)_2CH\cdot$	16	27 ,,
$(C_6H_5)_3C\cdot$	44	38 ,,
$\alpha C_{10}H_7—CH_2\cdot$	10	24 ,,
$p\cdot C_6H_5—C_6H_4—CH_2\cdot$	13	18 ,,
$(p\cdot C_6H_5—C_6H_4)_3C\cdot$	496	40 ,,

More recent measurements by Bent and his colleagues of the heats of reaction of hexaphenylethane with both oxygen and hydrogen† have confirmed that the energy to break the central C—C link is at least 30 k.cals. less in hexaphenylethane than in ethane, and in this respect the resonance theory is now so thoroughly justified that the experimental measurements made with compounds of the hexa-arylethane series can be used as the most reliable guides to the energy contents of complex polycyclic systems.

In order to account for the ease of dissociation of hexaphenylethane, Pauling and Wheland‡ assumed that the energy required to split the central C—C link was calculable as the corresponding bond energy in ethane (about 85 k.cals.) *minus* the stabilizing resonance energy of each radical.

† Bent, Cuthbertson, Dorfman, and Leary, *J.A.C.S.* 1936, **58**, 165; Bent and Cuthbertson, ibid., pp. 170, 2000; Bent and Cline, ibid., p. 1624.

‡ Pauling and Wheland, *J. Chem. Phys.* 1933, **1**, 362.

Thus for $Ph_3C—CPh_3$

$$E = 85-(2\times 38) = 9 \text{ k.cals.}$$

This assumption gives a reasonable value for the heat of dissociation of hexaphenylethane, but, as Ziegler has pointed out,† it does not give the correct value for the activation energy, whilst for derivatives of hexaphenylethane, such as diphenyl-tetramethylethane, it gives grossly incorrect values even for heats of dissociation.

It is, indeed, when one considers the dissociation *process* that one finds it difficult to formulate any simple but consistent theory. Why, for instance, are both diphenyl and tetraphenylmethane stable molecules, whilst hexaphenylethane dissociates to about 2 per cent. at room temperature and decaphenylbutane, $(Ph_3C—CPh_2)—(CPh_2—CPh_3)$, dissociates completely to pentaphenylethyl radicals, $Ph_3C—CPh_2\cdot$, but not to triphenylmethyl radicals? All these undissociated molecules should be stabilized resonance systems throughout, yet to account for the dissociation of the two latter compounds one must suppose that the valency electrons are drawn away from the central C—C bond into the aromatic rings. This cannot be a general effect of the aromatic ring system, since the central bond of diphenyl is both stronger, and shorter, than the normal carbon to carbon bond. Again both triphenylmethyl and nitrogen-dianisyl are fairly stable free radicals, yet they unite to a product, $(C_6H_5)_3C—N(C_6H_4—OCH_3)_2$, which shows no signs of dissociation.

Ziegler has suggested that the central C—C bond of hexaphenylethane, and of its analogues, is lengthened, and therefore weakened by the steric repulsion between the two large $Ph_3C—$ groups.† In support of Ziegler's theory, Morris, Byerly, and Selwood‡ have drawn attention to the fact that in hexamethylethane the central C—C bond has been shown to be 1·58 A long instead of the normal value of 1·54 A.§ More recently, Marvel and his colleagues have stressed the experimental fact that *ortho* substituents in the aromatic rings have an outstanding effect in increasing the degree of dissociation of hexaphenylethane derivatives, as Table XIV shows, though they reduce the velocity of dissociation.‖

It will be seen that two methyl groups in the *ortho* position to the central carbon link have a decidedly greater effect on the dissociability than four extra benzene rings in the *para* position.

† Ziegler, *Annalen*, 1942, **551**, 127. ‡ *J.A.C.S.* 1942, **64**, 1727.

§ Bauer and Beach, ibid. 1142.

‖ Compare Table XII. *PZ* values are particularly low when there are *ortho* substituents: this is the usual '*ortho* effect' of substituents on reaction velocity.

Table XIV

Degree of Dissociation of Substituted Hexaphenylethanes in M/10 solution in Benzene.† *(Magnetic susceptibility measurements)*

Substance	*Percentage dissociation* (= 100α)
Di-*para*-methyl-hexaphenylethane $(p\text{Tol}, Ph_2C)_2$	5
Di-*para*-isopropyl- "	8–10
Di-*ortho*-methyl- "	25
Di-*ortho*-ethyl- "	33
Di-*para*-phenyl- " $[(pPhC_6H_4)Ph_2C]_2$	12
Di-*meta*-phenyl- "	13
Di-α-naphthyl-tetraphenylethane	54
Tetra-*ortho*-ethyl-hexaphenylethane	82
Tetra-*para*-phenyl-hexaphenylethane	18

† Data collected from *J.A.C.S.* 1939, **61**, 2009, 2775; 1941, **63**, 1892; 1942, **64**, 1824.

Undoubtedly, therefore, the steric factor is of great importance, and in fairness to the earlier investigators, such as Gomberg and Schlenk, it should be pointed out that it was the conception of the difficulty in packing large aromatic rings around a carbon atom that led to the original discovery of triphenylmethyl. The newer valency theories have tended to obscure this point, but it is evident that the solution of the theoretical problem of bond stability in organic molecules is to be sought by means of calculations which will establish the energy content of the different parts of a single molecule, and not by those which sum the energy of its electronic system as a whole.

Bi-Radicals

Hydrocarbons such as (XXIII) are deeply coloured and react rapidly with oxygen, and for this reason it has been suggested that they may exist in the form of bi-radicals, such as (XXIV).

$$(C_6H_5)_2C{=}C_6H_4{=}C_6H_4{=}C(C_6H_5)_2 \qquad \text{(XXIII)}$$

$$(C_6H_5)_2\dot{C}{-}C_6H_4{-}C_6H_4{-}\dot{C}(C_6H_5)_2 \qquad \text{(XXIV)}$$

Magnetic measurements by Müller and his colleagues have shown, however, that substances of this type are, in general diamagnetic, and therefore quinonoid in structure (XXIII).‡

If, however, the co-planar configuration of the two central aromatic

‡ Müller and Müller-Rodloff, *Annalen*, 1935, **517**, 134.

rings is made impossible, by introducing large substituents into the *ortho* positions, as in (XXV), the quinonoid structure becomes impossible, the only alternative being that of a true bi-radical, in which two tervalent carbon atoms are linked by the twisted ring system of 2′:6-2′:6′-dichloro-diphenyl.

$$(C_6H_5{-}C_6H_4)_2\dot{C}{-}C_6H_2Cl_2{-}C_6H_2Cl_2{-}\dot{C}(C_6H_4{-}C_6H_5)_2 \qquad \text{(XXV)}$$

This product gives paramagnetic solutions,† though it is diamagnetic, presumably as a dimeride, in the solid state. As would be expected, it yields a di-peroxide.

Meta derivatives of diphenyl, such as (XXVI), which cannot form quinonoid structures analogous to (XXIII), can also form true bi-radicals, and so too can substances of the general type (XXVII) in which two triphenylmethyl systems are separated by a saturated carbon chain.

$$(C_6H_5)_2\dot{C}{-}C_6H_4{-}C_6H_4{-}\dot{C}(C_6H_5)_2 \quad (meta,\ meta') \qquad \text{(XXVI)}$$

$$(C_6H_5)_2\dot{C}{-}C_6H_4{-}(CH_2)_n{-}C_6H_4{-}\dot{C}(C_6H_5)_2 \qquad \text{(XXVII)}$$

† Müller and Tietz, *Ber.* 1941, **74**, 807. Compare *Ber.* 1939, **72**, 2063; *Angew. Chem.* 1941, **54**, 192.

IV

FREE RADICALS CONTAINING ELEMENTS OTHER THAN CARBON

Nitrogen Compounds

Nitric oxide, NO, is the simplest known molecule which possesses an odd number of electrons. However, though it is paramagnetic, it is very much less reactive than free atoms, such as hydrogen or even iodine, and shows little tendency to dimerize to N_2O_2, except when in the liquid or crystalline state.† This stability of nitric oxide is explainable by the fact that it is a resonance structure, with the canonical states:

$$:\dot{N}=\ddot{O}: \qquad :\overset{-}{\ddot{N}}=\overset{+}{\dot{O}}: \qquad \cdot\overset{+}{\ddot{N}}-\underset{\cdot\cdot}{\overset{-}{\ddot{O}}}:$$

and can, most adequately, be represented as having a *three-electron bond* supplementing a single N—O covalency,‡ i.e. as $:N\overset{\cdot\cdot\cdot}{—}O:$, since it has a very small dipole moment, and the internuclear distance between its two atoms, 1·14 A, lies between that calculated for double and triple covalent links (N=O, 1·18 A; N≡O, 1·06 A).

The nitrosyl cation, present in $NOClO_4$ and $NOBF_4$,§ probably has the structure $:\overset{+}{N}\equiv O:$, and the anion, present in $\overset{+}{Na}NO^-$,|| the structure $:\overset{-}{\ddot{N}}=\ddot{O}:$

The simple gas reactions of nitric oxide with chlorine,¶ bromine,†† and oxygen‡‡ involve termolecular collisions, e.g.

$$2NO + O_2 \longrightarrow 2NO_2,$$

rather than the bimolecular reaction chains that are characteristic of molecules containing unpaired electrons. They all proceed at measureable velocity at ordinary temperatures, but are reversible processes at higher temperatures. In high dilution the oxidation of nitric oxide in

† Goodeve, *Trans. Faraday Soc.* 1938, **34**, 791; Bizette and Tsai, *Compt. rend.* 1937, **204**, 1638; Johnston and Giauque, *J.A.C.S.* 1929, **51**, 3194; Lips, *Helv. Phys. Acta*, 1935, **8**, 247.

‡ Pauling, *The Nature of the Chemical Bond*, p. 266 (1940).

§ Klinkenberg, *Rec. trav. chim.* 1937, **56**, 749.

|| Frazer and Long, *J. Chem. Phys.* 1938, **6**, 462.

¶ Trautz, *Z. anorg. Chem.* 1914, **88**, 285; Krauss and Saracini, *Zeit. phys. Chem.* 1937, **178**, 245.

†† Trautz and Dalal, *Z. anorg. Chem.* 1918, **102**, 149; Bodenstein and Krauss, *Zeit. phys. Chem.* 1936, **175**, 294.

‡‡ Bodenstein, *Zeit. phys. Chem.* 1922, **100**, 68; Kornfeld and Klinger, ibid. 1929, **134**, 37.

air leads to the formation of N_2O_3, since the bimolecular reaction between nitric oxide and nitrogen peroxide

$$NO + NO_2 \longrightarrow N_2O_3$$

is a very much faster one than is its termolecular reaction with oxygen.†

The rate-controlling stage of the gas reaction between nitric oxide and hydrogen, which proceeds at higher temperatures,‡ is again essentially termolecular, though in this case there is some evidence that binary collision complexes of very short life are involved.

Nevertheless the odd-electron character of nitric oxide is sufficiently well marked for it to be a valuable diagnostic reagent for other free radicals. Thus it combines instantly in solution with triphenylmethyl, diphenyl-nitrogen, and their analogues (pp. 45, 65) and, in the gas phase, immediately terminates reaction chains involving neutral alkyl radicals (p. 134). Again, with salts of the transition metals, such as iron and cobalt, which possess unpaired *d* electrons, it forms coordination compounds—the nitrosyls—in which electron-pair bonds only are present. It is noteworthy that in all these compounds the fresh covalent bond involves the nitrogen atom, as would be expected of the structure $\cdot\ddot{N}{=}O:$.

Nitrogen peroxide, NO_2, is another simple paramagnetic molecule which has a resonance structure, and may be written as either

$$:\ddot{\underset{\cdot\cdot}{O}}{-}\dot{N}{=}\ddot{O}: \quad \text{or} \quad :\underset{\cdot\cdot}{O}\overset{\cdot\cdot\cdot}{-}N{=}\underset{\cdot\cdot}{\ddot{O}}\,;$$

but it has a much greater tendency to dimerize:

$$2NO_2 \rightleftharpoons N_2O_4 + 13 \text{ k.cals.},$$

and generally behaves as a mixed anhydride of nitrous and nitric acids.

The free radical character of monomeric nitrogen peroxide is, however, indicated by the fact that it will catalyse the chain oxidations of both carbon monoxide and methane,§ though it has been suggested that this may be due to its providing a trace of atomic oxygen.

Again monomeric nitrogen peroxide reacts with toluene to form HNO_2 and the free radical benzyl, $C_6H_5{-}CH_2\cdot$, which then combines both with more nitrogen peroxide to give phenyl-nitromethane, $C_6H_5{-}CH_2{-}NO_2$, or with nitric oxide to form $C_6H_5{-}CH_2{-}NO$, thus effecting substitution in the aliphatic side-chain.||

† Piankov, *J. Gen. Chem. Russia*, 1933, **3**, 652.

‡ Hinshelwood and Green, *J.* 1926, p. 730; Hinshelwood and Mitchell, ibid. 1936, p. 378.

§ Norrish and Wallace, *Proc. Roy. Soc.* 1934, A **145**, 307.

|| Titov, *J. Gen. Chem. Russia*, 1937, **7**, 1695; 1940, **10**, 1878.

Whenever the nitration of saturated hydrocarbons can be effected, it seems to occur by a chain-reaction of this type.

The exact electronic structure of the dimeride, nitrogen tetroxide, is uncertain. Spectral evidence and entropy measurements indicate that the molecule is symmetrical. This is usually taken as indicative of the dinitro structure (*a*), but since this has two positively charged nitrogen atoms in adjacent positions it should be less stable than the nitro-nitroso structure, (*b*):

$$\overset{-}{:\ddot{\underset{..}{O}}}\!\!\!\underset{O\!\!=}{\!\!>}\overset{+}{N}-\overset{+}{N}\!\!<\!\!\!\!\underset{=O}{\overset{-}{\ddot{\underset{..}{O}}:}} \qquad \overset{-}{:\ddot{\underset{..}{O}}}\!\!\!\underset{O\!\!=}{\!\!>}\overset{+}{N}-O-N=O \qquad \overset{-}{:\ddot{\underset{..}{O}}}-N\!\!<\!\!\underset{O}{\overset{O}{\diamond}}\!\!>\!\!\overset{+}{N}=O.$$

(*a*) (*b*) (*c*)

Chemical evidence accords better with structure (*b*), since nitrogen tetroxide can be used to diazotize aromatic amines,† or to nitrate both aromatic and paraffin hydrocarbons, though in this latter reaction the yields are usually poor.

However, as an alternative to (*b*), the resonance structure (*c*) is equally likely.

Nitrogen peroxide forms crystalline addition compounds with many olefines containing secondary and tertiary carbon atoms. It has been shown that with simple olefines, such as ethylene, the initial product is a mixture of the dinitro-compound, e.g. $NO_2—CH_2—CH_2—NO_2$ and the nitro-nitrite, e.g. $NO_2—CH_2—CH_2—O—NO$.‡

Diphenyl-nitrogen. Once the free radical nature of triphenylmethyl had been established, it was but natural that a search should be made for analogous properties in aromatic compounds of other elements.

Wieland, in 1911,§ showed that tetraphenyl-hydrazine, which can most easily be prepared by oxidizing diphenylamine with potassium permanganate in cold acetone,‖ acted in many ways like hexaphenylethane. It is a colourless crystalline solid, which can be preserved unchanged for years if protected from light and acids, but its solutions

† Houston and Johnson, *J.A.C.S.* 1925, **47**, 3011.

‡ Wieland, *Annalen*, 1921, **424**, 71; Levy and Scaife, *J.* 1946, pp. 1093, 1100; Levy, Scaife, and Smith, ibid., p. 1096.

§ *Annalen*, 1911, **381**, 200.

‖ See Gattermann–Wieland, *Laboratory Methods of Organic Chemistry* (Translation 1938, Macmillan, London).

in non-ionizing solvents become green when heated, and fade on cooling. This is evidently due to dissociation,

$$Ph_2N—NPh_2 \rightleftharpoons Ph_2N\cdot + \cdot NPh_2,$$

since Beer's law is not obeyed, the colour of dilute solutions being relatively more intense than that of more concentrated ones.

Fission at the N—N bond is definitely indicated by the fact that warm green solutions react promptly with nitric oxide to give diphenylnitrosamine, in exactly the same way as triphenylmethyl combines with nitric oxide:

$$Ph_2N\cdot + \cdot NO \rightleftharpoons Ph_2N—NO.$$

In the nitrogen series, however, this reaction is reversible since nitric oxide is liberated when diphenylnitrosamine is boiled in xylene.

The velocity of reaction between tetraphenyl-hydrazine and nitric oxide in *o*-dichlorobenzene solution has been measured by Cain and Wiselogle,† following the technique of Ziegler and his colleagues (p. 45). As with the corresponding reaction of hexaphenylethane, the process is strictly unimolecular (provided that the partial pressure of the nitric oxide is more than 0·2 atmosphere), and proportional to the molecular concentration of the tetraphenyl-hydrazine, but independent of the nitric oxide pressure. Thus the measured reaction velocity is that of the dissociation of the tetraphenyl-hydrazine. At 100° C. the observed time of half dissociation was 3·1 minutes, whilst from observations over the temperature range 75–100° C. the activation energy was estimated as 30 k.cals. $\pm$ 1·5. This activation energy is much greater than the estimated heat of formation of the N—N covalent link (about 20 k.cals.), just as the activation energy for the dissociation of hexaphenylethane is greater than its heat of dissociation (p. 56).

Several other reactions confirm the radical nature of diphenylnitrogen. Thus it reacts with triphenylmethyl to give a stable addition product,

$$Ph_3C\cdot + \cdot NPh_2 \longrightarrow Ph_3C—NPh_2,$$

and with metallic sodium to yield diphenylsodamide,

$$Ph_2\ddot{N}\cdot + Na\cdot \longrightarrow (Ph_2\ddot{N}:)^-Na^+.$$

It is very easily reduced to diphenylamine, but, unlike triphenylmethyl, it does not react with either oxygen or iodine, obviously because such additions would be endothermic processes giving unstable products.

At temperatures which permit of dissociation, tetraphenyl-hydrazine

† C. K. Cain and F. Y. Wiselogle, *J.A.C.S.* 1940, **62**, 1163.

undergoes disproportionation in neutral solvents, giving, by hydrogen transfer, diphenylamine and diphenyl-dihydrophenazine:

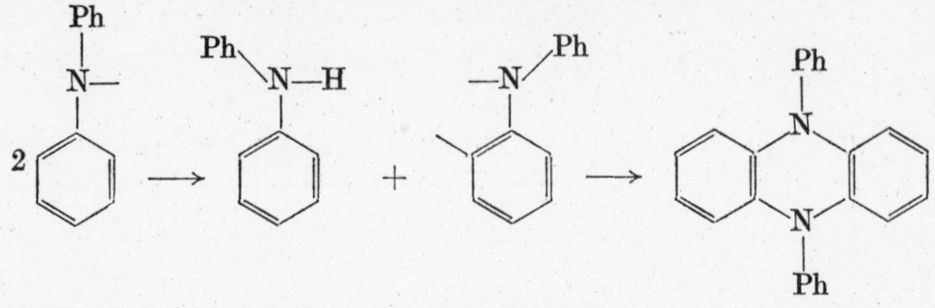

Dialkyl-diaryl-hydrazines, when heated, disproportionate similarly,†

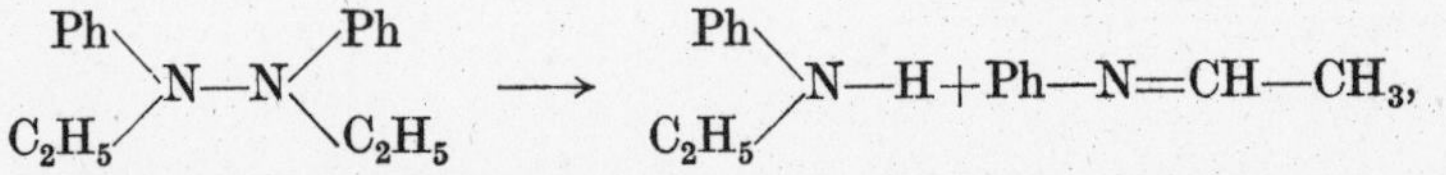

$$\frac{Ph}{C_2H_5}\!\!>\!N\!-\!N\!<\!\!\frac{Ph}{C_2H_5} \longrightarrow \frac{Ph}{C_2H_5}\!\!>\!N\!-\!H + Ph\!-\!N\!=\!CH\!-\!CH_3,$$

their reactions again being similar to the disproportionation reactions of hexaphenylethane analogues (pp. 49–52).

In the presence of acids, halogens, and salts such as ferric, zinc, aluminium, or antimony chlorides, still more complicated decompositions occur, and deep blue or violet products are formed. Tetraphenyl-hydrazine on treatment with hydrochloric acid yields, besides diphenylamine and diphenyl-dihydrophenazine, diphenyl-benzidine and *p*-chloro-anilido-triphenylamine, $Cl\text{—}C_6H_4\text{—}NH\text{—}C_6H_4\text{—}N(C_6H_5)_2$. This indicates that hydrogen can be abstracted from the *para* as well as from the *ortho* position in the benzene ring, and hence Wieland‡ assigned *para*-quinonoid structures to his highly coloured products. However, the coloured salts contain the N—N link unbroken, since the original hydrazine can be regenerated by treatment with alkali. Moreover, even *para*-substituted hydrazines, such as tetra-*p*-tolyl-hydrazine give these coloured compounds.

Their structures have been elucidated by Weitz and Schwechten,§ who have demonstrated that they are ***hydrazinium salts***, with a structure in which the positive ion is also a free radical, i.e. $\left(Ar_2\ddot{N}\text{—}\dot{N}\!<\!{Ar \atop Ar}\right)^+$, where one of the nitrogen atoms has only seven valency electrons. They showed that tetra-*p*-tolyl-hydrazine, in dry ether, when treated with iodine and silver perchlorate gave a blackish-violet crystalline salt, $(Tol_2\ddot{N}\text{—}\dot{N}Tol_2)ClO_4$, which liberated iodine from potassium iodide, with

† Wieland and Fressel, *Annalen*, 1912, **392**, 135.
‡ *Ber.* 1907, **40**, 4263.
§ Weitz and Schwechten, *Ber.* 1927, **60**, 1203.

regeneration of tetra-*p*-tolyl-hydrazine. This salt is strongly paramagnetic.† Salts of similar character can be obtained by oxidizing tri-*p*-tolylamine, together with picric acid, in dry benzene solution with lead peroxide.‡ From the corresponding perchlorate can be made a number of double salts with antimony, aluminium, mercury, and phosphorus halides:

$$[(C_7H_7)_3\dot{N}]^+(ClO_4)^- ; \qquad [(C_7H_7)_3\dot{N}]^+SbCl_6^-.$$

In these *aminium* and *hydrazinium* salts the aromatic amine acts like a metallic cation, but yet, like a neutral radical, promptly picks up an extra electron from a reducing agent, e.g.

$$(Tol_3\dot{N})^+(ClO_4)^- + Fe^{++} \longrightarrow Tol_3\ddot{N} + Fe^{+++} + (ClO_4)^-,$$

giving the free electrically neutral amine.

Radical–cation formation of this type only occurs with aromatic tertiary amines, and hydrazines, which are too feebly basic to form normal salts, i.e. cations of structure $(Ar_3NH)^+$, with acids. In the case of the tetra-aryl-hydrazines, the hydrazinium salt formation occurs in acid solution without the intervention of a separate oxidizing agent, for the dissociated diaryl-nitrogen radicals are sufficiently powerful oxidizing agents to abstract electrons from undissociated hydrazine molecules, e.g.

$$Tol_2N\cdot + Tol_2\ddot{N}{-}\ddot{N}Tol_2 \longrightarrow (Tol_2N\colon)^- + (Tol_2\ddot{N}{-}\dot{N}Tol_2)^+$$

or

$$3\,Tol_2\ddot{N}{-}\ddot{N}Tol_2 + 2HCl = 2\,Tol_2\ddot{N}H + 2(Tol_2\ddot{N}{-}\dot{N}Tol_2)^+Cl^-.$$

A number of substitution derivatives of tetraphenyl-hydrazine have been prepared by Wieland and his colleagues,§ who showed that *meta*-directing groups, such as NO_2, decreased the ease of dissociation whilst *ortho-para*-directing groups, such as CH_3O— and $(CH_3)_2N$—, increased it. They commented on the fact that this behaviour of substituents was opposite to that observed in the triphenylmethyl series, and a qualitative explanation for this difference has been proposed by Burton and Ingold‖ on the view that a net gain of electronic charge leads to an increase of stability of a nitrogen radical.

Hydrazyl radicals. Stefan Goldschmidt, in 1920,¶ found that dissociability of the N—N bond was much more evident in the tetrazane series. When a solution of triphenyl-hydrazine, in dry ether, is shaken

† Katz, *Zeit. für Physik*, 1933, **87**, 238; Müller and Wiesemann, *Ber.* 1936, **69**, 2157.
‡ Weitz and Schwechten, ibid., 1926, **59**, 2307; 1927, **60**, 551.
§ *Ber.* 1912, **45**, 2600; 1915, **48**, 1078, 1091; 1922, **55**, 1804.
‖ *Proc. Leeds Phil. Soc.* 1929, **1**, 430.
¶ *Ber.* 1920, **53**, 44.

with lead peroxide at room temperature there is formed a deep blue solution containing the radical triphenyl-hydrazyl (I), though when the reaction is carried out at $-55°$ to $-60°$ C. in dimethyl ether, hexaphenyl-tetrazane (II) can be isolated as a very pale green solid.

$$\underset{\text{(II)}}{Ph_2N-\underset{|}{\overset{}{N}}(Ph)-\underset{|}{N}(Ph)-NPh_2} \rightleftharpoons \underset{\text{(I)}}{2Ph_2N-\dot{N}(Ph)}$$

The colour of the blue solution does not obey Beer's dilution law, and solutions in chloroform are relatively darker than those in ether under the same conditions.

Triphenyl-hydrazyl combines immediately with nitric oxide, giving N-nitroso-triphenyl-hydrazine, reacts slowly with triphenylmethyl, and can be analysed by taking advantage of its immediate quantitative reduction with either quinol or hydrazobenzene:

$$2Ph_2N-\dot{N}(Ph) + C_6H_4(OH)_2 \longrightarrow 2Ph_2N-NHPh + C_6H_4O_2,$$

since the dissociation of the tetrazane to the hydrazyl is a slowish reaction. On keeping, solutions of triphenyl-hydrazyl decompose into diphenylamine and the diphenylhydrazone of quinone-anil, which can also be obtained by direct oxidation, with lead peroxide, of a mixture of triphenyl-hydrazine and aniline:

$$2Ph_2N-\dot{N}(Ph) \longrightarrow Ph_2N-H + Ph_2N-N{=}C_6H_4{=}N-Ph.$$

Goldschmidt considers that the radical Ph—N= may be involved in this latter oxidation.

The radical $\alpha\alpha$-diphenyl-β-trinitrophenyl-hydrazyl (III):†

$$\underset{\text{(III)}}{(C_6H_5)_2N-\dot{N}-C_6H_2(NO_2)_3} \qquad \underset{\text{(IV)}}{(C_6H_5)_2N-N(OH)-C_6H_2(NO_2)_3}$$

which may be prepared by condensing *as*-diphenyl-hydrazine with picryl chloride and oxidizing the product with lead peroxide in dry ether containing sodium sulphate, is much more stable, for the corresponding tetrazane is unknown.

(III) is a violet-black substance which shows a remarkable resemblance to potassium permanganate. It is a paramagnetic solid,‡ and the value

† Goldschmidt and Renn, *Ber.* 1922, **55**, 628.

‡ Müller, Müller-Rodloff, and Bunge, *Annalen*, 1935, **520**, 235.

of its magnetic moment is equal to that calculated for a molecule containing one unpaired electron. The colours of its solutions do not diminish in intensity even when the latter are cooled in ether-carbon dioxide. Unlike other compounds of divalent nitrogen, (III) does not react with nitric oxide, but it reacts readily with nitrogen peroxide, yielding eventually β-hydroxy-$\alpha\alpha$-diphenyl-β-trinitrophenyl-hydrazine (IV).

Tetrazanes containing acyl groups can also dissociate slightly to hydrazyl radicals, such as (V) and (VI):

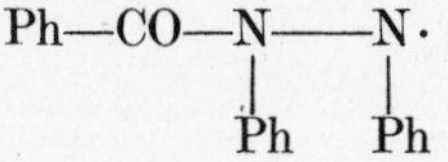

```
Ph—CO—N——N·          Ph—N——N·
      |    |               |    |
      Ph   Ph              Ph   CO—Ph
     (V)                  (VI)
```

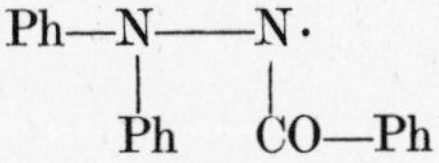

since they give coloured solutions, and combine easily with both nitric oxide and triphenylmethyl.† Since, in this series, the dissociation of the tetrazane is a much slower process than is the reduction of the free hydrazyl with hydrazobenzene or quinol, it is possible to determine dissociation constants by titrating solutions, at low temperatures, with these reagents until the colour vanishes. Therefrom, heats of dissociation may be calculated.‡ For compound (VI) the heat of dissociation varied from 10·3 k.cals. in toluene to 5·2 k.cals. in chloroform, the corresponding dissociation constants, at $-18°$ C., being of the order of 10^{-4}.

Heats of dissociation of the N—N link, measured for a series of diaryl-acyl-hydrazyls, analogous to (VI), ranged downwards from 18 k.cals., and thus are comparable in magnitude with heats of dissociation of the C—C link in compounds of the hexaphenylethane series (p. 54).

It is noticeable, however, that the velocity of dissociation of the arylated hydrazines, or tetrazanes, is very much less than that of analogous hexa-arylethanes.

Diphenyl nitric oxide, $\mathrm{Ph_2}\overset{+}{\mathrm{N}}\text{—}\overset{-}{\mathrm{O}}\mathrm{:}$

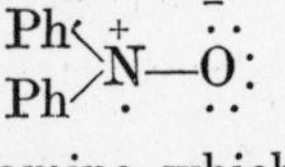

When diphenyl hydroxylamine, which is easily prepared by the action of phenyl magnesium bromide on nitrosobenzene, is oxidized with silver oxide in dry ether containing anhydrous sodium sulphate, it yields a deep red solution from which diphenyl nitric oxide, m.p. 62°, can be separated by freezing.§ Cryoscopic measurements show that this radical, unlike nitrogen peroxide, is a monomeric free radical which is

† Goldschmidt and Euler, *Ber.* 1922, **55**, 616; Goldschmidt, *Annalen*, 1924, **437**, 194.
‡ Goldschmidt and Bader, ibid. 1929, **473**, 137.
§ Wieland and Offenbächer, *Ber.* 1914, **47**, 2111.

unassociated even at very low temperatures. It is reduced at once by potassium iodide, and is decolorized immediately by both nitric oxide and triphenylmethyl, with which it reacts as follows:

$$Ph_2\overset{+}{\underset{\cdot}{N}}-\overset{-}{O} + \cdot NO \longrightarrow Ph_2\overset{+}{N}(-N{=}O)-\overset{-}{O} \longrightarrow Ph_2N-NO_2$$

$$Ph_2N-NO_2 \longrightarrow NO_2-C_6H_4-NH-Ph$$

$$NO_2-C_6H_4-NH-Ph \longrightarrow Ph_2N-OH + NO_2-C_6H_4-N(NO)-Ph$$

$$Ph_2\overset{+}{\underset{\cdot}{N}}-\overset{-}{O} + \cdot CPh_3 \longrightarrow Ph_2N-O-CPh_3$$

$$Ph_2N-O-CPh_3 \longrightarrow Ph_2N-OH + Ph_2N-O-C(Ph)_2-C_6H_4-CPh_3$$

and with nitrogen peroxide yields di-*p*-nitrophenyl nitric oxide, which, though much more stable, has similar reactions.† The tolyl nitric oxides are much less stable,‡ but di-*p*-anisyl nitric oxide is much more stable than is diphenyl nitric oxide.§ Cambi‖ has measured the magnetic susceptibilities of di-*p*-nitrophenyl nitric oxide and of di-*p*-anisyl nitric oxide; both are paramagnetic. Another paramagnetic compound of this type (VII) has been prepared by Banfield and Kenyon by the action of phenyl-hydroxylamine on acetone.¶

$$(CH_3)_2C(-\overset{+}{\underset{\cdot}{N}}(Ph)-\overset{-}{O})-CH_2-C(=\overset{+}{N}(Ph)-\overset{-}{O})-CH_3 \qquad \text{(VII)}$$

In all compounds of this group the bond between the nitrogen and oxygen atoms is a 'semi-polar', $>\overset{+}{N}-\overset{-}{O}$, or 'dative', $>N\rightarrow O$, link, and, in accordance with conceptions of resonance there is some probability that the odd electron may be located on the oxygen atom. Thus the structures (VIII) and (IX) are mesomeric

$$\underset{\text{(VIII)}}{Ph_2\dot{N}-\ddot{\underset{\cdot\cdot}{O}}:} \qquad \underset{\text{(IX)}}{Ph_2\ddot{N}-\ddot{\underset{\cdot\cdot}{O}}\cdot} \qquad \underset{\text{(X)}}{Ph_2N\cdot\!\cdot\!\cdot O:}$$

though of these canonical states (VIII) will undoubtedly have the

† Wieland and Roth, *Ber.* 1920, **53**, 210.
‡ Wieland and Kögl, ibid. 1922, **55**, 1798.
§ Kurt Meyer and Billroth, ibid. 1919, **52**, 1476.
‖ Cambi, *Gazzetta*, 1933, **63**, 579.
¶ Banfield and Kenyon, *J.* 1926, p. 1612; Kenyon and Sugden, *J.* 1932, p. 170.

lower energy level. Nevertheless, the resonance between the two states is undoubtedly conducive to the stability of the radical as a whole entity. This may be expressed by means of the three-electron bonded formula (X).

'Ammonium radicals.' When aqueous ammonia, or ammonium salts, are electrolysed at a low temperature using a mercury cathode, there is formed a curious type of amalgam, which, on warming puffs up and evolves gaseous nitrogen and hydrogen in the proportions corresponding to the radical NH_4.† A similar product can be obtained by acting on ammonia, or ammonium salts, with amalgams of potassium or sodium. A comparatively stable amalgam of a similar type can be prepared by electrolysing tetramethylammonium chloride in ether or alcohol.‡ These amalgams which will liberate hydrogen from water, and displace metals, such as copper and zinc, from solutions of their salts, thus have the chemical properties of the amalgams of the true alkali metals.

Deep blue solutions are formed when tetra-ethyl-ammonium chloride and analogous salts are electrolysed in liquid ammonia at $-70°$ C. in the absence of air.§ These are immediately decolorized by iodine or sulphur and decompose when warmed to about $-30°$ C.

All these properties have been looked upon as indicative of the existence of uncharged ammonium radicals, (NH_4), $N(C_2H_5)_4$, though the blue solutions in liquid ammonia may have the ionic structure $[N(C_2H_5)_4]^+NH_2^-$ similar to that of sodamide $Na^+NH_2^-$.

It is difficult to formulate a molecular structure for the neutral ammonium radical, since the ammonium cation cannot, as can a true metallic cation, pick up an extra electron, for this would have to be held in a new valency shell outside the coordinated hydrogen atoms.

$$\text{Compare}\quad Na^+ \longrightarrow Na\cdot \quad \text{with}\quad (NH_4)^+ \longrightarrow \left(\begin{matrix} & H & \\ & \cdot\cdot & \\ H{:} & N & {:}H \\ & \cdot\cdot & \\ & H & \end{matrix}\right).$$

Possibly, therefore, the amalgams contain ionized complexes, the mercury holding the extra electrons. It is significant that there is at present no evidence for the transient existence of the ammonium radical in the gas phase.

The true free radicals equivalent to ammonia are, of course, the

† Berzelius and Pontin, Gilbert's *Annalen*, 1810, **6**, 247.

‡ McCoy and Moore, *J.A.C.S.* 1911, **33**, 273.

§ Schlubach and Ballauf, *Ber.* 1920, **53**, 1689; 1921, **54**, 2811, 2825.

aminium salts, such as $[(C_6H_5)_3N\cdot]^+(ClO_4)^-$, which have been described on p. 67. In these the nitrogen atom has one electron less than the complete octet and acts as a pseudo-halogen.

Oxygen and Sulphur Compounds

Unstable coloured solutions can be obtained from many phenols by oxidation in cold dry ether with lead peroxide, and Goldschmidt† has suggested that these solutions contain neutral radicals with univalent oxygen, R—O·

By oxidizing phenanthraquinol monomethyl and mono-ethyl ethers with alkaline potassium ferricyanide, Goldschmidt and Schmidt‡ obtained almost colourless peroxides, which yielded greenish-yellow solutions which gradually darkened on standing. Cryoscopic measurements indicated that in solution the peroxides were gradually dissociating into radicals, the process reaching an equilibrium in about three hours. Similarly 9-chloro-10-hydroxy-phenanthrene can be oxidized to the colourless peroxide (XI), which eventually dissociates to the extent of 69 per cent., yielding a deep blue solution.§ This presumably contains the radical (XII), though an alternative formulation as (XIII) cannot be wholly excluded from consideration.

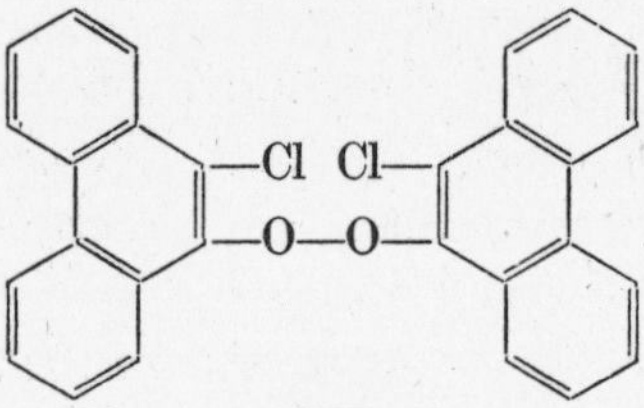

(XI) 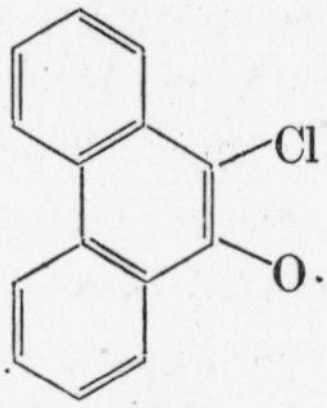 (XII) 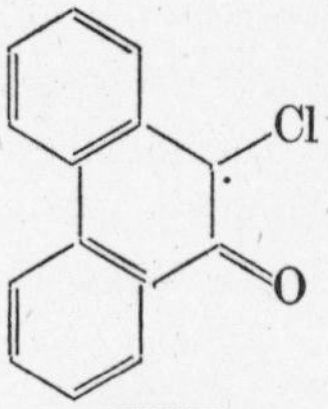 (XIII)

These coloured radicals of Goldschmidt are immediately reduced by quinol or phenylhydrazine, and are rapidly oxidized to phenanthraquinone by bromine or by oxygen. They do not react with nitric oxide, but combine additively with triphenylmethyl, giving products which can be hydrolysed to triphenyl-carbinol.

There is no evidence of the existence of stable radicals containing univalent sulphur. This is only to be expected, in view of the high bond strength (*ca.* 64 k.cals.) of the S—S covalent link.

However, reactive neutral radicals, Aryl—S·, of short life, can undoubtedly exist. Solutions of diphenyl-disulphide, Ph—S—S—Ph, and

† Goldschmidt, *Ber.* 1922, **55**, 3194.

‡ Goldschmidt and Schmidt, ibid., p. 3197.

§ Goldschmidt and Steigerwald, *Annalen*, 1924, **438**, 202; Goldschmidt, Vogt, and Bredig, ibid. 1925, **445**, 123.

of bis(thio-α-naphthoyl disulphide, $(C_{10}H_7—CS—S—)_2$, become yellow when heated and Beer's dilution law is not obeyed.† These aromatic disulphides will react with solutions of triphenylmethyl, giving thio-ethers, which are decomposed again by air into the original disulphide and triphenylmethyl peroxide:‡

$$Ph_2S_2 + 2\cdot CPh_3 \longrightarrow 2Ph—S—CPh_3,$$

$$2Ph—S—CPh_3 + O_2 \longrightarrow Ph—S—S—Ph + Ph_3C—O—O—CPh_3.$$

Again, warm solutions of disulphides readily react with metals such as sodium, silver, or zinc:†

$$(C_{10}H_7—CS—S—)_2 + 2Ag \longrightarrow 2C_{10}H_7—CS—S—Ag.$$

The fact that thiols can act as chain carriers in autoxidation§ (pp. 258, 283), and can add on to olefines by the peroxide-catalysed radical mechanism (pp. 188–9), are further indications of the transient existence of neutral thiol radicals. Whilst the polarographic behaviour of disulphides, such as cystine, seldom gives indications of stepwise reduction, anomalous effects have been recorded in the presence of traces of metals such as copper.

SEMI-QUINONES

The reduction of a quinone to a hydroquinone is usually a two-stage process. The intermediate product in acid solution is a quinhydrone (XIV), which is a resonance complex formed from one molecule each of quinone and hydroquinone in which the two ring systems are held together by hydrogen atoms. As Clemo and McIlwain have shown‖ in the phenazine series, the same quinhydrone can be obtained by mixing (i) a quinone with a substituent *A* and a hydroquinone with substituent *B* or (ii) the quinone with substituent *B* and the hydroquinone with substituent *A*.

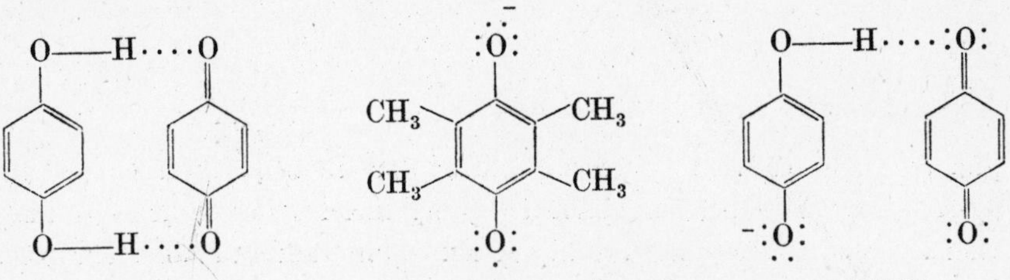

(XIV) (XV) (XVI)

† Schönberg, Rupp, and Gumlich, *Ber.* 1933, **66**, 1932.
‡ Lecher, ibid. 1915, **48**, 524; 1920, **55**, 577.
§ Ziegler and Gänicke, *Annalen*, 1942, **551**, 213.
‖ Clemo and McIlwain, *J.* 1934, p. 1992.

Quinhydrones act as very weak acids, and their anions, e.g. (XVI), are also resonance-stabilized systems.

In alkaline solution the intermediate stage in the reduction of a quinone is, initially, a paramagnetic *semi-quinone* anion, such as (XV), which may form a stabilized diamagnetic dimer (possibly of type XVI) but which, as Michaelis and his colleagues have shown by magnetic susceptibility measurement,† can often exist, in dilute solution, in the active free radical form. Thus in solutions of pH 9 or over duroquinone yields exclusively the free radical (XV).

The formation of semi-quinonoid radicals is a common feature of the reduction of indophenol and indamine dyestuffs and their heterocyclic analogues, such as Binschedler's green (XVII), Lauth's violet (XVIII), and pyocyanine (XIX):

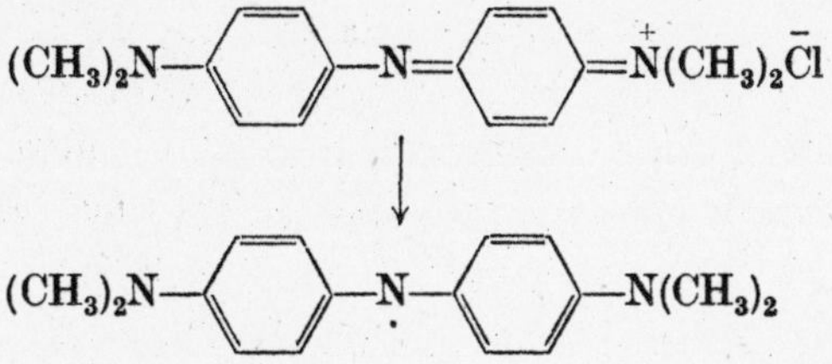

(XVII)

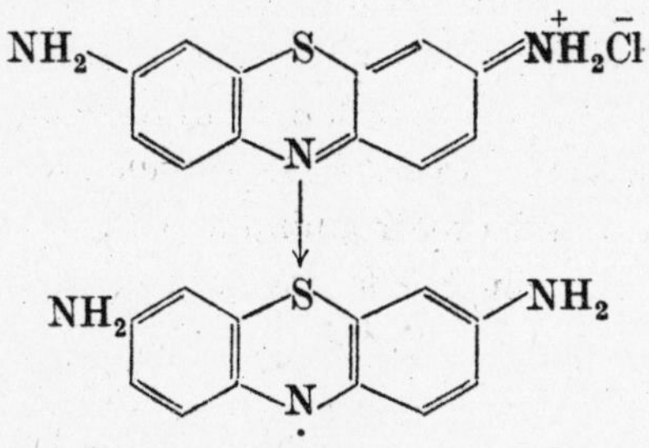

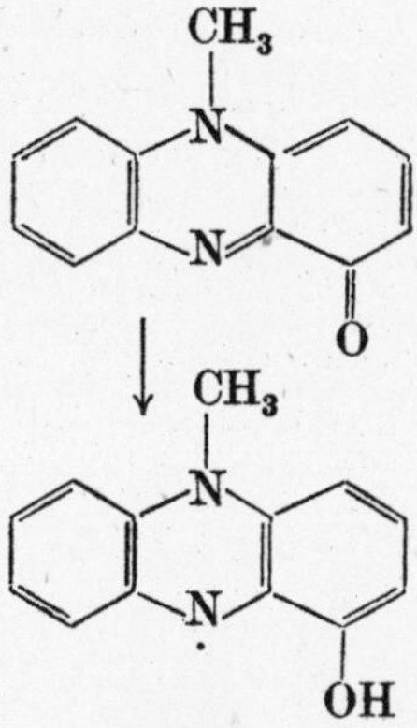

(XVIII) (XIX)

and always gives rise to intensely coloured products.‡ Heterocyclic ring systems in which there are extended possibilities of resonance stabilization are conducive to the stability of semi-quinonoid radicals. They can be formed for instance from simple thiazines not containing attached amino groups.§

† Michaelis *et al.*, *J.A.C.S.* 1938, **60**, 202, 1678.
‡ Ibid., p. 1666; 1940, **62**, 204.
§ Michaelis, Granick, and Schubert, *J.A.C.S.* 1941, **63**, 351.

Wurster's salts. Wurster's coloured salts, which are obtained when aromatic diamines are oxidized with bromine, are similar in character, compound (XVII) being in fact a typical member of this group of salts.

Michaelis, Schubert, and Granick† have examined the essential relationships between structure and stability in the highly coloured oxidation products of *p*-phenylene-diamine and its alkyl derivatives, and have pointed out that stable radicals can only be formed when the Wurster's salts have a molecular symmetry sufficiently high for the occurrence of resonance throughout the whole molecule. For this, the benzene ring, the *para*-nitrogen atoms, and the four attached groups must all lie in one plane,

(XX) (XXI)

since the contribution of the quinonoid canonical state (XXI) restricts the free rotation of the amino groups.

These simple Wurster's salts are stable only in the pH range of 3·5 to 6, obviously because the unipolar ion (XXIII) is a symmetrical resonance system, whereas both the free base (XXII) and the dipolar ion (XXIV) are unsymmetrical.

Methylation of the amino groups of *p*-phenylene-diamine enhances the stability of the Wurster's salts, but substitution in the benzene

$H_2\ddot{N}-C_6H_4-\dot{\ddot{N}}-H$ (XXII) $H_2\ddot{N}-C_6H_4-\dot{\overset{+}{N}}H_2$ (XXIII) $H_3\overset{+}{N}-C_6H_4-\dot{\overset{+}{N}}H_2$ (XXIV)

ring tends to reduce their stability. Thus, whereas the blue salt formed from tetramethyl-*p*-phenylene-diamine is stable indefinitely, dimethyl-amino-durene (XXV) does not yield a Wurster's salt. It has been suggested that in this case the steric hindrance of the nuclear methyl groups in the *ortho*-positions to the $NH-CH_3$ groups prevents the

† Michaelis, Schubert, and Granick, *J.A.C.S.* 1939, **61**, 1981.

latter from taking up a location coplanar with the benzene ring, as is necessary in a resonance-stabilized radical-ion.

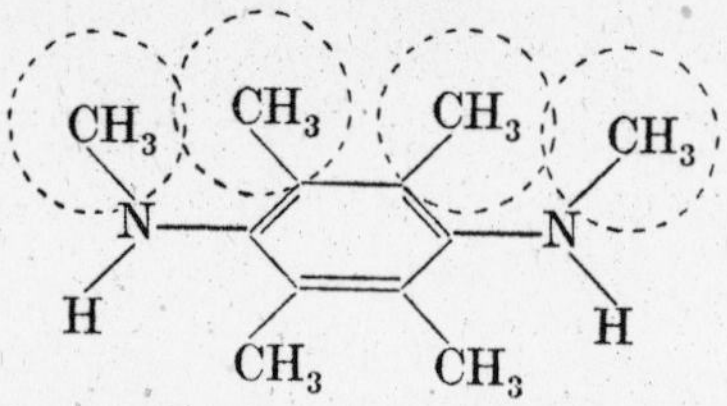

(XXV)

This explanation is identical with that invoked by Müller (p. 61) for explaining the conditions of formation of stable carbon bi-radicals.

Viologens. Another interesting series of semi-quinones which show no tendency to dimerize to quinhydrones† is afforded by the *viologens* which are the deep blue-violet reduction products of compounds of the dipyridyl series. Dimroth‡ and his colleagues first showed that the reduction of $\gamma\gamma'$-dipyridyl with zinc dust in acetic anhydride, or chromous chloride, gave deep violet products at the reduction stage corresponding to a quinhydrone, whilst Weitz, in a series of papers,§ has described two series of deeply coloured, very reactive salts obtainable by oxidizing tetrahydro-$\gamma\gamma'$-dipyridyl derivatives. For example, two hydriodides, $C_{24}H_{22}N_2$,HI and $C_{24}H_{22}N_2$,2HI, were obtained by oxidizing NN-dibenzyl-tetrahydro-$\gamma\gamma'$-dipyridyl (XXVI).

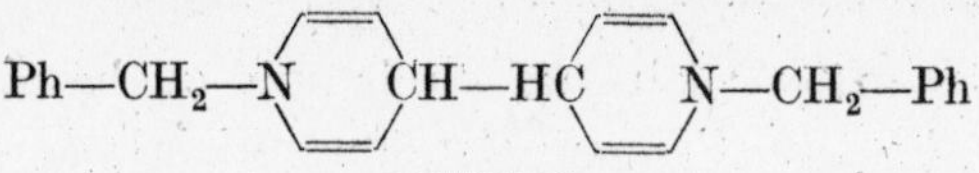

Ph—CH₂—N CH—HC N—CH₂—Ph

(XXVI)

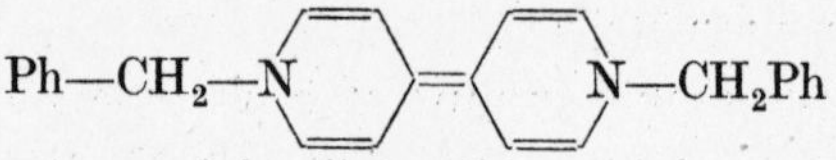

Ph—CH₂—N = N—CH₂Ph

(XXVII)

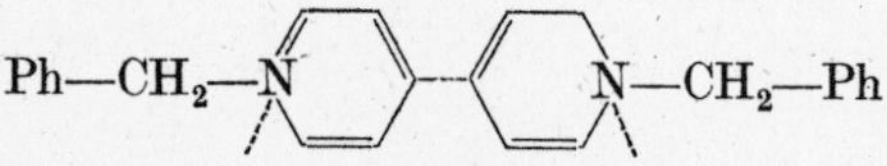

Ph—CH₂—N N—CH₂—Ph

(XXVIII)

Ph—CH₂—N = N⁺—CH₂Ph
H I⁻

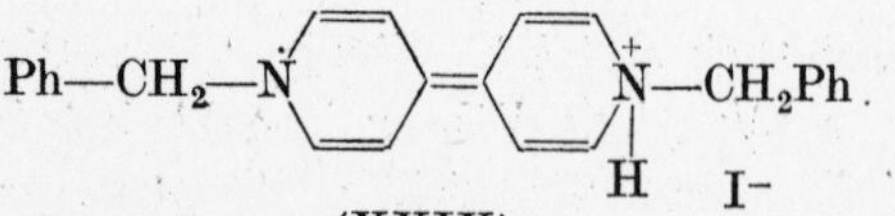

(XXIX)

Of these, the second is the salt of the quinonoid compound (XXVII),

† Michaelis and Hill, *J.A.C.S.* 1933, **55**, 1481.

‡ Dimroth and Heene, *Ber.* 1921, **54**, 2934; Dimroth and Frister, ibid. 1922, **55**, 3693.

§ *Annalen*, 1921, **425**, 161, 187; *Ber.* 1922, **55**, 395, 2864; 1924, **57**, 153.

which, however, Weitz wrote as the bi-radical (XXVIII), though it has since been shown to be diamagnetic.†

The sub-iodide (XXIX) is, however, a free semi-quinonoid radical in which one of the nitrogen atoms possesses only seven electrons. Weitz and his colleagues showed, by ebullioscopic measurements in methyl alcohol, that it had far too low a molecular weight for a quinhydrone, whilst Michaelis and his colleagues have found, by potentiometric measurements, no trace of dimerization in substances of this series, which, they note, exist only in acid solution.

It is significant to note that both the Wurster's salts, and these reduced dipyridyl derivatives, have found valuable applications as oxidation-reduction indicators.

Potentiometric detection of semi-quinones. Michaelis‡ has shown that semi-quinone formation can easily be detected potentiometrically, since the oxidation-reduction potential of a quinone, $E = E_0 + \frac{RT}{nF}\log\frac{[\mathrm{Ox}]}{[\mathrm{Red}]}$ varies more abruptly for a one-electron change ($n = 1$) than for a two-electron change. Analysis of potentiometric titration curves will indubitably differentiate between two-electron reduction, one-electron reduction leading to semi-quinone production, and one-electron reduction followed by dimerization to a quinhydrone, or a pinacone (compare p. 192). If the slope, dE/dx, of the electrode potential curve (where x is the fraction reduced) at the mid-point of the titration is greater than RT/F then either a semi-quinone radical or its dimer must be present in the solution. This slope of the electrode potential curve can be assessed most simply by estimating the 'index potential' of the system, which is defined as the potential difference between the equilibrium values for 25 and 75 per cent. reduction of the organic compound in aqueous solution. If this is greater than 14·3 millivolts at 30° C. (corresponding to $\Delta E = (RT/2F)\log 3$) then one-electron reduction must be occurring.

Dimerization of the primary radical (i.e. quinhydrone or pinacone formation) tends to increase the slope of the oxidation-reduction curve in the neighbourhood of 50 per cent. reduction, but since dimerization is a bimolecular process its extent will vary with the dilution of the solution. Consequently for semi-quinones which do not dimerize the form of the potentiometric titration curve will be independent of

† Müller and Wiesemann, ibid. 1936, **69**, 2157.

‡ Michaelis, *Chemical Reviews*, 1935, **16**, 243; Michaelis and Schubert, ibid. 1938, **22**, 437.

the concentration of the dissolved substance, whilst for substances which dimerize reversibly the slope of the potentiometric titration curve is given by

$$dE/dx = (RT/F)\surd(\tfrac{1}{2}K_d a),$$

where K_d is the dissociation constant of the dimer and a the molar concentration of the original quinone, ketone, etc. A simple dilution test is thus sufficient for differentiating between semi-quinones and quinhydrones.

Polarographic reduction (p. 12) can also be used to establish the existence of semi-quinone radicals. In this way it has been shown that free radicals can be formed by the partial reduction of heterocyclic compounds of the pyridine, quinoline, and acridine series,† including such biochemically important substances as nicotinamide (Chapter XII).

Organo-metallic Free Radicals‡

In a number of cases, molecular weight determinations have indicated that organo-metallic compounds, $Ar_3M—MAr_3$, analogous to hexaphenylethane, can dissociate into radicals $Ar_3M\cdot$, and this inference can often be substantiated by evidence of marked reactivity towards oxygen, sodium, iodine, and other halogens.

For instance, whilst hexaphenyl-digermanium, $Ph_3Ge—GePh_3$, does not appear to dissociate it is easily split to Ph_3GeNa by metallic sodium, and to Ph_3GeBr with bromine. Hexaphenyl-di-tin, Ph_6Sn_2, and its homologues all give abnormally low molecular weights and oxidize in the air. The analogous compounds with simple aliphatic radicals, again seem to exist in the dissociated forms, as trimethyl tin, $(CH_3)_3Sn\cdot$, and tri-ethyl tin, $(C_2H_5)_3Sn\cdot$, and react easily with oxygen, sulphur, iodine, and sodium giving stable products such as $(CH_3)_3Sn—O—Sn(CH_3)_3$, $(CH_3)_3Sn—I$, $(CH_3)_3SnNa$. With alkyl halides they react as follows:

$$2(C_2H_5)_3Sn + CH_3I \longrightarrow (C_2H_5)_3Sn—CH_3 + (C_2H_5)_3Sn—I,$$

$$(C_2H_5)_3Sn + C_2H_5I \longrightarrow (C_2H_5)_3Sn—I + C_4H_{10}.$$

Lead alkyls and aryls of the same type also have low apparent molecular weights, and decompose when heated in solution,

$$2(C_6H_5)_3Pb—Pb(C_6H_5)_3 \longrightarrow Pb + 3Pb(C_6H_5)_4;$$

whilst tetraphenyl-diarsine, Ph_4As_2, reacts similarly,

$$3Ph_4As_2 \longrightarrow 4Ph_3As + 2As.$$

† Stock, *J.* 1944, p. 427; Breyer, Buchanan, and Duewell, ibid., p. 360.

‡ For detailed information see Krause, *Die Chemie der Metall-organischen Verbindungen*, Berlin, 1937.

In many cases, however, the apparent molecular weight of a dissolved organo-metallic compound has been found to change irreversibly with time, this being particularly true of observations made by the ebullioscopic method, and quantitative recovery of the dissolved substance is often impossible. It seems, therefore, that many of the reported instances of dissociations of compounds $Ar_3M—MAr_3$ to radicals are in reality irreversible redistribution processes, examples of which have been illustrated in the equations given above.

Selwood and his colleagues† have more recently made a thorough search for organo-metallic free radicals, using magnetic susceptibility measurement as their criterion, and have shown that all previously reported instances of dissociation to radicals of compounds of germanium, tin, and lead give only diamagnetic products. It would thus seem that no genuine organo-metallic free radicals have yet been made.

The high chemical activity of organo-metallic compounds towards oxygen, iodine, etc., is explicable by the fact that carbon-metal bonds have low energy contents, and, in consequence sporadic molecular rearrangement, or *redistribution* as it has been termed, is possible.‡

† Selwood, *J.A.C.S.* 1939, **61**, 3168; 1940, **62**, 2765; 1941, **63**, 2509; Selwood, Byerly, and Morris, ibid. 1942, **64**, 1727.

‡ Calingaert, ibid. 1942, **64**, 462. See Calingaert's article in Gilman's *Organic Chemistry*, vol. ii, 1943 edn.

V

FREE ATOMS AND THEIR GAS REACTIONS

Electrical Dissociation and Spectral Analysis

With the exception of the inert gases, the non-metallic elements do not exist in the free atomic state at ordinary temperatures. They combine with themselves to form stable molecules, e.g. H_2, O_2, which, however, can be dissociated to atoms by heating to high temperatures. For many years, however, chemists have inferred that the stable diatomic gases dissociate when an electrical discharge is passed through them, since by this means reactions such as

$$2H_2+O_2 = 2H_2O \quad \text{and} \quad N_2+O_2 = 2NO,$$

which involve the breaking of diatomic molecules, can be brought about.

For a long time it was not certain whether these electrical decompositions involved the production of neutral atoms or of gaseous ions, but modern knowledge of spectroscopy has revealed the exact course of the disruption process. Thus passage of an electrical discharge through a Geissler tube containing hydrogen generates a pinkish light which can easily be resolved into a simple line spectrum, in which the wave-length of each line can be expressed as a term in the general equation

$$\nu = \frac{c}{\lambda} = R\left(\frac{1}{2^2}-\frac{1}{n^2}\right),$$

where R is constant and n is an integer.

In 1913 Niels Bohr interpreted this mathematically related series of spectral lines—the Balmer series—as being an emission spectrum characteristic of an *atom* of hydrogen, which, following Rutherford, he depicted as comprised of a nucleus, with a unit positive charge, and a single planetary electron, capable of existing in any one of a finite number of quantized orbits, with each of which was associated a definite amount of energy. Bohr's quantum theory has since been clarified, though not discredited, by the introduction of newer ideas of statistical mechanics, and so uniformly successful are the modern theories of spectroscopy that it cannot now be doubted that free *neutral* atoms of hydrogen are present in a discharge tube containing hydrogen gas.

To-day, theories of spectroscopy can safely be used to ascertain whether free atoms are present in any gas. If light of wave-lengths calculated to be characteristic of known atoms is being emitted, or can be absorbed, by any gas then these free atoms must definitely be present in it, although they may be incapable of detection by any other means. In this way can be investigated equally well the nature of a laboratory preparation or of a distant star.

In a similar way simple neutral compound radicals, such as OH and CN, can be identified, and shown to be capable of independent existence at high temperatures.

The production of these line spectra by passing electrical discharges through gases is of interest in connexion with theories of free radical formation. According to modern conceptions, a molecule when subjected to an electrical strain, acquires potential energy and may dissociate. As in the case of molecular dissociation by gain of thermal or photochemical energy, covalent bonds are most easily broken by the fission of the electron pair with the formation of two neutral radicals, one fragment having energy corresponding to the *ground*, or most stable, *state* of the radical concerned, and the other any excess energy acquired in the dissociation process.

This second fragment is an *activated* atom, or radical, which tends to revert to the ground state by emitting its excess of energy as a radiation *characteristic of the fragment produced by the dissociation process*, and not as radiation characteristic of the molecule which has been disrupted.†

Both neutral radicals and ions can be produced by passing electrical discharges through gases. Electric spark spectra frequently show spectral lines characteristic of ions, whereas arc spectra, and spectra produced by silent discharges, are more frequently emitted by neutral atoms or by activated molecules.

Atomic Hydrogen

In 1922 R. W. Wood first isolated, and described the properties of, atomic hydrogen, which he produced in an electrical discharge tube.‡ He found that when a heavy electrical discharge was passed through moist hydrogen gas dissociation is, after the first fraction of a second, complete, and that atomic hydrogen could be pumped along a glass tube a considerable way from the area affected by the electrical discharge without the occurrence of recombination. A tungsten wire placed in the stream of cold gas became white hot; the hydrogen atoms recombine on its surface and give up to the tungsten the energy of the recombination

† Compare Bonhoeffer, *Zeit. phys. Chem.* 1924, **113**, 199.
‡ *Phil. Mag.* 1922, vi, **44**, 538.

process $2H\cdot \rightarrow H_2+103$ k.cals. After passing the tungsten wire, the issuing gas gave the spectrum of molecular hydrogen and not the Balmer spectrum of atomic hydrogen. Recombination was also found to occur on the surface of thorium oxide, which became incandescent. Curiously enough, recombination of hydrogen atoms did not occur

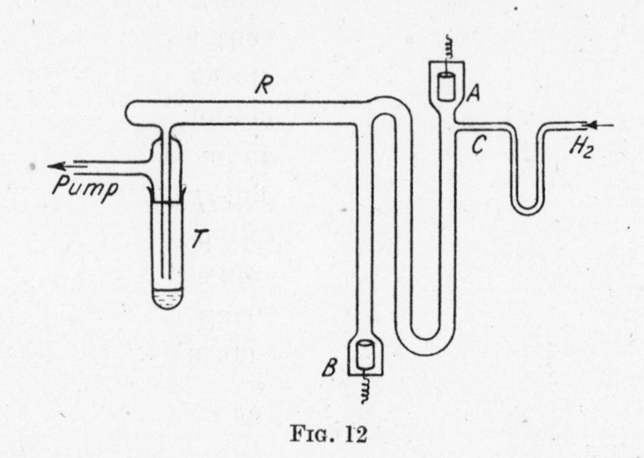

FIG. 12

appreciably on the surface of the glass tube, except in the complete absence of moisture, or at the temperature of liquid air. The atomic hydrogen was found to be chemically active, for it speedily reduced tin oxide to metallic tin.

The chemical properties of Wood's atomic hydrogen were investigated more fully by Bonhoeffer in 1924.† As indicated in Fig. 12, pure hydrogen, prepared by the electrolysis of caustic soda, and dried by passage through a liquid air trap, was passed through the capillary tube *C* into the long discharge tube *AB*, and pumped out, through the wide reaction tube *R* and the detachable trap *T*, to a high-speed mercury pump. It was essential to place the exit tube *R* well away from the electrodes, since recombination of hydrogen atoms is catalysed by the electrode surfaces. By passing a silent discharge between cylindrical aluminium electrodes at 10,000 volts potential difference, through the hydrogen stream in *AB*, maintained at between 0·1 and 1·0 mm. pressure, there was obtained in *R* a chemically active product which would, at distances of up to 10 cm. from the electrical discharge, reduce the oxides of copper, lead, bismuth, silver, and mercury, but not those of aluminium, magnesium, or chromium. Sulphur phosphorus and arsenic yielded their hydrides; oleic acid was reduced to stearic acid, but the carboxyl group was not further attacked.

† *Zeit. phys. Chem.* 1924, **113**, 199.

The following results were obtained by exposing small pieces of sulphur in a gas stream of velocity 30 cm. per second at a pressure of 0·5 mm. of mercury.

TABLE XV

Reaction between Atomic Hydrogen and Sulphur

Distance from discharge .	1·5 cm.	10 cm.	20 cm.	30 cm.
Loss of weight per minute .	3·2 mg.	1·6 mg.	0·9 mg.	0·4 mg.

The loss of weight falls off exponentially with distance, and in passing along 10 cm. of the tube—i.e. in $\frac{1}{3}$ second—the chemical activity of the hydrogen falls to one-half.

Hence Bonhoeffer concluded that at 0·5 mm. pressure the average life of atomic hydrogen is $\frac{1}{3}$ second, a value which was at first regarded as being surprisingly high, since at this pressure gas particles undergo about 10^{12} mutual collisions per second.

It is evident, therefore, that two hydrogen atoms do not recombine whenever they collide, although the process $2H\cdot \rightarrow H_2$ is very highly exothermic. This experimental fact can easily be explained on the basis of the quantum theory, for both hydrogen atoms and hydrogen molecules can only possess internal energy in fixed quantized amounts. Since the total energy content of two hydrogen atoms in the ground state is greater than that of a hydrogen molecule in any stationary state, it is impossible for two hydrogen atoms to recombine to form a diatomic molecule unless, at the instant of recombination, this excess of energy can be removed by some other means. On account of the conservation of linear and angular momentum none of the energy can go into rotation or translation. Consequently the recombination of hydrogen atoms can only take place in the gaseous phase upon the occurrence of a three-body collision between two hydrogen atoms and a third particle capable of absorbing the liberated energy.

A collision with the walls of the containing vessel, or with any solid substance, may also be an occasion upon which this recombination of atoms can occur, but, as Bonhoeffer showed, substances vary enormously in their catalytic (energy abstracting) capacity, metals being particularly effective, and salts, in general, ineffective. For instance, a thermometer showed no appreciable rise of temperature if its clean glass bulb was introduced into the hydrogen gas stream at a distance of 15 cm. from the electrical discharge, but if the bulb had first been dipped into a $N/10$ solution of silver nitrate, then the recorded temperature rose to

300° C. owing to recombination of the atomic hydrogen on the film of metallic silver which was formed instantly by reduction. This thermometric heating effect was measured at different distances from the electrical discharge, and the recorded temperature was found to decrease exponentially with distance in such a way as to confirm the conclusion, which had been reached by the chemical experiment with sulphur, that the half life of atomic hydrogen was about $\frac{1}{3}$ second at 0·5 mm. pressure.

The relative catalytic activity of different metals was established by comparing the temperatures recorded on coated thermometer bulbs, and was found to decrease in the order

$$\text{Pt} > \text{Pd} > \text{W} > \text{Fe} > \text{Cr} > \text{Ag} > \text{Cu} > \text{Pb} > \text{Hg}.$$

Appreciable recombination also took place on the surfaces of the stable oxides MgO, CaO, BaO, Al_2O_3, and Cr_2O_3.

Even dry glass surfaces are gradually attacked by atomic hydrogen with the formation of a dark deposit, thought to be metallic sodium, since light of the yellow *D*-line is then emitted. A damp glass surface does not favour the recombination of hydrogen atoms, and a film of phosphoric acid is still more effective in permanently deactivating the surface of the reaction vessel. This stabilizing action of a water film may in part result from the occurrence on the surface of exchange reactions, e.g.

$$H\cdot + \mathrm{O}\begin{smallmatrix}\mathrm{H}\\ \mathrm{H}\end{smallmatrix} \longrightarrow H\text{—}\mathrm{O}\text{—H} + \cdot\mathrm{H},$$

by which hydrogen atoms are regenerated.

Many metals react with atomic hydrogen, in addition to acting as catalysts for its surface recombination to hydrogen molecules. Thus with mercury there is formed an unstable product which gives rise to a characteristic band spectrum, believed to be due to HgH. By injecting mercury vapour into atomic hydrogen and cooling the mixture rapidly to the temperature of liquid air, Geib and Harteck† claim to have isolated this hydride in the form of a black solid, which decomposed at −125° C. Pietsch‡ has found that, after prolonged exposure to atomic hydrogen, the metals silver, beryllium, gallium, indium, and tantalum become covered with surface films of substances which evolve hydrogen and leave metallic hydroxides when treated with water. These surface

† *Ber.* 1932, **65,** 1550.
‡ *Z. Elektrochem.* 1933, **39,** 577.

films were therefore considered to be metallic hydrides of a salt-like character, analogous to lithium hydride, e.g.

$$Ag^+H^- + H_2O = Ag^+OH^- + H_2.$$

Some indication was obtained by Pietsch that lead and thallium formed volatile hydrides, similar in character to the covalent hydrides of phosphorus, arsenic, and antimony, which Bonhoeffer had obtained from atomic hydrogen and the corresponding elements, and had identified in the usual manner. Pearson, Robinson, and Stoddart,† however, found that whilst atomic hydrogen readily attacks germanium, tin, arsenic, antimony, and tellurium, forming volatile hydrides, it does not attack either pure lead or bismuth. They were unable to confirm the existence of lead hydride, which Paneth had claimed to have prepared by the electrolysis of acids at lead cathodes.

The absence of a reaction between atomic hydrogen and metallic lead has been used for differentiating between atomic hydrogen and the free alkyl radicals, such as methyl and ethyl, both of which react easily with lead mirrors (compare pp. 7 and 122).

A valuable industrial application of the fact that a great deal of heat is evolved on the catalytic recombination of hydrogen atoms has been developed by Langmuir,‡ who has devised an atomic hydrogen torch for high temperature welding. A current of hydrogen gas is blown through an electric arc struck between tungsten electrodes, and then is made to impinge upon the metal surfaces to be welded. The hydrogen atoms, formed by thermal dissociation in the electric arc, recombine on the metal surface, heating it locally, whilst the hydrogen itself prevents the occurrence of any oxidation. By this means refractory metals, such as tungsten and tantalum, can be melted and worked, and satisfactory joints can be made in special alloy steels which are difficult to weld in an ordinary flame on account of oxidation.

Atomic hydrogen can also be prepared photochemically (Chapter VI); again, the energy of photochemically activated mercury atoms can be used to disrupt the hydrogen molecule (p. 110). However, in studies of the mercury-sensitized reactions of gas mixtures it is not always certain that it is the hydrogen and not the other molecules which have been dissociated by collisions with the excited mercury atoms.

Gas Reactions of Atomic Hydrogen

As explained on p. 83, it is impossible for two atoms to unite upon collision in the gaseous phase except with the participation of a third

† Pearson, Robinson, and Stoddart, *Proc. Roy. Soc.* 1933, A **142**, 275.
‡ Langmuir, *Ind. Eng. Chem.* 1927, **19**, 667.

body. Also it is most improbable, though not always impossible, for an atom, or radical, to combine with any other atom or radical to form a single stable product unless there is available some vehicle for the removal of the heat of the chemical combination, since again there must be conservation of momentum, and quantization of internal energy. Consequently gas reactions, such as $H_2+Cl_2 = 2HCl$, which can be initiated by electrical discharges, and involve the participation of free atoms, are not simple combination processes, but are essentially substitution reactions in the gaseous phase together with more complex processes involving three-body collisions or surface reactions. Nearly all gas reactions are, in fact, complicated chain processes which involve a succession of atomic substitutions. Information concerning the kinetics of these chain reactions can be found in other treatises†; evidence for their atomic mechanism is given below.

1. Interchange of atomic and molecular hydrogen. The simplest case of substitution by atomic hydrogen is afforded by the reaction between atomic and molecular hydrogen by means of which *para*-hydrogen and *ortho*-hydrogen may be interconverted, or deuterium exchanged for its isotope.

It has already been explained (p. 31) that the *para* and *ortho* forms of molecular hydrogen do not, at ordinary temperatures, interchange spontaneously, except in the immediate vicinity of molecular magnetic fields. At a temperature of 700–800° C., however, this interconversion is a homogeneous gas reaction of the order 3/2, corresponding to a reaction between $1\frac{1}{2}$ molecules of hydrogen, and then is most simply explicable as an atomic substitution

$$H\cdot + \underset{para}{\downarrow H\text{—}H \uparrow} \rightleftharpoons \underset{ortho}{\downarrow H\text{—}H \downarrow} + \cdot H,$$

brought about by the initial slight thermal dissociation of the hydrogen molecule, and collision of atomic and molecular hydrogen, whereupon from either *ortho*- or *para*-hydrogen the same mixture is finally produced in statistical ratio, although every such collision does not necessarily lead to an interconversion of the two forms.‡

Geib and Harteck§ have confirmed this by showing that atomic hydrogen, formed by an electric discharge, converted *para*-hydrogen to *ortho*-hydrogen at the much lower temperature of +10° to +100° C.

† Hinshelwood, *The Kinetics of Chemical Change*, Oxford, 1940; Semenoff, *Chemical Kinetics and Chain Reactions*, Oxford, 1932; Rollefson and Burton, *Photochemistry and the Mechanism of Chemical Reactions*, 1939.

‡ Bonhoeffer and Harteck, *Zeit. phys. Chem.* 1929, B **4**, 113; A. Farkas, ibid. 1929, B **10**, 419.

§ *Zeit. phys. Chem.* 1931, Bodensteinfestband, p. 638.

They estimated the energy of activation of the substitution reaction as only about 7 k.cals. per gram molecule.

Moreover, at 600–700° C. the interchange between hydrogen and deuterium, $H_2+D_2 \rightarrow 2HD$, is also a homogeneous gas reaction of the order 3/2 with an activation energy of 7·4 k.cals.,† and there can be no doubt that this isotope exchange is a substitution process involving the rupture of a H—H bond.

The activation energy of these hydrogen exchange reactions represents the energy required for the system $\underset{atom}{H\cdot}+\underset{molecule}{H—H}$ to reach the symmetrical transition state H···H···H. This necessitates the stretching of the covalent bond of molecular hydrogen and the approach of the hydrogen atom into the vicinity of a strong electronic field. It is significant that this activation energy is only a small fraction of the energy needed to disrupt molecular hydrogen into free atoms.

2. Reactions with the halogens. Nernst in 1916‡ suggested that the combination of hydrogen and chlorine gases is a chain reaction involving the presence of free atoms:

$$Cl_2 + h\nu \longrightarrow 2Cl\cdot \qquad \text{(i)}$$

$$Cl\cdot + H_2 \longrightarrow HCl + H\cdot \qquad \text{(ii)}$$

$$H\cdot + Cl_2 \longrightarrow HCl + Cl\cdot \qquad \text{(iii)}$$

Evidence for the existence of atomic hydrogen in this reacting mixture has been obtained by Geib and Harteck,§ who showed that when a weak stream of chlorine was passed into *para*-hydrogen, and irradiated, some conversion to *ortho*-hydrogen occurred. In the dark, or in the absence of chlorine, there was no transformation of hydrogen allotropes. Previously Boehm and Bonhoeffer|| had shown that a considerable amount of heat was evolved when atomic hydrogen was mixed with chlorine or bromine vapours. The exothermic reactions

$$H\cdot + Cl_2 = HCl + Cl\cdot + 45{\cdot}0 \text{ k.cals.}$$

$$H\cdot + Br_2 = HBr + Br\cdot + 40{\cdot}5 \text{ k.cals.}$$

$$H\cdot + I_2 = HI + I\cdot + 33{\cdot}7 \text{ k.cals.}$$

require very small amounts of activation energy, estimated as 3,000 cals., 1,000 cals., and zero respectively.¶ Hence these substitutions occur at practically every collision between a hydrogen atom and a

† A. Farkas and L. Farkas, *Proc. Roy. Soc.* 1935, A **152**, 124–57.
‡ *Z. Elektrochem.* 1916, **22**, 62; 1918, **24**, 1916.
§ *Zeit. phys. Chem.* 1931, B **15**, 116.
|| *Zeit. phys. Chem.* 1926, **119**, 385.
¶ Morris and Pease, *J. Chem. Phys.* 1935, **3**, 796.

halogen molecule even at room temperature. At 150–200° C. the same is true for the vapour phase reaction between atomic hydrogen and carbon tetrachloride:†

$$H\cdot + CCl_4 = HCl + \cdot CCl_3,$$

which requires an activation energy of 3·5 k.cals.

3. Reaction with oxygen.‡ The combination of hydrogen and oxygen to form water is a much more complex chain reaction than that between hydrogen and chlorine, for it can take different courses according to conditions of temperature and pressure. When atomic hydrogen is introduced into oxygen both hydrogen peroxide and water are formed, and the presence of the free hydroxyl radical, ·OH, can be detected by means of its characteristic spectral lines.§ By working at temperatures down to that of liquid air, Geib and Harteck|| have shown that the percentage yield of hydrogen peroxide increases as the reaction temperature is lowered, and can be made to approach 100 per cent. at very low temperatures. They therefore suggested that the initial product of the reaction between atomic hydrogen and molecular oxygen was the compound radical H—O—O·, which subsequently either united with hydrogen to give hydrogen peroxide or else split up giving other products from which water was eventually formed.

Hydrogen peroxide is also formed when atomic hydrogen is produced photochemically in mixtures of oxygen and hydrogen gases both by direct illumination,¶ by sensitized irradiation in presence of mercury,†† and by photolysis of ammonia.‡‡ These facts, together with much kinetic evidence, support the theory originally due to Taylor and Marshall§§ that the following reactions occur when hydrogen and oxygen combine under these conditions:

$$H\cdot + O_2 \longrightarrow HO_2\cdot \quad \text{(i)}$$

$$HO_2\cdot + H_2 \longrightarrow H_2O_2 + H\cdot \quad \text{(ii)}$$

$$H\cdot + H_2O_2\cdot \longrightarrow H_2O + \cdot OH \quad \text{(iii)}$$

$$HO\cdot + H_2 \longrightarrow H_2O + H\cdot \quad \text{(iv)}$$

† Vance and Bauman, *J. Chem. Phys.* 1938, **6**, 811.

‡ For details on this subject see *The Hydrogen-Oxygen Reaction* by Williamson and Hinshelwood, Oxford, 1934.

§ Boehm and Bonhoeffer, *Zeit. phys. Chem.* 1926, **119**, 385.

|| *Ber.* 1932, **65**, 1551.

¶ Frankenburger and Klinkhardt, *Zeit. phys. Chem.* 1932, B **15**, 421; *Trans. Faraday Soc.* 1931, **27**, 431.

†† Bates and Salley, *J.A.C.S.* 1933, **55**, 110; Volman, *J. Chem. Physics*, 1946, **14**, 12.

‡‡ Taylor and Salley, ibid., p. 96.

§§ *J.A.C.S.* 1926, **48**, 2840; 1927, **49**, 2763; *J. Phys. Chem.* 1925, **29**, 1140.

Of these, reaction (i) probably requires a three-body collision† or alternatively leads to the production of an activated radical of high energy content.

Other reactions which have been suggested are

$$HO_2\cdot + HO_2\cdot \longrightarrow H_2O_2 + O_2 \qquad \text{(v)}$$

and

$$H_2O_2 \longrightarrow 2\cdot OH \qquad \text{(vi)}$$

(vi) is probably a wall reaction.‡

The reaction $H\cdot + O_2 \rightarrow HO\cdot + \cdot O$ does not participate in any of these chain processes, for the energy available is not sufficient to break completely the strong double bond of the oxygen molecule.

Interesting experimental evidence that hydrogen atoms can bring about the combination of hydrogen and oxygen gases at room temperature is afforded by the fact that hydrogen-oxygen mixtures can be exploded by adding a little chlorine and then illuminating with ultraviolet light.§ Under these conditions hydrogen and chlorine react, generating free hydrogen atoms which then initiate the chain reaction with oxygen molecules. Iodine, in contrast, is an inhibitor of the hydrogen-oxygen reaction, since it reacts with the free atoms giving products, such as atomic iodine, which have too little intrinsic energy to interact with either hydrogen or oxygen molecules.

4. Reactions with other inorganic molecules. The inert gases, such as argon and neon, are of course incapable of undergoing chemical reaction, and may therefore be used as diluents for atomic hydrogen in gas mixtures. Harteck‖ has made use of this fact in studying the reactions between atomic hydrogen and aqueous solutions of inorganic salts, since atomic hydrogen, generated by Wood's method from a mixture of hydrogen at 0·3 mm. partial pressure and neon at 16 mm. partial pressure, can be passed into water without causing immediate evaporation of the latter.

Another gas which does not react with atomic hydrogen is nitrogen. This lack of chemical reactivity is due to the great stability of the triple bond $N{\equiv}N$.

Both carbon monoxide and carbon dioxide react only very slowly with atomic hydrogen, for the reactions

$$H\cdot + CO \longrightarrow H\dot{C}O \quad \text{and} \quad H\cdot + CO_2 \longrightarrow O\dot{C}{-}OH$$

are not exothermic, and require an appreciable amount of activation

† Compare Bates and Lavin, *J.A.C.S.* 1933, **55**, 81; Cook and Bates, ibid. 1935, **57**, 1775; Von Elbe and Lewis, ibid. 1937, **59**, 656; Bray, ibid. 1938, **60**, 82.

‡ Urey, Dawsey, and Rice, ibid. 1929, **51**, 1380.

§ Norrish, *Proc. Roy. Soc.* 1931, **135**, 334.

‖ *Z. Elektrochem.* 1936, **42**, 536.

energy.† Bonhoeffer and Boehm‡ failed to bring about either of these reactions with atomic hydrogen prepared by Wood's method, but they can be effected by using atomic hydrogen produced by mercury sensitization.§ Each of these reactions can, of course, only occur during a three-body collision, and each yields a radical which is very unstable. When hydrogen reacts with carbon monoxide there are formed both glyoxal and solid polymers, in addition to formaldehyde, and the following reactions are therefore considered to be possible:

$$H\cdot + CO + M \longrightarrow H\dot{C}O + M^* \text{ (= third body)} \qquad \text{(i)}$$

$$H\dot{C}O + H_2 \longrightarrow H_2CO + H\cdot \qquad \text{(ii)}$$

$$H\dot{C}O + H\dot{C}O \longrightarrow H_2CO + CO \qquad \text{(iii)}$$

$$H\cdot + H\dot{C}O \longrightarrow H_2 + CO \qquad \text{(iv)}$$

$$H\dot{C}O + H\dot{C}O \longrightarrow HCO\text{—}CHO. \qquad \text{(v)}$$

Nitric oxide, which may itself be regarded as a free radical, reacts readily with atomic hydrogen, even at the temperature of liquid air, giving a yellow substance, thought to be $(HNO)_2$, which explodes on warming to $-95°$.‖

Just as atomic hydrogen reacts with molecular hydrogen so also it can react with many inorganic hydrides. Thus much heat is evolved when atomic hydrogen is passed into hydrogen bromide,¶ and this is ascribed to the exothermic reaction

$$H\cdot + HBr \longrightarrow H_2 + Br\cdot + 16{\cdot}2 \text{ k.cals.}$$

The subsequent reaction $Br\cdot + H_2 \rightarrow HBr + H\cdot$, taking place in the presence of an excess of hydrogen, will, of course, prevent the liberation of any free bromine.

The activation energies for the reactions

$$H\cdot + HCl \longrightarrow H_2 + Cl\cdot + 0{\cdot}8 \text{ k.cals.}$$

$$H\cdot + HBr \longrightarrow H_2 + Br\cdot + 16{\cdot}2 \text{ k.cals.}$$

$$H\cdot + HI \longrightarrow H_2 + I\cdot + 32{\cdot}1 \text{ k.cals.}$$

have been computed to be 5 k.cals., 1 k.cal., and 1 k.cal. respectively,†† which is only a very little less than those required for the reactions

† Farkas and Sachsse, *Zeit. phys. Chem.* 1934, B **27**, 111.

‡ *Zeit. phys. Chem.* 1926, **119**, 385.

§ Marshall, *J. Phys. Chem.* 1925, **29**, 1140; Frankenburger, *Z. Elektrochem.* 1930, **36**, 757.

‖ Harteck, *Ber.* 1933, **66**, 423.

¶ Boehm and Bonhoeffer, *Zeit. phys. Chem.* 1926, **119**, 385.

†† Pease and Morris, *J. Chem. Phys.* 1935, **3**, 796.

between atomic hydrogen and the corresponding halogen elements (p. 87).

Similar reactions of hydrogen atoms are believed to occur with hydrogen sulphide, arsine, and phosphine, and have been taken into consideration as probable reactions involved in photochemical decompositions of these substances.

5. Reactions with hydrocarbons.† Reactions between atomic hydrogen and hydrocarbons have been studied extensively, and particularly valuable information has been obtained by using deuterium to indicate the exact mechanisms of the changes involved.

Atomic hydrogen, prepared by Wood's method, does not react with methane below 200° C.‡ Above this temperature there occurs an exchange reaction which requires an activation energy of 16–18 k.cals. This is thought to be an atomic substitution process, e.g.

$$D\cdot + CH_4 \longrightarrow CH_3D + H\cdot, \quad \text{(i)}$$

and not a chain reaction (ii) involving the formation of alkyl radicals, e.g.§

$$\left.\begin{array}{l} D\cdot + CH_4 \longrightarrow CH_3\cdot + HD \\ CH_3\cdot + D_2 \longrightarrow CH_3D + D\cdot \end{array}\right\}. \quad \text{(ii)}$$

However, the chain process (ii) may possibly occur at temperatures above 300° C., since some higher hydrocarbons are formed when heated mixtures of methane and deuterium containing mercury vapour are photochemically activated.|| The higher hydrocarbons are considered to be secondary reaction products of free methyl radicals, though these may be produced either by reaction (ii) or by a mercury sensitized decomposition of methane,

$$Hg^* + CH_4 \longrightarrow CH_3\cdot + H\cdot + Hg. \quad \text{(iii)}$$

In marked contrast to the above, it has been found that atomic hydrogen will react with ethane at much lower temperatures, converting it to methane. Deuterium has been shown to react with ethane at 26° C. according to equation (iv),

$$C_2H_6 + D\cdot \longrightarrow CH_3\cdot + CH_3D, \quad \text{(iv)}$$

and not by isotopic exchange (reaction (i)), since the residual ethane from these low temperature experiments is quite free from deuterium.¶ Isotopic exchange of atomic deuterium with ethane can occur at

† Compare Steacie, *Atomic and Free Radical Reactions*, Reinhold Pub. Corp., New York, 1946.

‡ Trenner, Morikawa, and Taylor, *J. Chem. Phys.* 1937, **5**, 203.

§ Steacie, *Chemical Reviews*, 1938, **22**, 311.

|| Morikawa, Benedict, and Taylor, *J. Chem. Phys.* 1937, **5**, 212.

¶ Trenner, Morikawa, and Taylor, loc. cit.

temperatures over 100° C., but requires a greater activation energy (11 k.cals.) than does the fission reaction (iv) (needing 7 k.cals.).

Propane also reacts readily with atomic hydrogen at low temperatures† and appears to be hydrogenated directly to methane. Thus both the reactions

$$C_3H_8 + H\cdot \longrightarrow CH_4\cdot + C_2H_5\cdot$$

and

$$C_2H_5 + H\cdot \longrightarrow 2CH_3\cdot$$

must be very facile. The higher paraffins probably react in a similar manner.

The experimental fact that fission of a carbon to carbon link by atomic hydrogen, e.g. $H\cdot + C_2H_6 \rightarrow CH_4 + CH_3\cdot$, occurs in preference to dehydrogenation, $C_2H_6 + H\cdot \rightarrow H_2 + C_2H_5\cdot$, is not unexpected, since the bond energy of the C—H link (*c.* 100 k.cals.) is decidedly greater than that of a C—C link (*c.* 80 k.cals.). The former reaction is possibly a process in which there occurs a Walden inversion of the groups about the carbon atom to which the free hydrogen (or D) atom ultimately becomes attached.

Light is emitted when atomic hydrogen reacts with ethylene at ordinary temperatures‡ and ethane is produced. This hydrogenation reaction can take place even at the temperature of liquid air. Dehydrogenation reactions can also occur, for Klemenc and Patat§ have isolated acetylene as a reaction product.

When mixtures of ethylene and hydrogen are photosensitized by means of mercury a large proportion of the gaseous hydrocarbon is converted into a liquid polymer of molecular weight over 200,|| and a similar polymerization occurs when ethylene containing traces of ammonia or methylamine is irradiated with ultra-violet light.¶ This polymerization is undoubtedly a chain addition process:

$$H\cdot + C_2H_4 \longrightarrow C_2H_5\cdot,$$

$$C_2H_5\cdot + C_2H_4 \longrightarrow C_2H_5{-}C_2H_4\cdot, \text{ etc.,}$$

in which a free radical adds on to one end of a double bond, thereby generating a more complex alkyl radical of similar high chemical reactivity (compare p. 130).

Atomic hydrogen reacts vigorously with acetylene. Much heat is evolved, and the recombination of hydrogen atoms is thereby effected, but the acetylene itself can be recovered unchanged at the end of the

† Steacie and Parlee, *Trans. Faraday Soc.* 1939, **35**, 854.
‡ Von Wartenberg and Schultze, *Zeit. phys. Chem.* 1929, B **2**, 1.
§ *Zeit. phys. Chem.* 1929, B **3**, 289. Compare Bates and Taylor, *J.A.C.S.* 1927, **49**, 2438.
|| Taylor and Hill, ibid. 1929, **51**, 2922.
¶ Taylor and Emeleus, ibid. 1930, **52**, 2150.

reaction.† By carrying out this reaction with deuterium, Geib and Steacie‡ found that normal acetylene was very rapidly converted into C_2D_2, and concluded that the reaction processes involved were

$$C_2H_2 + D\cdot \longrightarrow HD + C_2H\cdot,$$

$$C_2H\cdot + D\cdot \longrightarrow C_2HD, \text{ etc.}$$

This reaction illustrates the weakness of the C—H bond in acetylene, in which the hydrogen atoms are sufficiently reactive to be replaceable by metals such as sodium and copper.

Polymerization of acetylene to the explosive yellow solid *cuprene*, C_nH_n, which is probably a chain polymer, is another reaction which can occur.§ This product may be made by irradiating mixtures of hydrogen and acetylene containing mercury. The ring polymer, benzene, is not formed so easily under these conditions.

Atomic Oxygen

Harteck and Kopsch|| prepared atomic oxygen by passing a stream of purified dry oxygen gas at 1 mm. pressure through a cooled tube, inside which a heavy discharge current was passed between aluminium electrodes maintained at a potential difference of 5,000 volts. The existence of the free oxygen atoms was established spectrographically, and it was shown that, at a distance of 7 cm. from the discharge, a platinum wire could be melted by the energy liberated by the surface recombination process

$$2O \longrightarrow O_2 + 116{,}400 \text{ cals.}$$

Atomic oxygen has also been obtained by the direct photochemical dissociation of molecular oxygen with ultra-violet light of wave-length less than 1,750 A.¶ It may possibly be formed indirectly (see below) by means of light of up to 2,500 A wave-length, and can undoubtedly be formed still more easily by the photochemical dissociation of ozone.

Reactions of Atomic Oxygen

1. Ozone formation. It is well known that ozone is prepared by passing an electrical discharge through oxygen gas at atmospheric pressure. This conversion of oxygen into ozone probably involves the primary dissociation of molecular oxygen into atomic oxygen and a

† Bonhoeffer and Harteck, *Zeit. phys. Chem.* 1928, **139**, 64.
‡ *Zeit. phys. Chem.* 1935, B **29**, 215.
§ Bates and Taylor, *J.A.C.S.* 1927, **49**, 2438.
|| *Zeit. phys. Chem.* 1931, B **12**, 327.
¶ Neujmin and Popov, ibid. 1934, B **27**, 15; Kistiakowsky, *J.A.C.S.* 1930, **52**, 1868.

subsequent three-body collision between an oxygen atom, an oxygen molecule, and an energy acceptor, which may be either another gas particle or a catalytically active surface,

$$O_2 \longrightarrow 2O, \tag{i}$$

$$O + O_2 + M \longrightarrow O_3 + M\ (+\ 24{\cdot}1\ \text{k.cals.}), \tag{ii}$$

for free atomic oxygen has been shown to react in this way.

The photochemical formation of ozone can also be an atomic reaction of this type, but another possible reaction, which may proceed at wavelengths between 1,750 and 2,500 A is a chain process initiated by a collision between a photochemically activated oxygen molecule and a normal oxygen molecule,

$$O_2^* + O_2 \longrightarrow O_3 + O, \tag{iii}$$

followed by (ii) above.†

The percentage yield of ozone which can be obtained from oxygen depends upon the gas pressure. At atmospheric pressure free oxygen atoms would be able to make over 10^6 three-body collisions (ii) per second in the gas phase, and hence under these conditions their conversion to ozone should be virtually complete in 10^{-4} second. At a pressure of 1 mm., however, the frequency of three-body collisions falls to about 10 per second, and thus the mean free life of atomic oxygen increases correspondingly until at very low pressures the catalysed surface recombination

$$O + O + M \longrightarrow O_2 + M\ (+\ 116{\cdot}4\ \text{k.cals.})$$

becomes their more prevalent mode of destruction,‡ and no ozone is formed. The reaction $O+O_3 \rightarrow 2O_2$ may also bring about the destruction of atomic oxygen, and is a strongly exothermic process. The activation energies for the reactions $O+O_2 \rightarrow O_3$ and $O+O_3 \rightarrow 2O_2$ have been computed as 4 k.cals. and 6·2 k.cals. respectively.

Kistiakowsky§ has shown that just as all surfaces are not equally effective as catalysts for bringing about the recombination of free atoms so also all gas particles are not equally effective as energy acceptors in the three-body collisions which lead to ozone formation. He has given the following figures for the relative efficiency of different gases as energy acceptors:

O_2	CO_2	CO	N_2	A
1·0	0·8	0·62	0·28	0·13

† Compare Rollefson and Burton, *Photochemistry*, 1939, p. 328.
‡ Harteck and Kopsch, loc. cit.
§ *Zeit. phys. Chem.* 1925, **117**, 337.

As one would infer, it has been found experimentally that an inert gas such as neon can act as a carrier for atomic oxygen in a mixture at a relatively high pressure (compare p. 89). In this way it has been shown that when gas containing atomic oxygen is passed into aqueous solutions of chlorides, or bromides, oxidation to chlorates, or bromates, occurs. Oxalates are oxidized to carbon dioxide.† Thus atomic oxygen is a more powerful oxidizing agent than is ozone.

2. Reaction with hydrogen. The reaction between atomic oxygen and molecular hydrogen leads to the formation of water and *not* hydrogen peroxide. The following primary reactions are possible:

$$O\cdot + H_2 \longrightarrow \cdot OH + H\cdot, \qquad \text{(i)}$$

$$O\cdot + H_2 + M \longrightarrow H_2O + M \text{ (three-body process)}, \qquad \text{(ii)}$$

and reaction (i) most probably occurs at high temperatures (above 400° C.)‡ when hydrogen is present in excess, although this conclusion has not been verified conclusively by establishing spectrographically the presence of the free hydroxyl radical. By reaction (i) each oxygen atom produces *two* highly reactive products. This brings about a chain-branching process, typical of the high-velocity explosive combination of oxygen and hydrogen, which can occur between certain well-defined pressure limits. Reaction (ii) in contrast would tend to inhibit the occurrence of any chain reaction, and may occur in non-explosive mixtures which have been greatly diluted by the addition of an inert gas.

Free oxygen atoms are considered to be the initiators of the combination between hydrogen and oxygen gases when reaction is brought about by ultra-violet light or by an electric spark (except when a hydrogen sensitizer such as mercury vapour is present.) It has been suggested that some promoters of the hydrogen-oxygen combination, such as nitrogen peroxide, may act by supplying oxygen atoms to initiate the explosive chain reaction,§ though more probably radicals such as NO_3 are concerned.||

In this reaction the production of some ozone as by-product can be taken as diagnostic of the transient existence of free oxygen atoms, just as the formation of hydrogen peroxide can be taken as diagnostic of the production of free hydrogen atoms (p. 88).

† Harteck, *Z. Elektrochem.* 1936, **42**, 536.
‡ Kistiakowsky, *J.A.C.S.* 1930, **52**, 1868.
§ Norrish and Griffiths, *Proc. Roy. Soc.* 1933, A **139**, 147.
|| Von Elbe and Lewis, *J.A.C.S.* 1937, **59**, 2022; 1939, **61**, 1350.

3. Reaction with hydrides. The free hydroxyl radical seems to be a regular initial product of the reaction between atomic oxygen and a hydride,

$$O + HR \rightarrow \cdot OH + R\cdot,$$

but, since two free radicals are produced simultaneously by this process, the subsequent course of the oxidation process is exceedingly complicated. Thus the reaction between atomic oxygen and hydrogen cyanide has been shown spectrographically to lead to the formation of both free hydroxyl and free cyanide radicals,

$$O + HCN \longrightarrow HO\cdot + \cdot CN \text{ (+ 17 k.cals.)},$$

though the final reaction products are water, carbon dioxide, and nitric oxide.†

The reaction $O + H—O—H \rightarrow 2HO\cdot$ is believed to occur with water, since atomic oxygen is rapidly destroyed by the presence of a trace of moisture. Hydrogen chloride and hydrogen bromide are believed to react in the same way as hydrogen cyanide:

$$O + HCl \longrightarrow \cdot OH + \cdot Cl \text{ (+ 1 k.cal.)},$$

$$O + HBr \longrightarrow \cdot OH + \cdot Br \text{ (+ 20 k.cals.)}.$$

Ammonia is easily oxidized, and even at the temperature of liquid air it reacts slowly with atomic oxygen to form an explosive yellow substance, possibly HNO, which may be identical with the product of the reaction between atomic hydrogen and nitric oxide.

So much energy is liberated in the reaction between atomic oxygen and hydrogen sulphide that the mixture emits a bluish light.

Similarly, hydrocarbons inflame when mixed with atomic oxygen, and their flame spectra contain bands due to the hydroxyl radical and also those ascribed to C—H and C—C groups. The oxidation of hydrocarbons does not immediately proceed to completion. Thus a great deal of carbon monoxide results from the reaction between atomic oxygen and methane, and with methyl alcohol as much as 62 per cent. of the product is carbon monoxide.† In accordance with this, it has been found that dry carbon monoxide is only attacked slowly by atomic oxygen at room temperature, though in presence of moisture, when the hydroxyl radical may be present, the oxidation proceeds much more rapidly.

Since the direct dissociation of molecular oxygen to give atomic oxygen (a reaction requiring the fission of a double bond) is much less easy that the decomposition of a hydrocarbon molecule (the reaction $H—C_nH_{2n+1} \rightarrow H\cdot + \cdot C_nH_{2n+1}$ requiring only the fission of a single

† Harteck and Kopsch, *Zeit. phys. Chem.* 1931, B **12**, 327.

bond), it is most improbable that many of the reactions which occur in the burning of organic compounds should involve the presence of atomic oxygen, except perhaps in flames at very high temperatures.

Atomic Chlorine

Since 1916 chemists have correctly inferred that some atomic chlorine is produced when chlorine gas is exposed to ultra-violet light, and this hypothesis has consistently proved to be an accurate guide to the interpretation of the mechanisms of chlorination reactions in the gaseous phase.

In 1928 Polanyi produced traces of atomic chlorine by passing sodium vapour into chlorine gas (see pp. 100–103) and showed that he could thereby initiate the combination of hydrogen and chlorine gases in the absence of light.

Appreciable quantities of atomic chlorine were first obtained in 1933 by the electrical dissociation method. Rodebush and Klingelhoefer† subjected chlorine at 1 mm. pressure to an electrodeless discharge, whilst Schwab and Friess‡ used a glow discharge between electrodes at 4,000 volts potential difference and demonstrated the presence of the free atoms spectrographically. According to the latter investigators the mean life of atomic chlorine at room temperature and 0·1 mm. pressure is 3×10^{-3} second, so that a chlorine atom may make on the average a dozen collisions with the dry glass wall of the reaction vessel before recombination takes place. Most metal surfaces bring about the rapid recombination of chlorine atoms, with evolution of heat, though a platinum surface is a very poor catalyst for this process, whilst gas carbon is a very effective catalyst. According to Rodebush and Klingelhoefer, bright silver foil is an excellent material for detecting atomic chlorine, since it immediately turns white when exposed to chlorine atoms, but is not attacked by chlorine molecules.

Gas Reactions of Atomic Chlorine

1. Reaction with hydrogen. One aspect of the mechanism of the reaction between hydrogen and chlorine has already been discussed (p. 87). Evidence that the reaction is initiated by the photochemical dissociation of molecular chlorine (i),

$$Cl_2 + h\nu \longrightarrow 2Cl\cdot, \quad \text{(i)}$$

$$Cl\cdot + H_2 \longrightarrow HCl + H\cdot, \quad \text{(ii)}$$

$$H\cdot + Cl_2 \longrightarrow HCl + Cl\cdot, \quad \text{(iii)}$$

† *J.A.C.S.* 1933, **55**, 130. ‡ *Z. Elektrochem.* 1933, **39**, 586.

was obtained by Jost and Schweizer,† who showed that hydrogen chloride was formed in total darkness when a rapid stream of chlorine gas was illuminated and then passed into a blackened vessel containing hydrogen. Rodebush and Klingelhoefer passed free atomic chlorine into hydrogen and estimated that only about 1 in 10^5 of the collisions of type (ii) were effective in producing chemical change. From reaction velocity measurements carried out at different temperatures they concluded that reaction (ii) requires an activation energy of 6·1 k.cals. ($\pm$1 k.cal.).

It has been found that oxygen does not react rapidly with atomic chlorine‡ and therefore the very marked retarding effect which traces of oxygen have on the reaction between hydrogen and chlorine is not so much due to the removal of chlorine atoms by the reaction

$$Cl\cdot + O_2 \rightarrow ClO_2$$

as to the rapid reaction between atomic hydrogen and molecular oxygen. This conclusion is supported by much kinetic evidence.

2. Reaction with carbon monoxide. Atomic chlorine combines with carbon monoxide to form phosgene, according to the following chain mechanism:

$$Cl\cdot + CO + M \longrightarrow \cdot COCl + M^* \text{ (M is probably } Cl_2), \quad \text{(i)}$$

$$\cdot COCl + Cl_2 \longrightarrow COCl_2 + Cl\cdot \quad \text{(ii)}$$

but the overall rate of reaction is not high since (*a*) the initial reaction (i) requires a three-body collision, (*b*) the intermediate radical tends to dissociate,

$$\cdot COCl \longrightarrow CO + Cl\cdot, \quad \text{(iii)}$$

and (*c*) may be decomposed by atomic chlorine

$$Cl\cdot + \cdot COCl \longrightarrow Cl_2 + CO. \quad \text{(iv)}$$

The velocity of the combination is still further diminished by the addition of oxygen, which reacts with the intermediate $\cdot COCl$ radical to form carbon dioxide.

Nevertheless, the photochemical dissociation of one chlorine molecule may lead to the production of up to 2,000 molecules of phosgene.

3. Reaction with paraffin hydrocarbons. Atomic chlorine reacts rapidly with methane with much evolution of heat,§ giving a mixture of chlorination products.‖ The reaction proceeds in stages, each of

† *Zeit. phys. Chem.* 1931, B **13**, 373.
‡ Schwab and Friess, loc. cit.; Rodebush and Klingelhoefer, loc. cit.
§ Schwab and Friess, *Z. Elektrochem.* 1933, **39**, 586.
‖ Cf. Coehn and Cordes, *Zeit. phys. Chem.* 1930, B **9**, 1.

which is similar to the reaction between hydrogen and chlorine, alkyl radicals being intermediate products:

$$Cl\cdot + CH_4 \longrightarrow H{-}Cl + CH_3\cdot, \qquad \text{(i)}$$

$$CH_3\cdot + Cl_2 \longrightarrow CH_3{-}Cl + Cl\cdot, \qquad \text{(ii)}$$

$$Cl\cdot + CH_3Cl \longrightarrow H{-}Cl + \cdot CH_2Cl, \qquad \text{(iii)}$$

$$\cdot CH_2Cl + Cl_2 \longrightarrow CH_2Cl_2 + Cl\cdot, \text{ etc.} \qquad \text{(iv)}$$

Carbon tetrachloride is the final reaction product, and this too may react with atomic chlorine:

$$Cl\cdot + CCl_4 \rightleftharpoons Cl{-}Cl + \cdot CCl_3, \qquad \text{(v)}$$

just as atomic hydrogen reacts with molecular hydrogen (p. 86), since it has been noticed that on a glass surface initially flushed with methane the life of atomic chlorine is eventually longer than on a clean glass surface.

Oxygen retards the rate of chlorination of methane,† just as it retards the hydrogen-chlorine reaction, and phosgene is then a reaction product which is evidently produced by the interaction of oxygen and chlorinated hydrocarbon radicals. Similarly, the formation of phosgene on the exposure of chloroform to air and sunlight is probably due to the oxidation of $\cdot CCl_3$ radicals.‡

The vapour phase chlorination of higher paraffins is again a chain process which can be accelerated by free ethyl radicals produced by the addition of a little lead tetra-ethyl, and retarded by the addition of oxygen.§ Experimental evidence suggests that though the reaction chains are propagated in the gas phase, the initial chlorine atoms are produced by molecular dissociation at the surface of the reaction vessel, where, too, the reaction chains usually terminate.

4. Reaction with olefines. The addition of chlorine to olefines is usually a surface reaction,|| but can be accelerated by photochemical activation and may under these circumstances have an atomic chain mechanism

$$Cl\cdot + C_2H_4 \longrightarrow C_2H_4Cl\cdot,$$

$$C_2H_4Cl\cdot + Cl_2 \longrightarrow C_2H_4Cl + Cl\cdot,$$

even at comparatively low temperatures.¶

Dickinson and Carrico†† in 1934 showed that the vapour phase

† Pease and Walz, *J.A.C.S.* 1931, **53**, 3728; Jones and Bates, ibid. 1934, **56**, 2282.
‡ Schumacher and Wolff, *Zeit. phys. Chem.* 1934, B **26**, 453.
§ Vaughan and Rust, *J. Org. Chem.* 1940, **5**, 449.
|| Norrish, *J.* 1926, p. 55.
¶ Stewart and Weidenbaum, *J.A.C.S.* 1935, **57**, 2036.
†† *J.A.C.S.* 1934, **56**, 1473; 1935, **57**, 1343.

addition of chlorine to tetrachloro-ethylene was a chain reaction which could be inhibited by traces of oxygen, whilst Rust and Vaughan† have shown more recently that the same is true for the *high-temperature* reaction between ethylene and chlorine, which can be accelerated by adding lead tetra-ethyl.

At temperatures above 350° C., however, substitution of olefines by chlorine,

$$C_2H_4 + Cl_2 \longrightarrow C_2H_3Cl + HCl,$$

predominates over addition, and even at 250° C. higher olefines, such as propylene and *iso*-butylene, substitute in the allyl position more easily than they will add on chlorine to the double bond:‡

$$Cl_2 + CH_2{=}C(CH_3)_2 \longrightarrow CH_2{=}C(CH_3){-}CH_2Cl + HCl.$$

This is due to the enhanced reactivity of the α-methylene group in the system $CH_2{-}C{=}C$ in which less energy is needed for atomic disruption of the C—H link than for addition of atomic chlorine to one end of a double bond (compare pp. 242, 256). This substitutive tendency is much more pronounced with bromine than with chlorine, probably because the initial atomic dissociation of the halogen molecule requires less activation energy. At 300° C. bromine substitutes propylene,

$$Br_2 + CH_2{=}CH{-}CH_3 \longrightarrow HBr + CH_2{=}CH{-}CH_2Br,$$

though at 200° C., or below, the addition reaction predominates.

At temperatures of over 450° C. the reaction between chlorine and olefines or paraffins becomes still more complicated, for thermal dissociation of the C—Cl bond can then occur, leading to extensive molecular decomposition. For instance, pyrolysis of carbon tetrachloride yields hexachloroethane, tetrachloro-ethylene, and hexachloro-benzene, whilst trichloro-ethylene is a regular end-product from less completely chlorinated hydrocarbons.

Reactions of Atomic Sodium

1. Reactions with the halogens. When monatomic sodium vapour is allowed to pass into chlorine gas, kept at a steady temperature between 250 and 300° C. and at a low pressure of 10^{-2} to 10^{-3} mm., sodium chloride is formed and there is emitted a 'highly attenuated flame' with the wave-length of the characteristic D-line of sodium.

Using an apparatus shown schematically in Fig. 13 Polanyi and his

† *J. Org. Chem.* 1940, **5**, 472.

‡ Groll, Hearne, *et al.*, *Ind. Eng. Chem.* 1939, **31**, 1239, 1413, 1530; Rust and Vaughan, loc. cit.

colleagues† measured, at varying distances from the nozzle, both the intensity of the emitted light and the local concentration of the sodium chloride which deposited on the walls of the tube. Sodium was vaporized inside an electrically heated furnace *F*, and the vapour, at low pressure, issued through the nozzle *N* into the evacuated tube *AB*, into which, at *E*, there was also allowed to enter the vapour of a halogen. Chemical

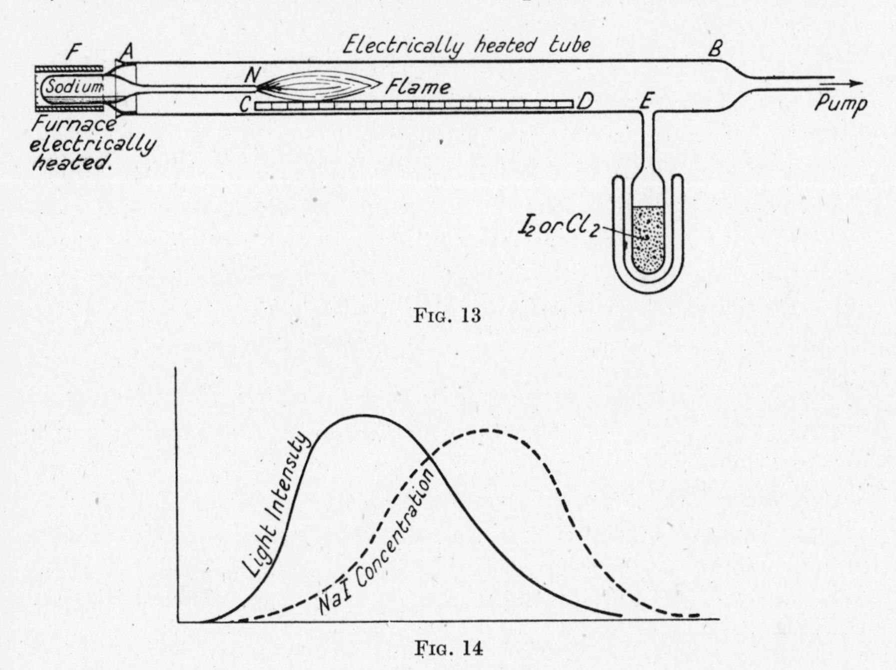

FIG. 13

FIG. 14

reaction occurred in the space between *E* and *N*, with emission of light, and separation of a sodium halide. The local concentration of the sodium salt was measured by placing inside the tube a graduated rod *CD*, which, at the end of the experiment, was removed and washed, section by section, into distilled water. The halide deposited on each section was then estimated by titration with silver nitrate.

The results of a typical experiment are shown in Fig. 14. From a knowledge of the temperature, the pressure, and the velocity of flow of gas along the tube, they calculated both the velocity with which the sodium atoms entered the reaction vessel and also the initial frequency of collisions between sodium atoms and halogen molecules. With these data it was possible to elucidate the kinetic mechanism of the reactions involved.

† *Zeit. phys. Chem.* 1928, B **1**, 1, 21, 30, 62; *Atomic Reactions*, London, 1932.

They found that a sodium chloride molecule was produced upon every collision occurring between a sodium atom and a chlorine molecule, and that a free chlorine atom was formed thereby,

$$Na\cdot + Cl_2 \longrightarrow NaCl + Cl\cdot + 35 \text{ k.cals.}$$

The formation of the atomic chlorine was verified by showing that a trace of sodium vapour served to initiate the atomic chain combination between hydrogen and chlorine gases (p. 97).

The reaction $Na\cdot + \cdot Cl \rightarrow NaCl + 93{\cdot}4$ k.cals. cannot occur directly in the gas phase, for a third particle must participate in any collisions between two atoms leading to combination.

To a great extent, the reaction between sodium and chlorine atoms takes place on the walls of the apparatus, but in addition sodium chloride can be formed in the gas phase by collisions between single chlorine *atoms* and two sodium atoms, in the form of the weakly bound molecule Na_2, for the existence of which there is spectroscopic evidence. In the reaction

$$Na_2 + Cl\cdot \longrightarrow NaCl + Na\cdot$$

the liberated chemical energy can be shared as internal, and kinetic, energy between the two reaction products. At some stage in the reaction, sodium atoms are activated to such an extent that they emit the D-line radiation after an interval of about 10^{-8} seconds. The balance of experimental evidence indicates that the initial reaction of the atomic chlorine produces an activated form of sodium chloride, which, by a subsequent collision, hands on energy to atomic sodium, which then irradiates light:†

$$Na_2 + Cl\cdot \longrightarrow NaCl^* + Na\cdot,$$
$$NaCl^* + Na\cdot \longrightarrow NaCl + Na^*,$$
$$Na^* \longrightarrow Na + h\nu.$$

Since the reaction which produces light is not the primary reaction at which sodium chloride is formed, it follows that the flame produced by the chemical combination of sodium and chlorine vapours has its greatest intensity not in the region where there is the greatest formation of sodium chloride, but in the region in which there is the greatest concentration of sodium atoms. Thus the most intense flame is obtained when the chlorine gas is allowed to stream into the sodium vapour and not vice versa.

Exactly similar gas reactions occur between atomic sodium and both bromine and iodine vapours. Cyanogen, however, does not react

† Compare Bowen, *The Chemical Aspects of Light*, p. 174 (Oxford, 1942).

similarly, for the molecule C_2N_2 is far too stable to be disrupted with ease by free atoms.

2. Reactions with halides. Sodium vapour, under the same conditions, reacts in a very similar manner with both inorganic and organic halides, and reactions of the types

$$Na\cdot + HCl \longrightarrow NaCl + H\cdot,$$
$$Na\cdot + HgCl_2 \longrightarrow NaCl + \cdot HgCl,$$
$$Na\cdot + CH_3Cl \longrightarrow NaCl + CH_3\cdot,$$

which generate free atoms or free neutral organic radicals, have been proved to occur. In many of these reactions the liberation of energy,

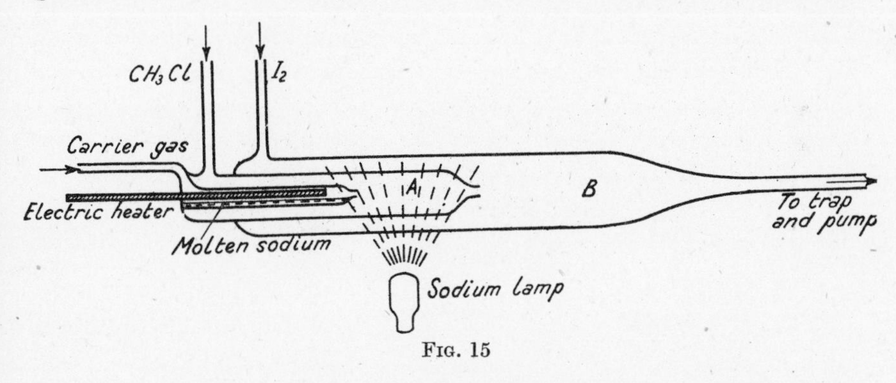

Fig. 15

which is shared between the reaction products, is too small to permit of the emission of visible light; in fact chemical change does not always take place upon every collision between a sodium atom and a halide molecule.† In order to determine the rate of reaction under these circumstances it is necessary to find the mean free life of the atomic sodium after its introduction into the reaction mixture. This can be done by mixing the sodium vapour with a stream of an inert carrier gas, injecting this into an excess of halide vapour, and irradiating the reaction vessel with white light from an adjacent source. The Fraunhofer effect of selective absorption of the sodium D-line can then be observed through the reaction vessel only in the region in which free sodium atoms are present. In this way the zone of chemical reaction can be mapped out with accuracy.

By using a double reaction vessel, indicated schematically in Fig. 15, Polanyi, Horn, and Style‡ proved conclusively that neutral organic radicals, having an appreciable independent existence, are produced by

† von Hartel and Polanyi, *Zeit. phys. Chem.* 1930, B **11**, 97.
‡ *Trans. Faraday Soc.* 1934, **30**, 179.

these reactions of sodium vapour. Sodium vapour was allowed to stream into vessel *A* containing an alkyl chloride, and the position of the nozzle, and the gas velocities, were so adjusted that no sodium passed through into vessel *B* to deposit sodium chloride there. The gaseous products which passed into vessel *B* reacted there with iodine vapour, and formed alkyl iodides which were isolated in quantity, i.e.

$$Na\cdot + CH_3Cl \longrightarrow NaCl + CH_3\cdot \quad \text{(vessel } A\text{)},$$
$$CH_3\cdot + I_2 \longrightarrow CH_3I \quad \text{(vessel } B\text{)}.$$

They found in this way that free alkyl radicals could be carried along the reaction tube for distances of up to 8 cm. beyond the limit of the passage of the sodium vapour.

Later, Allen and Bawn† showed that the free methyl produced by this sodium vapour reaction would attack mirrors of antimony and tellurium, whilst Paneth and Lautsch‡ by the same method found that the free benzyl radical, $C_6H_5—CH_2\cdot$, could be detected at a distance of 15 cm. from the reaction zone. Allen and Bawn found some evidence of the production of the free phenyl radical from sodium and chloro-benzene, though undoubtedly it has a very brief life. Its presence could not definitely be established by Paneth and his colleagues.

When a second reagent is not added, the free organic radicals generated by the reaction between sodium vapour and organic halides interact to give a mixture of hydrocarbons similar to that produced by the thermal fission of organic molecules. When hydrogen is used as the carrier gas, the chief products are saturated hydrocarbons, for reactions such as

$$CH_3\cdot + H_2 \longrightarrow CH_4 + H\cdot$$

then predominate, but when an inert gas such as nitrogen is used un-saturated hydrocarbons, such as ethylene, are also formed.

This sodium vapour reaction has been used to prepare alkyl and aryl radicals, such as methyl, phenyl, and benzyl, and also di-radicals such as trimethylene, $\cdot CH_2—CH_2—CH_2\cdot$, which is obtainable from tri-methylene dibromide and which, in part, cyclizes to *cyclo*-propane.§

It has been suggested that the reaction between sodium vapour and methylene bromide yields both the methylene di-radical $\cdot CH_2\cdot$, which dimerizes to ethylene, and the bromo-methyl radical $Br—CH_2\cdot$.||

The chemical kinetics of reactions between atomic sodium and both organic and inorganic halides have been studied extensively, since the

† *Trans. Faraday Soc.* 1938, **34**, 463.
‡ *J.* 1935, p. 382.
§ Bawn, *Trans. Faraday Soc.* 1938, **34**, 598, 606; 1939, **35**, 185, 889.
|| Bawn, loc. cit.

experimental results so obtained provide a valuable check on calculations of bond strengths and activation energies.†

The chemical change involves the fission of a stable molecule by the advent of an extra electron, which is provided by the sodium atom. As this single electron is picked up an electron *pair* is released simultaneously to the exclusive control of the halogen atom, which separates as a halide anion, e.g.

$$\mathrm{Na\cdot} + \mathrm{H{:}\overset{H}{\underset{H}{\ddot{\underset{..}{C}}}}{:}\ddot{\underset{..}{Cl}}{:}} \longrightarrow \mathrm{Na^{+}} + \mathrm{\overset{H\,.\,.\,H}{{:}C{:}}\atop{\cdot H}} + \mathrm{{:}\ddot{\underset{..}{Cl}}{:}}$$

The spatial configuration of the original halide will not be the same as that of the free radical, which probably has a planar structure. An appreciable, but difficultly calculable, amount of energy is required to effect this bond deformation.

When sodium atoms react with organic halide vapours only a fraction of the binary collisions results in chemical change. By assuming that the reaction constant B of the Arrhenius equation $k = Be^{-E/RT}$ is equal to the frequency of collision between sodium atoms and halide molecules it is possible to calculate from the reaction velocity k the activation energy E which is required. Table XVI gives experimental data which have been obtained in this way.

TABLE XVI

The Reaction between Sodium Vapour and Organic Halides

Halide	*Fraction of effective collisions*	*Activation energy*
Methyl iodide	1:1·5	0 cal.
Methyl bromide	1:25	3,200 ,,
Methyl chloride	1:5,000	8,800 ,,
Methyl fluoride	$1:10^7$	25,000 ,,
Ethyl iodide	1:5	1,700 ,,
Ethyl bromide	1:70	4,400 ,,
Ethyl chloride	1:1,000	7,300 ,,
n-Propyl chloride	1:20	3,000 ,,
Iodobenzene	1:1	0 ,,
Bromobenzene	1:20	3,100 ,,
Chlorobenzene	1:1,000	7,200 ,,
Benzyl chloride	1:1	0 ,,
Acetyl chloride	1:5	1,700 ,,
Benzoyl chloride	1:1	0 ,,
Chloroform	1:6	2,000 ,,
Carbon tetrachloride	1:2	0 ,,

Throughout, the order of reactivity is Iodides > Bromides > Chlorides > Fluorides, and also Tertiary halides > Secondary halides > Primary halides.

† Compare, *inter alia*, Stevels, *Trans. Faraday Soc.* 1938, **34,** 431; Heller and Polanyi, ibid. 1936, **32,** 633; Haresnape, Stevels, and Warhurst, ibid. 1940, **36,** 465.

VI

PHOTOCHEMICAL DECOMPOSITIONS

General Theory†

When a molecule absorbs a quantum of radiation, the extra energy thus gained may be utilized in any of the following ways:

1. The molecule may retain this extra energy, and may remain as an *activated molecule*, capable of losing the extra energy at some subsequent time. The energy can be retained in, and distributed within, the molecule as extra electronic energy, as vibrational energy, or as rotational energy, but it is not immediately converted into translational energy, except as a result of processes 3 or 4.

2. The molecule may lose this extra energy by the emission of radiation. This emission of radiant energy is termed *fluorescence*. It usually occurs in about 10^{-8} second from the instant of activation. The term *phosphorescence* is used to denote the emission of light from activated molecules which have persisted as such for an appreciable period of time.

3. The molecule may dissociate into fragments.

4. The molecule may, by collision with another, hand on its energy, as a whole or in part, to a second molecule which thus becomes activated. Intermolecular collisions can, in consequence, lead to the quenching of the fluorescence of molecules which have absorbed radiant energy. Collisions may also lead to (*a*) the fluorescence of a molecule which has gained energy from another, (*b*) the dissociation of this second molecule, or (*c*) chemical reactions between the colliding particles.

The energy changes which may occur within molecules on absorption or emission of radiation are most simply illustrated by reference to Figs. 16 and 17, which show graphically the connexions which exist between the dimensions of any chemical link and its energy content.

The lowest vibrational state of a molecule is represented by the energy level E_1 of Fig. 16, where d is the average distance between the atoms AB, which vibrate (with zero-point energy) from bond distance a to bond distance b. When a molecule possesses a higher *vibrational* energy, corresponding to level E_2, it vibrates from distance x to distance y. Since one quantum of vibrational energy amounts to about 5 k.cals. per gram-molecule, whereas the statistical average energy available

† For a concise account of this subject see Bowen, *The Chemical Aspects of Light* (Oxford, 1942).

per degree of freedom ($\frac{1}{2}RT$) is only about 0·3 k.cals. at normal temperatures, it follows that under ordinary circumstances a small

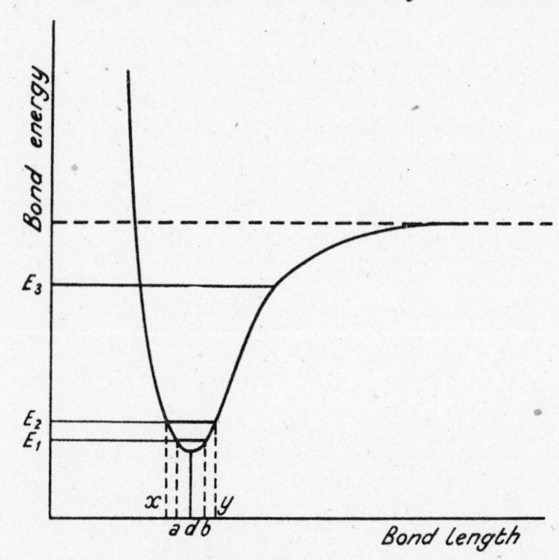

FIG. 16

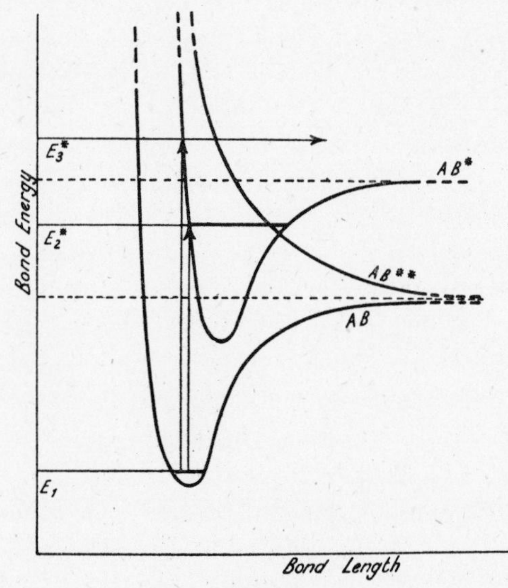

FIG. 17

fraction only of all molecules have vibrational energy greater than that of the lowest level E_1.

When a molecule absorbs radiation of visible, or ultra-violet, frequencies (corresponding to 30–130 k.cals. per gm.-mol.) it does not pass from level E_1 to a level E_3 of high vibrational energy because of the excessively small absorption coefficient.

If absorption of radiant energy takes place, it is due to a transition of a valency electron from one quantum orbit to another. This creates a new chemical link, with a new binding energy, corresponding to a level on a new potential energy curve AB^* (Fig. 17).

The passage of an electron from one orbit AB to another AB^* is an extremely rapid process compared with a bond vibration. Consequently when an electronic transition occurs the inter-nuclear distance has no time to alter much. The newly-formed excited molecules AB^* are therefore in compressed states, as represented by the vertical line transitions of Fig. 17. These excited molecules at once start to vibrate. If, as shown for AB^*, a level such as E_3^* is reached, the first outward swing has in fact infinite amplitude, and the molecule consequently separates into two fragments. This process is commonly called *photo-dissociation*, and when it occurs the spectrum becomes continuous on the short-wave side, with no trace of vibrational structure.

Sometimes it happens that two upper potential energy curves, AB^* and AB^{**}, cross one another. Under these circumstances it may happen that a transition can occur from AB to level E_2^* on curve AB^* giving a molecule which vibrates on this curve (AB^*) for some time, and then switches over on to the crossing curve AB^{**}, at a level corresponding to bond dissociation. Such a process of dissociation, which involves a delay of time corresponding to many vibrational periods from the instant of activation, is called *pre-dissociation* and can sometimes be recognized by a diffuseness in the absorption spectrum.

Unfortunately the conclusions that can be derived from spectral evidence are not as clear-cut as the foregoing would indicate. The spectra of organic molecules in the vapour state are sometimes continuous through the overlapping of very complicated fine structures, and in solution, of course, spectra are always lacking in fine structure due to the disturbance of the molecular levels by the solvent. Pre-dissociation is not always shown by a diffuseness of fine structure in the gaseous state, since when there is a very long delay in dissociation the structure is sharp (e.g. in formaldehyde), whilst in other cases (e.g. sulphur dioxide) diffuse bands are observed without dissociation. The disappearance of fluorescence as one goes from long waves to short waves is perhaps a better criterion of dissociation from a spectral point of view, but is again of limited applicability.

A photochemical activation of a molecule insufficient to produce complete dissociation may nevertheless bring about a chemical reaction such as a molecular rearrangement. For example, by absorption of visible light stable *trans*-azobenzene in solution can be changed into *cis*-azobenzene,† but there is no evidence that this molecular rearrangement involves the disruption of the molecule into fragments, for separated radicals, such as $C_6H_5\cdot$ and $C_6H_5{-}N{=}N\cdot$, would immediately react with vicinal solvent molecules, and this does not occur. Again, the photochemical conversion of *o*-nitrobenzaldehyde to *o*-nitroso-benzoic acid‡ takes place without the occurrence of any side reactions. The photochemical quantum efficiency of this molecular rearrangement is about 0·5,§ and this may be taken as an indication that the photo-activated molecule may either revert to its original structure or, equally probably, change to the new electronic configuration, which, in this case, does not require any appreciable movement of the component atoms.

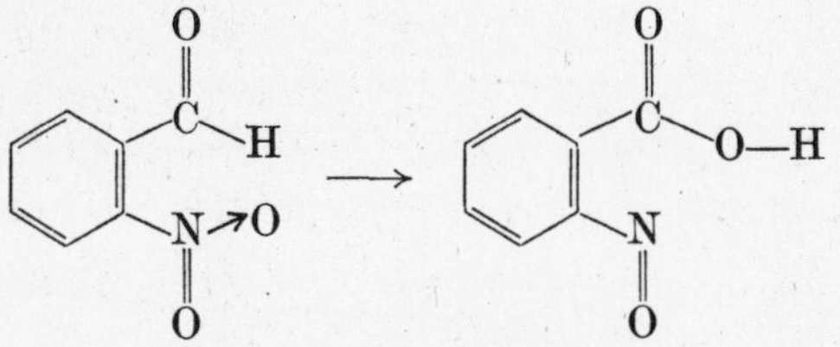

Photo-sensitization

Any atom or molecule which has absorbed radiant energy is, theoretically, capable of fluorescence—i.e. of the emission of radiation, but most substances do not visibly fluoresce on exposure to light. If a substance has absorbed radiant energy and does not re-emit this as fluorescence then it follows that the photochemical energy has been dissipated by some other means.

An atom which has been activated can lose its energy in two ways only: (*a*) by fluorescing, or (*b*) by energy transference to another particle with which it may collide:

$$(a)\quad A^* \longrightarrow A + h\nu; \qquad (b)\quad A^* + X \longrightarrow A + X^*.$$

Process (*b*) necessarily involves a molecular collision with a particle which can utilize the exact energy quantum $h\nu$ which the activated atom A* can supply. Naturally it follows that the occurrence of fluorescence in a condensed system is much less probable than in a gas at a low pressure. It has been shown experimentally that in gases, such

† Hartley, *J.* 1938, p. 633. ‡ Ciamician and Silber, *Ber.* 1901, **34**, 2040.

§ Leighton and Lucy, *J. Chem. Phys.* 1934, **2**, 756.

as sodium or mercury vapours, at low pressures, the quenching of fluorescence can be expressed by the formula

$$\frac{I_p}{I_0} = \frac{1}{1+k[X]},$$

where I_p is the intensity of fluorescence at pressure p of the gas X, I_0 is the extrapolated intensity at zero pressure, and k is a constant depending upon the chemical nature of the colliding particles X.

Activation by collision is a very specific process, and, in a gaseous mixture, particles X of one molecular species only may receive, by collision, practically all the photochemical energy available. For instance, hydrogen is about 100 times as effective as helium for quenching the fluorescence of sodium vapour.†

Particles which quench fluorescence necessarily gain energy thereby, and, in general, become activated particles possessing extra internal energy, rather than particles with extra translational energy. This activation of molecules is termed *photo-sensitization*, and is a very potent mechanism of catalysis of gas reactions, for it frequently brings about molecular dissociation. For example, photochemically activated atoms of the inert gas xenon are able to bring about the dissociation of molecular hydrogen to hydrogen atoms,‡

$$Xe + h\nu \longrightarrow Xe^*,$$

$$Xe^* + H_2 \longrightarrow Xe + 2H\cdot,$$

the production of which can be established spectroscopically.

A trace of mercury vapour on illumination with the mercury resonance line of 2,537 A will also bring about the dissociation of the hydrogen molecule, though in this dissociation process the unstable molecule HgH may possibly be involved. In 1922 Cario and Franck§ showed that the illumination by ultra-violet light of hydrogen gas containing a little mercury vapour led to the production of an active form of hydrogen capable of reducing metallic oxides, and in general behaving like the atomic hydrogen prepared by Wood's method (pp. 81–93). Atomic hydrogen obtained by photo-sensitization can initiate the chain reaction between hydrogen and oxygen gases, the reduction of carbon monoxide, and many other gas reactions of the types discussed in Chapter V.

Many other molecules can also be dissociated to atoms by similar photo-sensitization processes. Photo-sensitization may also initiate

† Mannkopf, *Z. Physik*, 1926, **36**, 315. ‡ Calvert, ibid. 1932, **78**, 479.
§ *Z. Physik*, 1922, **11**, 161.

reactions occurring in solution, or on the surfaces of solids, such as zinc oxide and titanium oxide.†

The energy transferences that can occur with photochemically activated *molecules* are, naturally, much more complex than those possible with atoms. In molecules the transference process

$$AB^* + X \longrightarrow AB + X^*$$

more commonly leads to the excitation of vibrational energy in X which may ultimately appear as heat, or may lead to chemical reaction in X.

It is also quite possible for radiant energy absorbed by one atom, or covalent bond, in a complex molecule to be transferred internally in such a way as to lead to the dissociation of a more distant covalent bond. For instance, the absorption of light at the C=O bond of aliphatic aldehydes and ketones leads eventually to the fission of C—C links, with the production of neutral alkyl radicals. All photochemical decompositions of this type could be regarded as internally photo-sensitized processes, and the study of the influence of chromophoric groups on photochemical changes remains a vast field for future research.

The Chemical Nature of Photochemical Decomposition

From the chemist's point of view the physical picture of photochemical decomposition given above needs to be amplified by consideration of the electronic structures and chemical properties of the immediate decomposition products.

Photochemical reactions generally require more energy than do the corresponding chemical changes. For example, hydrogen iodide needs at least 69 k.cals. for photochemical dissociation into atoms:

$$HI \longrightarrow H\cdot + \cdot I;$$

while only 42 k.cals. are necessary for its thermal decomposition, which is bimolecular:

$$2HI \longrightarrow H_2 + I_2.$$

Again, the spectral convergence limits which are observed in the spectra of the halogens, and correspond to dissociation energies, are greater than the thermal dissociation energies of these molecules, since they correspond to dissociation into one normal and one excited atom, instead of into two normal atoms. Such spectral limits of this photo-dissociation type, as well as pre-dissociation limits, do not therefore represent the lowest energies required to split molecules into normal atoms or radicals. Nevertheless, in many cases, the extra energy is not

† Goodeve, *Trans. Faraday Soc.* 1937, **33**, 340; Goodeve and Kitchener, ibid. 1938, **34**, 570.

very large, so that some degree of approximation to the energies of linking of simple bonds, like C—H and C—C has been obtained from spectral evidence.

The direct application of the above spectroscopic considerations to liquids or solutions is precluded by the fact that no suitably detailed structure is observable in the spectrum, but often arguments by analogy can be advanced. For example, it can be presumed that halogens dissociate in carbon tetrachloride solution just as they do in the gas phase in view of the general similarity of their vapour and solution spectra.

Arguments for photo-dissociation in condensed systems, however, must usually be based on chemical evidence. It seems that covalent molecules dissociate to neutral radicals when irradiated, whilst ions can undergo the analogous change of losing a single electron, e.g.

$$SO_3^{=} + h\nu \longrightarrow \cdot SO_3^{-} + e.\dagger$$

Very many kinetic studies of photochemical reactions have been formulated as processes involving neutral free atoms or radicals merely because the measured activation energies corresponded closely with theoretical computations of covalent bond strengths, without proofs being given of the actual separation and independent existence of the molecular fragments supposed to be involved. Nevertheless there has been discovered a great deal of direct experimental evidence justifying the general conclusion that the electron-pair bond is broken whenever photochemical dissociation occurs. This chemical evidence is set forth in some detail in the following sections of this chapter. Relevant physical evidence has been summarized in a number of detailed monographs‡ and therefore need not be repeated here.

Photolysis of Inorganic Molecules

1. The halogens. Reference has already been made to the spectroscopic evidence of the dissociation of halogen molecules into free neutral atoms. With both bromine and iodine it has been possible to calculate, from measurements of absorption intensities, the chemical composition of the photo-stationary state of equilibrium which is reached, under constant illumination, between the dissociation and recombination processes (i) and (ii)§

$$Br_2 + h\nu \longrightarrow 2Br\cdot, \quad \text{(i)}$$

$$2Br\cdot + X \longrightarrow Br_2 + X^*. \quad \text{(ii)}$$

† Compare Haber and Wansbrough-Jones, *Zeit. phys. Chem.* 1932, B **18**, 103.

‡ Bonhoeffer and Harteck, *Grundlagen der Photochemie*, Dresden, 1933; Rollefson and Burton, *Photochemistry*, New York, 1939.

§ Rabinowitch and Wood, *Trans. Faraday Soc.* 1936, **32**, 547; Rabinowitch and Lehmann, ibid. 1935, **31**, 689.

The recombination reaction (ii) necessarily involves a three-body collision with another particle which is capable of receiving the liberated energy. This energy is in part converted into heat, and consequently when a photochemically dissociable gas, such as bromine, is first illuminated there is an increase of pressure, known as a *Budde effect*, owing to the gain in the total kinetic energy of the gas particles.

Decisive chemical evidence of the formation of free atoms of both chlorine and bromine upon irradiation is afforded by the fact that these molecules react photochemically with hydrogen gas by a chain process which is kinetically similar to the combination reaction which can be initiated in the dark by the addition of traces of externally prepared free halogen atoms (p. 98). The photosynthesis of hydrogen bromide is a reversible process and kinetic studies have fully justified the assumption that free atoms are formed by its decomposition.

To illustrate the great chemical reactivity of free atoms, it may be mentioned here that iodine atoms, produced photochemically, will unite, in chloroform solution, with ethylene and propylene at temperatures as low as $-55°$ C.†

2. Water and hydrogen peroxide. Water is thought to decompose photochemically into hydrogen atoms and neutral hydroxyl radicals,

$$H{-}OH \longrightarrow H\cdot + \cdot OH,$$

since hydrogen peroxide can be obtained by prolonged exposure of water to very short-wave ultra-violet light.‡ It has been suggested, however, that this decomposition is photo-sensitized by impurities or by the walls of the reaction vessel.§ Hydrogen peroxide decomposes much more easily, giving water and oxygen as the final products. Spectroscopic evidence indicates that hydroxyl radicals are produced,‖ $HO{-}OH + h\nu \rightarrow HO\cdot + \cdot OH$, and this view is supported by the fact that the mercury photo-sensitized decomposition of hydrogen peroxide can be used to effect the production of glycols from olefines (Chapter XI, pp. 246–7).

3. Hydrogen sulphide. The analogous decomposition of hydrogen sulphide, $H_2S + h\nu \rightarrow H\cdot + \cdot SH$, has been established by Avery and Forbes,¶ who studied this photo-decomposition in dry carbon tetrachloride solution. Production of atomic hydrogen was conclusively

† Forbes and Nelson, *J.A.C.S.* 1937, **59**, 693.
‡ Kernbaum, *Compt. rend.* 1909, **149**, 273.
§ Goodeve and Stein, *Trans. Faraday Soc.* 1931, **27**, 393.
‖ Urey, Dawsey and Rice, *J.A.C.S.* 1929, **51**, 1371.
¶ *J.A.C.S.* 1938, **60**, 1005.

proved by the formation of hydrogen chloride, since the substitution process

$$H\cdot + CCl_4 \longrightarrow HCl + \cdot CCl_3$$

is a well-known reaction of atomic hydrogen.† Other reaction products were trichloromethyl mercaptan and hexachloroethane, produced by the reactions

$$HS\cdot + \cdot CCl_3 \longrightarrow HS{-}CCl_3 \quad \text{and} \quad 2\cdot CCl_3 \longrightarrow C_2Cl_6$$

respectively. Hydrogen chloride was also a product of the photochemical decomposition of hydrogen sulphide in solutions in chloroform and in methylene chloride. Applications of this subject in organic chemistry are dealt with in Chapter IX (pp. 188–9).

Physical evidence indicates that the photochemical decomposition of gaseous hydrogen sulphide, and also of hydrogen selenide and of hydrogen telluride, takes the same initial course.‡

4. Ammonia is another simple hydride which undoubtedly gives free neutral radicals by photochemical decomposition according to the equation $NH_3 + h\nu \rightarrow H\cdot + \cdot NH_2$. Several investigators have proved that hydrogen and hydrazine are found as reaction products, thus establishing evidence for the production of the $\cdot NH_2$ radical.§

Moreover, the reaction products of the photochemical decomposition of ammonia can bring about the conversion of *para*-hydrogen to *ortho*-hydrogen, and must therefore contain free hydrogen atoms.|| Kinetic measurements have established that this photochemical decomposition is reversible.¶ Further evidence of the formation of atomic hydrogen by the photochemical decomposition of ammonia is afforded by the fact that traces of ammonia serve, on irradiation, to initiate the combination between hydrogen and oxygen gases (p. 88). Phosphine and arsine are thought to decompose in a similar way.††

5. Oxides of nitrogen. Nitrous and nitric oxides are decomposed only by ultra-violet light of wave-lengths below 2,200 A since they do not absorb light of longer wave-length, but nitrogen peroxide can be decomposed by blue light (*c.* 4,000 A). Its photochemical decomposition

$$NO_2 + h\nu \longrightarrow NO + O$$

† Cremer, Polanyi, and Curry, *Zeit. phys. Chem.* 1933, B **23**, 445.

‡ Forbes, Cline, and Bradshaw, *J.A.C.S.* 1938, **60**, 1431; Goodeve and Stein, *Trans. Faraday Soc.* 1931, **27**, 393.

§ Welge and Beckman, *J.A.C.S.* 1936, **58**, 2462; Bates and Taylor, ibid. 1927, **49**, 2438; Gedye and Rideal, *J.* 1932, p. 1158.

|| Geib and Harteck, *Zeit. phys. Chem.* (Bodenstein-Festband), 1931, 849.

¶ Melville, *Trans. Faraday Soc.* 1932, **28**, 885.

†† Melville, *Proc. Roy. Soc.* 1933, A **139**, 541; 1937, A **160**, 406; Simmons and Beckman, *J.A.C.S.* 1936, **58**, 454.

which is a bimolecular reaction involving excited nitrogen peroxide molecules† yields either atomic oxygen, as suggested by Norrish and Griffiths (compare p. 95) or perhaps the active radical NO_3. Mixtures of oxides of nitrogen are decomposed more easily than the carefully purified substances. Thus a trace of nitrogen peroxide sensitizes the decomposition of nitrogen pentoxide, possibly by initiating the reaction-chain

$$NO_2 \longrightarrow NO + O,$$
$$N_2O_5 + O \longrightarrow N_2O_4 + O_2.$$

Chlorine dioxide undergoes an entirely similar decomposition. In general, however, the formation of oxygen atoms from oxides is much less facile than the production of atomic hydrogen from hydrides, probably since the latter usually absorb at longer wave-lengths. Apart from kinetic evidence there is very little, if any, direct proof of the production of free oxygen atoms by photolysis of any oxide.

Photolysis of Organic Molecules

1. Alkyl halides. All alkyl halides have continuous absorption spectra in the ultra-violet region, and this has been taken as indicative of some molecular decomposition, but only in the case of the simpler alkyl iodides has there been put forward any definite chemical evidence of dissociation into free radicals. Even with the iodides the quantum yields of decomposition products are very low, due to the fact that halogenations of organic compounds by free halogen atoms are invariably fast reactions.

Both in the vapour and in the liquid phases it has been proved conclusively that alkyl iodides decompose photochemically into free iodine atoms and free alkyl radicals, which then interact to give molecular iodine and a mixture of paraffins and olefines, together with some alkylene di-iodides; e.g.

$$C_2H_5I + h\nu \longrightarrow C_2H_5\cdot + I\cdot$$

followed by

$$C_2H_5 + C_2H_5I \longrightarrow C_2H_6 + C_2H_4I\cdot,$$
$$C_2H_4I\cdot \longrightarrow C_2H_4 + I\cdot,$$
$$C_2H_4I\cdot + \cdot I \longrightarrow C_2H_4I_2,$$
$$2C_2H_5\cdot \longrightarrow C_2H_6 + C_2H_4.$$

The production of free radicals by the photochemical decomposition of methyl iodide has been proved conclusively by West,‡ who showed that the photochemical decomposition products were able to effect the

† Norrish, *J.* 1929, pp. 1158, 1604; Holmes and Daniels, *J.A.C.S.* 1934, **56**, 630.
‡ *J.A.C.S.* 1935, **57**, 1931.

conversion of *para*-hydrogen to *ortho*-hydrogen. Moreover, by carrying out the reaction in the presence of metallic silver, which promptly removed the atomic iodine, West and Schlessinger† were able to increase fortyfold the rate of decomposition, and to show that all the subsequent reactions, attributable to free alkyl radicals, still occurred. Previously, the formation of olefines had been attributed to the molecular decomposition, e.g. $C_2H_5I \rightarrow C_2H_4 + HI$, though the fact that a paraffin hydrocarbon is formed in considerable quantities indicates that olefine formation is a secondary process only. Further evidence of the production of free radicals from alkyl halides has been drawn from the fact that their atmospheric oxidation takes place very readily in sunlight, undoubtedly by a chain reaction involving the presence of free alkyl radicals.‡

The photochemical decomposition takes the same course in hydrocarbon solvents as it does in the gaseous states,§ but in solvents of high dielectric constant ionic dissociation is favoured as an alternative. Whenever attack on a metal such as silver or mercury is found to occur the transient existence of neutral radicals and not of ions can be inferred.

2. Aldehydes and Ketones. Aliphatic compounds containing the carbonyl group show continuous and not banded absorption spectra in the region of 2,700 A, and this is an indication of the occurrence of molecular decomposition brought about by absorption of energy by the carbonyl group, since hydrocarbons do not absorb light in this region. Chemical investigations have shown that light of up to 3,300 A will dissociate both aldehydes and ketones, but that the carbonyl group itself is not disrupted; it splits off in the form of carbon monoxide.

At first it was thought that aldehydes decomposed photochemically by a single process, eliminating carbon monoxide and leaving fragments which united immediately to form a single paraffin hydrocarbon, e.g.

$$\begin{matrix} CH_3 \diagdown \\ \quad CO \\ H \diagup \end{matrix} \longrightarrow \begin{matrix} CH_3 \\ | \\ H \end{matrix} + CO,\|$$

but exact analyses of the gaseous reaction products of the higher aldehydes disproved this, since it was then found that some hydrogen was

† *J.A.C.S.* 1938, **60**, 961.

‡ Bates and Spence, *J.A.C.S.* 1931, **53**, 1689; *Trans. Faraday Soc.* 1931, **27**, 414; Jones and Bates, *J.A.C.S.* 1934, **56**, 2285; Iredale and Stephan, *Trans. Faraday Soc.* 1937, **33**, 800.

§ Emschwiller, *Compt. rend.* 1931, **192**, 799; West and Paul, *Trans. Faraday Soc.* 1932, **28**, 688; Gibson and Iredale, ibid., 1936, **32**, 571.

‖ Norrish and Kirkbride, ibid. 1931, **27**, 378; *J.* 1932, p. 1518.

formed, together with a mixture of paraffin hydrocarbons.† In 1935 Pearson and Purcell,‡ after failing in earlier attempts,§ showed that free methyl radicals were formed by the photolysis of acetaldehyde, by demonstrating the attack of the primary photochemical decomposition products upon warmed mirrors of tellurium, using apparatus indicated schematically in Fig. 18, and proving that dimethyl telluride was formed.

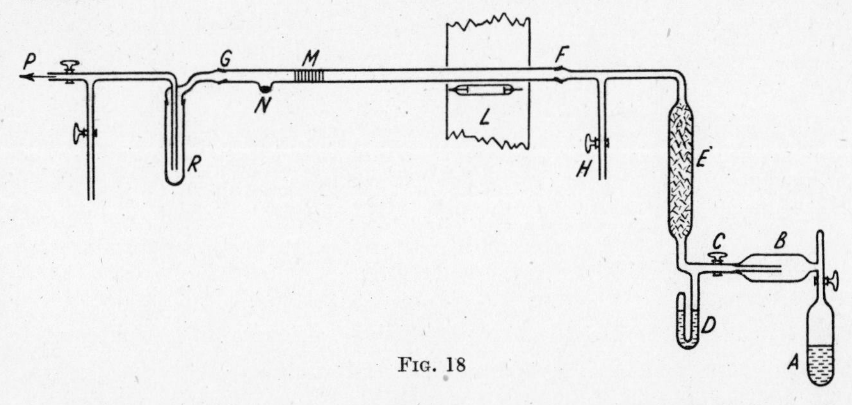

FIG. 18

Carefully fractionated acetaldehyde vapour was pumped from the cooled bulb A, through the capillary tube B and regulating tap C, to the quartz tube FG which could be irradiated at one place by the shielded mercury vapour lamp L. At M there was deposited a tellurium mirror, of which the temperature could be adjusted by external cooling. Condensable reaction products were caught in the receiver R, which was cooled in liquid air, whilst gaseous products were sucked off by a mercury vapour pump at P. The pressure in the gas stream was measured by the manometer D, and a tube E packed with silver foil served to prevent any traces of mercury vapour from entering the quartz tube FG. The tellurium mirrors were prepared by heating in pure hydrogen, which could be introduced at H, a pellet of tellurium which was initially placed in a depression N in the quartz tube.

When the tellurium mirror was kept cold it was not attacked, presumably because it became coated with polymerization products of acetaldehyde, but at temperatures over 40° C. it was rapidly attacked when the light L was switched on. When the acetaldehyde was not irradiated the tellurium mirror was not attacked even at 150° C. Dimethyl telluride was identified in the condensation products which

† Leighton and Blacet, *J.A.C.S.* 1932, **54**, 3165; Leermakers, ibid. 1934, **56**, 1537; Blacet and Volman, ibid. 1938, **60**, 1243.

‡ *J.* 1935, p. 1151.

§ Ibid. 1934, p. 1718.

collected in the receiver *R*. It was mixed with polymerization products of acetaldehyde, and in this connexion it should be mentioned that polymerization is one of the regular photochemical reactions of all aldehydes.

This work provides conclusive chemical evidence for the view that acetaldehyde and its analogues decompose photochemically (i) to give free alkyl radicals together with the formyl radical, which eventually yields carbon monoxide consequent on reactions such as (ii)–(v).

$$CH_3\text{—}CHO + h\nu \longrightarrow CH_3\cdot + \cdot CHO \qquad \text{(i)}$$

followed by

$$\cdot CH_3 + \cdot CHO \longrightarrow CH_4 + CO, \qquad \text{(ii)}$$

$$\cdot CHO + CH_3\text{—}CHO \longrightarrow CH_3CO\cdot + H_2 + CO, \qquad \text{(iii)}$$

$$\cdot CH_3 + CH_3\text{—}CHO \longrightarrow CH_4 + CH_3CO\cdot, \qquad \text{(iv)}$$

$$2\cdot CHO \longrightarrow H_2 + CO\cdot \qquad \text{(v)}$$

This mechanism accords with thermodynamic evidence, since the magnitude of the limiting energy quantum which can bring about aldehyde decomposition is about 89 k.cals., corresponding to a wave-length of 3,200 A. This amount of energy is sufficient to break a single C—C bond but not to break a C—H bond, for the disruption of which about 100 k.cals., corresponding to 2,700 A are needed.† Moreover, at elevated temperatures the photochemical decomposition is undoubtedly a chain reaction.‡ There is no evidence of the formation of free hydrogen atoms from aldehydes at temperatures below 100° C.,§ and consequently the formyl radical must have a reasonably high stability. However, reaction (ii) above, which would be of frequent occurrence in the decomposing gas on account of the initial proximity of the two radicals, will account for the apparent decomposition of aldehydes to carbon monoxide and paraffins by a one-stage process.

With higher aliphatic aldehydes, such as *n*-butyraldehyde‖ and *iso*-valeraldehyde,¶ another reaction, in which an olefine is formed, also occurs, e.g.:

$$Me_2CH\text{—}CH_2\text{—}CHO \longrightarrow MeCH{=}CH_2 + CH_3CHO.$$

Decompositions of this type were first discovered with ketones (p. 120).

Polymerization of aldehydes invariably accompany their photo-chemical decompositions to carbon monoxide and hydrocarbons. Since these polymerization reactions indicate activation of the carbonyl group

† Compare Norrish, *Trans. Faraday Soc.* 1934, **30**, 108.
‡ Leermakers, *J.A.C.S.* 1934, **56**, 1899.
§ Burton, ibid. 1936, **58**, 1645, 1655; 1938, **60**, 212.
‖ Leighton, Blacet, and Rowe, ibid. 1937, **59**, 1843.
¶ Bamford and Norrish, *J.* 1935, p. 1504.

they may be represented as reactions of the $\underset{\cdot}{C}\text{—}\underset{\cdot}{O}$ diradical (compare the photo-polymerization of ethylene): e.g.

$$\mathrm{Ph\text{—}CHO} + h\nu \longrightarrow \mathrm{Ph\text{—}}\underset{\cdot}{\overset{H}{\mathrm{C}}}\mathrm{\text{—}}\underset{\cdot}{\mathrm{O}},$$

$$\mathrm{Ph\text{—}}\underset{\cdot}{\overset{H}{\mathrm{C}}}\mathrm{\text{—}}\underset{\cdot}{\mathrm{O}} + \mathrm{Ph\text{—}CHO} \longrightarrow \mathrm{Ph\text{—}}\underset{\cdot}{\overset{H}{\mathrm{C}}}\mathrm{\text{—}O\text{—}H} + \mathrm{Ph\text{—}}\underset{\cdot}{\mathrm{C}}\mathrm{{=}O},$$

$$\mathrm{Ph\text{—}}\underset{\cdot}{\overset{H}{\mathrm{C}}}\mathrm{\text{—}OH} + \mathrm{Ph\text{—}}\underset{\cdot}{\mathrm{C}}\mathrm{{=}O} \longrightarrow \mathrm{Ph\text{—}CH(OH)\text{—}CO\text{—}Ph}.\dagger$$

This mechanism will explain satisfactorily many of the photochemical reactions of aldehydes and ketones in solution.‡

The evidence for the formation of free alkyl radicals by the photochemical decomposition of ketones is more abundantly conclusive still. In 1934 Pearson,§ using the apparatus described above (Fig. 18), showed that the photochemical decomposition products of acetone readily reacted with mirrors of antimony, tellurium, and lead. The active product had a half-life period of $5{\cdot}3 \times 10^{-3}$ seconds, which is the same as the half-life period of the free methyl radical. Subsequently, Pearson and Purcell‖ confirmed that the active product was the free methyl radical by isolating and characterizing its combination products with mercury, tellurium, and arsenic. In the same way it was proved that the free ethyl radical was formed from diethyl ketone. From acetophenone both methyl and phenyl radicals are produced,¶ whilst, curiously enough, the *n*-propyl radical is the chief active product formed from di-*iso*-propyl ketone.††

The production of free radicals by the photolysis of acetone has also been confirmed by West,‡‡ who showed that the active reaction products were able to effect the *ortho-para* conversion of molecular hydrogen (p. 86).

The exact mechanism of the photochemical decomposition of acetone and its homologues has been a controversial subject, but it is now agreed that at low temperatures the primary decomposition reaction leads to the formation of both the methyl and the acetyl free radicals, i.e.

$$\mathrm{CH_3\text{—}CO\text{—}CH_3} + h\nu \longrightarrow \mathrm{CH_3}\cdot + \cdot\mathrm{CO\text{—}CH_3}.$$

† Bäckström, *Zeit. phys. Chem.* 1934, B **25**, 99.

‡ Hirshberg and L. Farkas, *J.A.C.S.* 1937, **59**, 2453; Weizmann, Bergmann, and Hirshberg, ibid. 1938, **60**, 1530.

§ *J.* 1934, p. 1718.

‖ Ibid. 1935, p. 1151.

¶ Glazebrook and Pearson, ibid. 1939, p. 589.

†† Ibid. 1936, p. 1777.

‡‡ *J.A.C.S.* 1935, **57**, 1931.

Evidence for the existence of the very unstable acetyl radical $CH_3—CO\cdot$ was first obtained by Barak and Style,† and soon afterwards confirmed both by Spence and Wild‡ and by Glazebrook and Pearson,§ who showed that diacetyl was a reaction product by isolating its 2:4-dinitrophenylhydrazone, and also by converting it to nickel dimethylglyoxime. They found that diacetyl could not be isolated from photochemical decompositions carried out at temperatures of over 60° C., and thus the free acetyl must be a most unstable substance, easily prone to break down to carbon monoxide and free methyl:

$$CH_3—CO\cdot \longrightarrow CH_3\cdot + CO.$$

Confirmatory evidence for the existence of the free acetyl radical has been obtained by Rice and Schildknecht,‖ who have studied the photochemical oxidation of acetone and have shown that both dimethyl and diacetyl peroxides are formed.

As already mentioned, substances other than paraffin hydrocarbons are formed in photochemical decompositions of the higher aldehydes. Ketones containing paraffin chains decompose to give an olefine, as well as some carbon monoxide,¶ e.g.

$$CH_3CH_2CH_2CH_2COCH_3 \longrightarrow CH_3CH{=}CH_2 + CH_3COCH_3,$$

whilst cyclic ketones may also give *cyclo*-paraffins.†† Hence it can be concluded that the radiant energy which is initially absorbed by the carbonyl group may be transferred to a distant bond in the photochemically activated molecule, to bring about eventually the disruption of the molecule at its weakest bond. This would appear to be the α–β carbon to carbon link of the paraffin chain.

The irradiation of cold solutions of aldehydes and ketones gives no gaseous products,‡‡ and this is attributed to the 'primary recombination' effect first described by Franck and Rabinowitch (p. 18).

In hot solutions of hydrocarbons, such as *iso*-octane or medicinal paraffin, the photolysis of aldehydes and ketones yields some carbon monoxide.§§ Evidently although alkyl radicals must be liberated, under these circumstances, by reactions such as

$$C_2H_5—CO—CH_3 \longrightarrow C_2H_5\cdot + \cdot CO—CH_3,$$
$$\cdot CO—CH_3 \longrightarrow CO + \cdot CH_3,$$

† *Nature*, 1935, **135**, 307. ‡ *J*. 1937, p. 352. § Ibid. p. 567.

‖ *J.A.C.S.* 1938, **60**, 3044.

¶ Norrish and Appleyard, *J*. 1934, p. 874; Bamford and Norrish, ibid. 1935, p. 1505.

†† Saltmarsh and Norrish, ibid., p. 455; Bamford and Norrish, ibid. 1938, p. 1521.

‡‡ Bowen and de la Praudière, ibid. 1934, p. 1503; Bowen and Horton, ibid., p. 1505.

§§ Bamford and Norrish, *Nature*, 1936, **138**, 1016; 1937, **140**, 195; *Trans. Faraday Soc.* 1937, **32**, 1522: *J*. 1938, pp. 1531, 1544.

they must react almost exclusively with the solvent, from which they abstract hydrogen, since methane, ethane, and acetaldehyde can easily be separated by fractionation of the resultant mixture of evolved gases, and there is left, in the high-boiling residue, an equivalent amount of unsaturated substances.

Thus whereas any free radicals produced by photolysis of vapours of aldehydes and ketones have a reasonable probability of surviving until they meet and dimerize (by three-body collisions or wall reactions),

$$2\cdot CH_3 \longrightarrow CH_3{-}CH_3,$$
$$2CH_3{-}CO\cdot \longrightarrow CH_3{-}CO{-}CO{-}CH_3,$$

the probability of a dissolved free radical surviving activated collision, and consequent reaction with a solvent molecule,

$$CH_3\cdot + C_nH_{2n+2} \longrightarrow CH_4 + C_nH_{2n+1}, \quad \text{(i)}$$
$$CH_3{-}CO\cdot + C_nH_{2n+2} \longrightarrow CH_3{-}CHO + C_nH_{2n+1}, \quad \text{(ii)}$$

is almost negligible. The higher hydrocarbon radicals produced from the solvent evidently become stabilized by disproportionation,

$$\cdot C_nH_{2n+1} + \cdot C_mH_{2m+1} \longrightarrow C_nH_{2n} + C_mH_{2m+2}, \quad \text{(iii)}$$

whilst at low temperatures the cage of surrounding molecules evidently prevents the separation of any free radicals.

From these investigations of Bamford and Norrish it has been estimated that the activation energy for the hydrogenation of an alkyl radical by interaction with a paraffin (reaction (i)) is 12·3 k.cals., a value almost identical with that found by Taylor for the reaction of free methyl with molecular hydrogen, but larger than that reported for the gas phase reaction between free methyl and ethane or butane (p. 130).

The course of the photolysis of the higher ketones, such as *n*-butyl methyl ketone (p. 120) which, in the gaseous phase, split off an olefine molecule, is not changed when the decomposition is carried out in paraffin solution, and it has therefore been concluded that this reaction does not involve the transient formation of free radicals, but is a direct conversion to stable molecular products. With substances such as di-*n*-propyl ketone which decompose to give both alkyl radicals and olefines, the relative velocities of the two reaction processes are greatly altered by changing the reaction conditions. In particular, the evolution of carbon monoxide is almost entirely suppressed in cool solutions, but as the temperature is raised more and more carbon monoxide is evolved, and proportionately less acetaldehyde is formed owing to the increasing probability of occurrence of direct thermal decomposition of the unstable acetyl radical to yield methyl and carbon monoxide.

3. Carboxylic acids. The photochemical decomposition of carboxylic acids requires a light of lower wave-length (*c.* 2,300 A) than does that of the ketones, and this must undoubtedly be attributed to the stabilization of the carboxyl group by resonance. Moreover, hydrogen-bonded dimerides are present even in the vapour phase of many carboxylic acids, and there is evidence to suggest that the decomposition reactions of the monomers and dimers are different.

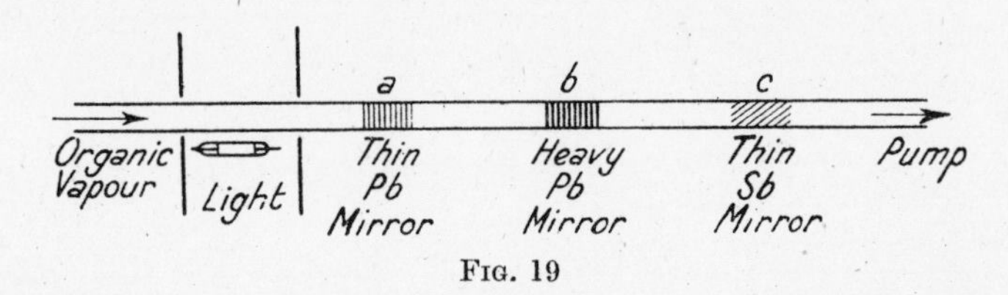

Fig. 19

Formic acid seems to decompose in two ways, yielding either water and carbon monoxide or hydrogen and carbon dioxide, without liberating free radicals, since the immediate photolysis products do not promote the *ortho–para* conversion of hydrogen, or attack antimony mirrors.† In contrast, both acetic and propionic acids have been shown to decompose to give atomic hydrogen, and possibly the hydroxyl radical, though alkyl radicals are *not* formed,‡ since the reaction products will attack antimony mirrors but not lead mirrors. In establishing this fact the guard mirror method was used by Burton, who passed the irradiated acid vapours successively over (*a*) a thin lead mirror for detection of methyl, (*b*) a heavy lead mirror to remove all free methyl, and (*c*) a thin antimony mirror to detect atomic hydrogen (compare pp. 7–8). (Fig. 19.)

Pure acetic acid had very little effect on mirrors *a* and *b*, but removed mirror *c*, whilst acetone removed mirror *a*, attacked mirror *b*, but had no effect on mirror *c*.

The decomposition reactions involved are therefore thought to be

$$CH_3COOH + h\nu \longrightarrow CH_3COO\cdot + \cdot H,$$
$$H\cdot + CH_3COOH \longrightarrow H_2 + CH_3COO\cdot,$$
$$H\cdot + CH_3COOH \longrightarrow CH_4 + \cdot COOH,$$
$$H\cdot + CH_3COO\cdot \longrightarrow CH_4 + CO_2,$$
$$\cdot COOH \longrightarrow CO + \cdot OH,$$
$$2CH_3COO\cdot \longrightarrow C_2H_6 + 2CO_2.$$

† Gorin and Taylor, *J.A.C.S.* 1934, **56**, 2042; Burton, ibid. 1936, **58**, 1655.
‡ Ibid. 692, 1645; 1938, **60**, 831.

The course of photolysis of acids in aqueous solution is still more complicated, but the main overall reaction is usually of the type of

$$CH_3COOH \longrightarrow CH_4 + CO_2.\dagger$$

Amino acids are deaminated in aqueous solution by light of 2,100–2,300 A.‡

4. Alcohols do not absorb light of over 2,000 A, and their overall decomposition reaction, both in the gas phase and in aqueous solution is given by the equation

$$R—CH_2OH \longrightarrow R—CHO + H_2.\S$$

Though no conclusive evidence for the transient existence of hydrogen atoms has been obtained it is thought that the initial decomposition reaction is

$$R—CH_2OH \longrightarrow R—\dot{C}HOH + \cdot H,$$

which is followed rapidly by $R—\dot{C}HOH \rightarrow R—CHO + \cdot H$, since, when the decomposition is carried out in heavy water the evolved gas is hydrogen containing deuterium, H—D. This hypothesis accords with thermochemical data which indicate that a C—H link should be more easily broken than either an O—H link or a C—O link.

5. Amines. The stable products of the photochemical decomposition of primary aliphatic amines are hydrogen, ammonia, paraffin hydrocarbons, and traces of aldehydic substances and polymerides which are thought to be derived from Schiff's bases.|| Nitrogen gas is not formed. Bamford¶ established the formation of atomic hydrogen in the photolysis of methylamine, by adding propylene to the reaction mixture and showing that hexane was then formed, together with an increased amount of polymers:

$$H\cdot + C_3H_6 \longrightarrow C_3H_7\cdot\ ; \qquad 2\cdot C_3H_7 \longrightarrow C_6H_{14}.$$

This conclusion has been substantiated by Wetmore and Taylor,†† who in addition have shown that, at 100° C., atomic hydrogen reacts with methylamine to form ammonia, and traces of methane:

$$H\cdot + CH_3NH_2 \longrightarrow NH_3 + \cdot CH_3 \longrightarrow CH_4.$$

† Pierce and Morey, ibid. 1932, **54**, 467.

‡ Weizmann, Bergmann and Hirshberg, ibid. 1936, **58**, 1675.

§ Patat and Hoch, *Z. Elektrochem.* 1935, **41**, 494; L. Farkas and Hirshberg, *J.A.C.S.* 1937, **59**, 2450.

|| Emeleus and Jolley, *J.* 1935, p. 1612.

¶ Bamford, ibid. 1939, p. 17.

†† Wetmore and H. A. Taylor, *J. Chem. Physics*, 1944, **12**, 61.

The primary photochemical decomposition of methylamine is therefore thought to be

$$CH_3{-}NH_2 + h\nu \longrightarrow CH_3{-}NH\cdot + \cdot H,$$

following which there probably occur

$$CH_3{-}NH\cdot \longrightarrow CH_2{=}NH + \cdot H \quad \text{(methylene-imine)},$$

$$CH_2{=}NH + CH_3{-}NH_2 \longrightarrow NH_3 + CH_2{=}NCH_3 \longrightarrow (CH_2N{-}CH_3)_3,$$

whereby the Schiff's base, giving positive reactions for formaldehyde, and the polymers are produced.

Together with these reactions, molecular hydrogen is probably formed by the reaction

$$H\cdot + CH_3{-}NH_2 \longrightarrow CH_3{-}NH\cdot + H_2.$$

Secondary bases decompose similarly, but do not give ammonia, whilst tertiary bases may give free alkyl radicals.†

6. Other nitrogen compounds. Since azomethane was one of the first compounds to be used for the preparation of free methyl radicals (p. 8), it is not surprising that its photochemical decomposition has been extensively studied. Decomposition can be brought about by light of 4,000 A, or under, and the final reaction products are nitrogen and ethane, together with traces of methane and propane. Though it was originally thought that the decomposition was a one-stage process,

$$CH_3{-}N{=}N{-}CH_3 \longrightarrow C_2H_6 + N_2,$$

it has now been fairly conclusively established that one quantum of light suffices to break the azomethane molecule into nitrogen and *two* methyl radicals, which subsequently unite or undergo disproportionation; i.e.

$$CH_3{-}N{=}N{-}CH_3 + h\nu \longrightarrow CH_3\cdot + N{\equiv}N + \cdot CH_3.\ddagger$$

There is no evidence for the transient existence of the radical $CH_3{-}N{=}N\cdot$.

Diazomethane decomposes in a similar manner, giving nitrogen and ethylene as the final stable products.§ The latter is derived from the diradical methylene, the formation of which has been established conclusively by Pearson, Purcell, and Saigh|| by its reaction with tellurium mirrors and isolation of telluroformaldehyde. There is, however, a rapid reaction between the methylene radical and molecular diazomethane.

† Bamford, *J.* 1939, p. 17.

‡ Burton, Davis and Taylor, *J.A.C.S.* 1937, **59**, 1038; Davis, Jahn, and Burton, ibid. 1938, **60**, 10.

§ Norrish and Kirkbride, *J.* 1933, p. 119.

|| *J.* 1938, p. 409.

Aromatic azo compounds, in contrast to their aliphatic analogues, are not easily decomposed by visible light, though, as mentioned previously (p. 109), irradiation may convert the stable *trans* isomer to the labile *cis* isomer without the occurrence of any bond fission. In contrast, it is well known that aromatic diazo-compounds can be decomposed by light, and a number of diazotype printing processes, used commercially both on paper and on fabrics, are based upon this reaction. The double zinc salts of diazotized dimethyl-*p*-phenylenediamine or *p*-amino-diphenylamine are frequently used for photographic printing. After exposure to bright light these salts lose their power of coupling with phenols in alkaline solution, and consequently can be used to prepare a positive print directly from a drawing on tracing cloth. However, the exact natures of the photochemical decomposition products of these diazonium salts have not yet been established with certainty.

Photochemical investigations of other organic compounds of nitrogen are still somewhat scanty, and would repay further investigation. Thus, whereas aliphatic nitrosamines decompose at 4,000 A, or under, with elimination of nitric oxide,† e.g.

$$(CH_3)_2N—NO \longrightarrow (CH_3)_2N\cdot + \cdot NO,$$

nitroso compounds, such as nitroso-*iso*-propylacetone,‡ nitroparaffins,§ and alkyl nitrites,|| appear to eliminate the NOH group; e.g.

$$CH_3—O—N{=}O \longrightarrow CH_2O + NOH.$$

This is an unusual photochemical reaction, since it involves the fission of two covalent bonds, and may well be due to the immediate reaction between an activated form of nitric oxide and an adjacent reactive (acidic) hydrogen atom.¶

7. Organo-metallic compounds, such as lead tetramethyl, mercury dimethyl, and zinc dimethyl also decompose photochemically in the same manner as they do thermally. Thus Leighton and Mortensen†† have shown that, at room temperature, a stream of lead tetramethyl vapour after irradiation attacked a mirror of radioactive lead (containing radium D), since radioactive lead methyl could be recovered afterwards by cooling the effluent in liquid air.

† Bamford, *J.* 1939, p. 12.

‡ Anderson, Crumpler, and Hammick, ibid. 1935, p. 1670

§ Hirschlaff and Norrish, ibid. 1936, p. 1580.

|| Purkis and Thompson, *Trans. Faraday Soc.* 1936, **32,** 1465; Thompson and Dainton, ibid. 1937, **33,** 1546.

¶ Compare Steacie and Shaw, *Proc. Roy. Soc.* 1934, A **146,** 388.

†† *J.A.C.S.* 1936, **58,** 448.

The production of methyl radicals from mercury dimethyl has been established by carrying out the photolysis in the presence of nitric oxide, which immediately reacts with free methyl radicals (p. 134),† and confirmed by studies of the reactions of the free methyl produced thereby with hydrogen, methane, and other hydrocarbons (pp. 129–31). Taylor and Jones‡ have shown that the radicals produced by the photochemical decomposition of mercury dimethyl at 200–300° C. will bring about the chain polymerization of ethylene. The elimination of carbon monoxide from metallic carbonyls is undoubtedly a reaction of similar character.§

† Thompson and Linnett, *Trans. Faraday Soc.* 1937, **33**, 501, 874.

‡ *J.A.C.S.* 1930, **52**, 1111.

§ Garratt and Thompson, *J.* 1934, pp. 524, 1817.

VII

REACTIONS OF FREE ALKYL RADICALS

The Average Life of Free Methyl

In their original experiments with free methyl (Chapter I, pp. 5–7) Paneth and Hofeditz found that the distance between the point of decomposition of the lead tetramethyl and the cold lead mirror could not be extended to much more than 30 cm. without reaction at the latter ceasing. This indicated that the reactive methyl radical was fairly rapidly destroyed by collisions either with gaseous particles or with the walls of the reaction tube.

Similar results were obtained when antimony mirrors were used, and by making comparative experiments with antimony mirrors of constant thickness (estimated by matching the opacity of the deposit with that of a standard, as in the Marsh technique for arsenic analysis) the following figures were obtained for the time of removal, r, of a mirror placed d cm. from the point at which the radicals were formed. In these tests the streaming velocity of the gases was 14 metres per second and hence the life of the free radical t is $d/1{,}400$ seconds.

Table XVII

Rate of Disappearance of Free Methyl Radicals

Distance d	*Life t*	*Removal time r*	log 1000/r
4 cm.	$2{\cdot}9 \times 10^{-3}$ sec.	4 sec.	2·4
8	5·7	11	1·96
13	9·3	20	1·70
18	12·9	25	1·60
22	15·7	45	1·35
28	20·0	70	1·16
33	23·6	100	1·00
37	26·4	150	0·82

The life, t, of the free radical is proportional to $\log 1/r$, so that evidently the concentration of radicals reaching the antimony mirror can be expressed by the usual equation for a unimolecular decomposition, $C_t = C_0 e^{-kt}$, since obviously the concentration C_t of radicals reaching the antimony mirror must be inversely proportional to the removal time r.

From the figures given in Table XVII the average life ($= 1/k$) of a free methyl radical was calculated to be $8{\cdot}4 \times 10^{-3}$ seconds and the half-life period (i.e. $\log_e 2/k$), $5{\cdot}8 \times 10^{-3}$ seconds.

Since at the pressure used the collision frequency between gas particles is of the order of 10^8 per second it follows that free methyl is not destroyed instantly by collision with hydrogen or nitrogen molecules. Later experiments† have shown that many other gases, such as argon, helium, carbon dioxide, and even water vapour can be used as carriers of active alkyl radicals (compare p. 89). The mean free life of the methyl radical does, however, depend to some extent upon the diameter of the reaction tube, its temperature, and the nature of the carrier gas,‡ and it has been concluded that under the conditions originally used by Paneth most of the destruction of the methyl radicals is brought about by their recombination to ethane on the walls of the reaction tube. It has been estimated that when a cold glass or quartz tube is used a methyl radical makes, on the average, 1,000 collisions with the walls of the tube before recombination occurs: at 500° when helium is the carrier gas, only about one wall collision in 10,000 destroys its activity. Every collision of a methyl radical with a surface of lead or antimony is thought to result in chemical combination. Methyl radicals, unlike atomic hydrogen (p. 81), do not recombine catalytically on platinum, iron, copper, or nickel surfaces, for wires of these metals do not become hot when placed in the gas stream near the source of the free radicals. Rapid reactions, however, occur with the alkali metals, lithium, sodium, and potassium, and with the metals thallium, tin, arsenic, and bismuth, of which stable organo-metallic compounds are well known, but not with silver or gold which form organo-metallic compounds of low stability. As would be expected, the Group VI elements, sulphur, selenium, and tellurium, all react rapidly.§

Gas Reactions of Free Alkyl Radicals

1. Reaction with hydrogen. When hydrogen is used as the carrier gas in the Paneth apparatus up to 60 per cent. of the methyl radicals are converted to methane, but in the absence of a carrier gas, or when an inert gas such as helium or nitrogen is used, over 80 per cent. gives ethane. The production of methane is attributed to the occurrence of the homogeneous gas reaction

$$CH_3\cdot + H_2 \longrightarrow CH_4 + H\cdot \qquad \text{(i)}$$

The formation of ethane is considered to be mainly a wall reaction,

$$2CH_3\cdot + M\ (= \text{wall}) \longrightarrow CH_3{-}CH_3 + M, \qquad \text{(ii)}$$

† Rice, Johnston, and Evering, *J.A.C.S.* 1932, **54**, 3529.

‡ Paneth and Herzfeld, *Z. Elektrochem.* 1931, **37**, 577; Paneth, Hofeditz, and Wunsch. *J.* 1935, p. 372; Forsyth, *Trans. Faraday Soc.* 1941, **37**, 312.

§ Rice and Rice, *The Aliphatic Free Radicals*, Baltimore, 1935.

supplemented by reaction occurring upon termolecular collisions between two methyl radicals and a molecule of a carrier gas. Reaction (i) which yields atomic hydrogen, can be measured by following the rate of interconversion of the *ortho* and *para* forms of hydrogen by their collisions with atomic hydrogen (p. 86).

From kinetic studies of the rate of production of methane by the thermal and photochemical decompositions of mercury dimethyl vapour in a hydrogen atmosphere, Cunningham and Taylor† have estimated the activation energy for the reaction between free methyl and hydrogen to be 9 ± 2 k.cals. This agrees with results obtained from studies of the photolysis of acetone vapour in hydrogen at 160–300° C.‡ but is slightly less than the estimates (*c.* 15 k.cals.) of earlier workers.§

2. Reactions with paraffin hydrocarbons. When the higher paraffin hydrocarbons are decomposed thermally the main decomposition products are methane, ethane, hydrogen, and simple olefines such as ethylene. Direct evidence of the existence of free radicals other than methyl and ethyl has rarely, if ever, been obtained. The same is generally true for the thermal decomposition of other aliphatic compounds, such as ethers, ketones, and aldehydes. It is evident, therefore, either that a paraffin chain tends to break at the terminal carbon atom, or that higher hydrocarbon radicals must rapidly decompose to yield an olefine and methyl or ethyl; e.g.

$$\cdot C_nH_{2n+1} \longrightarrow \cdot CH_3 + C_{n-1}H_{2n-2}. \qquad \text{(iii)}$$

This latter reaction may of course be either a direct decomposition similar to the photochemical decomposition of the higher ketones (p. 120) or, alternatively, the olefine may be produced by hydrogen transference, or as it is termed, disproportionation, between two radicals:

$$\cdot C_nH_{2n+1} + \cdot C_mH_{2m+1} \longrightarrow C_nH_{2n+2} + C_mH_{2m}. \qquad \text{(iv)}$$

Methane is a final reaction product of all thermal or photochemical reactions in which free methyl can be shown to have been formed, and it is evident that the hydrogen transference

$$\cdot CH_3 + C_mH_{2m+2} \longrightarrow CH_4 + \cdot C_mH_{2m+1} \qquad \text{(v)}$$

must require relatively little activation energy.

From studies of the rate of methane formation from the photochemical decomposition of mercury dimethyl in hydrocarbons,‖ Smith

† Cunningham and Taylor, *J. Chem. Phys.* 1938, **6**, 359.
‡ Taylor and Rosenblum, ibid. 119.
§ See, however, H. A. Taylor and Burton, ibid. 1939, **7**, 675.
‖ Smith and Taylor, ibid. 390.

and Taylor estimate the activation energy for the reaction of methyl radicals and ethane as 8·3 k.cals., that between methyl and *n*-butane as 5·5 k.cals., and that between methyl and *iso*-butane as 4·2 k.cals., though earlier workers have given estimates as high as 15–20 k.cals. for the energy requirement.†

In general, free methyl, and other hydrocarbon radicals, react with paraffins and other saturated organic molecules by abstracting hydrogen from the periphery of the molecule, and do not affect the carbon skeleton. Thus a reaction such as (vi) occurs less easily than either (i) or (v) although the bonding energy of a C—C link is less than that of a C—H link, since ethane decomposes to give methyl radicals rather than ethyl radicals and atomic hydrogen.

$$\cdot CH_3 + CH_3{-}C_nH_{2n+1} \longrightarrow CH_3{-}CH_3 + \cdot C_nH_{2n+1}. \qquad \text{(vi)}$$

As reactions in solution have shown (p. 19) spatial proximity can be a decisive factor in determining the course of reactions of the active free radicals. Though atomic hydrogen can apparently bring about the fission of a C—C bond on reaction with a paraffin, the more bulky methyl radical apparently can only displace the outermost atoms (i.e. hydrogen) of a molecule with which it may collide.‡

3. Reactions with olefines. Free alkyl radicals are undoubtedly able to react with the carbon atoms of olefines: they add on, individually, to the centres of unsaturation. In 1930, Taylor and Jones showed that when lead tetra-ethyl, or mercury dimethyl, vapours were thermally decomposed, at 250–300° C., in an atmosphere of ethylene, polymerization of the ethylene occurred.§ Later, Rice and Sickman|| showed that methyl radicals generated by the thermal decomposition of azomethane, $CH_3{-}N{=}N{-}CH_3$, would also polymerize ethylene. Free methyl or ethyl radicals produced photochemically act in the same way. Danby and Hinshelwood, for example,¶ have studied in detail the kinetics of the polymerization of ethylene which is induced by the photochemical decomposition of aldehydes and ketones.

This polymerization is obviously a chain addition process in which free alkyl radicals add on to a carbon atom of an olefine,

$$CH_3\cdot + CH_2{=}CH_2 \longrightarrow CH_3{-}CH_2{-}CH_2\cdot, \qquad \text{(vii)}$$

thereby leaving the other carbon atom with an odd electron. This

† e.g. Rice and Herzfeld, *J.A.C.S.* 1934, **56**, 284.

‡ For a discussion of this, see Steacie, *Chemical Reviews*, 1938, **22**, 311; 1942, **31**, 227; also Rice and Teller, *J. Chem. Phys.* 1938, **6**, 489.

§ *J.A.C.S.* 1930, **52**, 1121.

|| Ibid. 1935, **57**, 1384.

¶ Danby and Hinshelwood, *Proc. Roy. Soc.* 1941, A **179**, 169.

initial reaction product is thus itself a free radical, and since the probability of its encountering another olefine molecule is very much larger than that of encountering another radical, further addition processes

$$CH_3—CH_2—CH_2\cdot + CH_2=CH_2 \longrightarrow CH_3—CH_2—CH_2—(CH_2—CH_2)\cdot \quad \text{(viii)}$$

will occur until, at last, two radicals will meet and combine to a stable product, which is of course a paraffin hydrocarbon, or interact by disproportionation (equation (iv) above).

By a reaction of this type, ethylene, at high pressure, is converted into the saturated polymer *polythene*, whilst isoprene, butadiene, and similar di-olefines give rubber-like products. Acetylene also gives the chain polymer cuprene, and not benzene. It will be recalled that atomic hydrogen reacts with unsaturated compounds in the same way (pp. 91–3).

4. Reactions with oxygen. Oxidation reactions of alkyl radicals are undoubtedly involved in the combustion of hydrocarbon vapours. For a long time it was thought that the oxidation of hydrocarbons was a hydroxylation process, but whilst aldehydes, such as formaldehyde, can frequently be isolated as partial oxidation products in combustion, there is very little experimental evidence for the intermediate formation of alcohols. To-day there is no doubt that gas-phase combustions are chain processes in which a series of exceedingly rapid reactions follows a brief induction period, and that hydrocarbon combustion resembles in many ways the reaction between hydrogen and oxygen (pp. 88–9).

Since the initial induction period can be shortened by adding a trace of nitrogen peroxide, which may yield atomic oxygen, it was suggested by Norrish† that the chain process was

$$O + CH_4 \longrightarrow CH_2: + H_2O,$$
$$CH_2: + O_2 \longrightarrow CH_2O + O,$$

involving the methylene diradical, $CH_2:$, but it is more probable that, except in explosions occurring at very high temperatures, univalent radicals rather than divalent radicals are present, and that both the free hydroxyl radical, $\cdot OH$, and organic peroxides are involved. These oxygenated radicals are thought to act as dehydrogenators of hydrocarbon molecules, yielding alkyl radicals which then attack molecular oxygen. Thus:

Hydroxyl mechanisms‡

$$\cdot OH + CH_4 \longrightarrow H_2O + \cdot CH_3; \qquad \cdot CH_3 + O_2 \longrightarrow CH_2O + \cdot OH$$
$$\cdot OH + CH_2O \longrightarrow \cdot CHO + H_2O; \qquad \cdot CHO + O_2 \longrightarrow CO + HO_2\cdot$$

† Norrish, ibid. 1936, A **150**, 36.
‡ Von Elbe and Lewis, *J.A.C.S.* 1937, **59**, 976.

Peroxide mechanisms†

$$\begin{cases} R{-}CH_2\cdot + O_2 \longrightarrow R{-}CH_2{-}O{-}O\cdot \\ R{-}CH_2{-}O{-}O\cdot + R{-}CH_3 \longrightarrow R{-}CH_2{-}O{-}O{-}H + R{-}CH_2\cdot \end{cases}$$

$$R{-}CH_2{-}O{-}O{-}H \longrightarrow R{-}CHO + H_2O$$

$$R{-}CH_2O{-}O\cdot \longrightarrow R{-}CHO + \cdot OH$$

The aldehydes formed by this primary attack may either decompose thermally, yielding carbon monoxide and simpler alkyl radicals, or may be oxidized farther, most probably via easily formed peroxides:‡

i.e.
$$\begin{cases} R{-}CHO + R{-}C(=O){-}O{-}O\cdot \longrightarrow R{-}C(=O){-}O{-}O{-}H + R{-}\dot{C}O \\ R{-}\dot{C}O + O_2 \longrightarrow R{-}C(=O){-}O{-}O\cdot \end{cases}$$

$$R{-}C(=O){-}O{-}O{-}H \longrightarrow R{-}CO{-}O{-}O{-}CO{-}R \longrightarrow CO_2 + R\cdot + \cdot O{-}CO{-}R$$

The slow accumulation of aldehydes is thought to occur during the induction period which, as one might expect, can often be inhibited by adding a little acetaldehyde, formaldehyde, or ethyl alcohol to the initial gas mixture.

In support of these suggestions there is abundant spectroscopic evidence of the presence of the hydroxyl radical in flames, whilst organic peroxides can frequently be isolated from products of vapour phase oxidations. They are formed in quantity by the photochemical oxidation of aldehydes and ketones‡ and appear to be the sole initial products of low-temperature autoxidation processes in liquid systems (Chapter XI).

Catalysis and Anti-catalysis of Thermal Decomposition

Kinetic measurements have shown that the thermal decomposition of many aliphatic vapours, such as those of dimethyl ether or acetaldehyde, is apparently a simple unimolecular process, but, as Rice and

† Ubbelohde, *Proc. Roy. Soc.* 1936, A **152,** 354; *Zeit. für Elektrochem.* 1936, **42,** 468; Bäckström, *Zeit. phys. Chem.* 1934, B **25,** 99.

‡ Bowen and Tietz, *J.* 1930, p. 234; Norrish and Carruthers, ibid. 1936, p. 1036; Rice and Schildknecht, *J.A.C.S.* 1938, **60,** 3044.

Herzfeld pointed out,† most thermal decompositions involve complex chain reactions in which free radicals react with undissociated organic molecules, and this conclusion can be substantiated by carrying out exact analyses of the resultant gaseous products, which are usually complex mixtures.

Moreover, quite a number of apparently homogeneous unimolecular thermal decompositions of organic vapours can be catalysed by adding substances which easily dissociate. Thus the unimolecular decomposition of di-*iso*-propyl ether is noticeably catalysed by the addition of a little *iso*-propyl iodide, or iodine,‡ though the catalysed reaction still appears, from pressure measurements, to be a simple unimolecular process. Again the thermal decomposition of diethyl ether at 500° C. can be catalysed by the addition of a little acetaldehyde,§ which is, in fact, one of its normal decomposition products.

It has not been a difficult matter to show that in many of these cases the true catalysts are free alkyl radicals, which act by abstracting hydrogen from the more stable molecule (reaction (v) of p. 129), e.g.||

$$R\cdot + C_2H_5—O—C_2H_5 \longrightarrow R—H + \cdot C_2H_4—O—C_2H_5.$$

For example, free methyl radieals produced by the photochemical decomposition of acetone by light of 3,130 A wave-length, which is not absorbed by dimethyl ether, can bring about the decomposition of the latter at as low a temperature as 400° C.,¶ whilst radicals produced from the lead alkyls can act in a similar way.

It does not follow, however, that the higher temperature, uncatalysed, reaction is kinetically identical with the more rapid radical catalysed reaction, whilst some of the catalysed reactions may involve molecular processes such as

$$Me_2CH—O—CHMe_2 + I_2 = Me_2CHI + HI + Me_2CO,$$
$$Me_2CHI + HI = Me_2CH_2 + I_2.††$$

Whereas free alkyl radicals catalyse the thermal decomposition of organic vapours, Staveley and Hinshelwood‡‡ have been able to show that both thermal and photochemical decompositions can be inhibited

† Rice and Herzfeld, *J.A.C.S.* 1934, **56,** 284.
‡ Glass and Hinshelwood, *J.* 1929, p. 1815; *Proc. Roy. Soc.* 1930, A **128,** 75.
§ Fletcher and Rollefson, *J.A.C.S.* 1936, **58,** 2129.
|| Compare Hobbs, *Proc. Roy. Soc.* 1938, A **167,** 456.
¶ Leermakers, *J.A.C.S.* 1934, **56,** 1899.
†† Faull and Rollefson, ibid. 1936, **58,** 1758.
‡‡ Staveley and Hinshelwood, *Proc. Roy. Soc.* 1936, A **154,** 335; 1937, A **159,** 192; *J.* 1936, p. 812; 1937, p. 1568; *Trans. Faraday Soc.* 1939, **35,** 845.

by adding a trace of nitric oxide (Fig. 20). They pointed out that nitric oxide, which contains an odd number of electrons, combines instantly with neutral radicals such as triphenylmethyl (p. 45) to produce normal molecules and suggested that it might act on free methyl

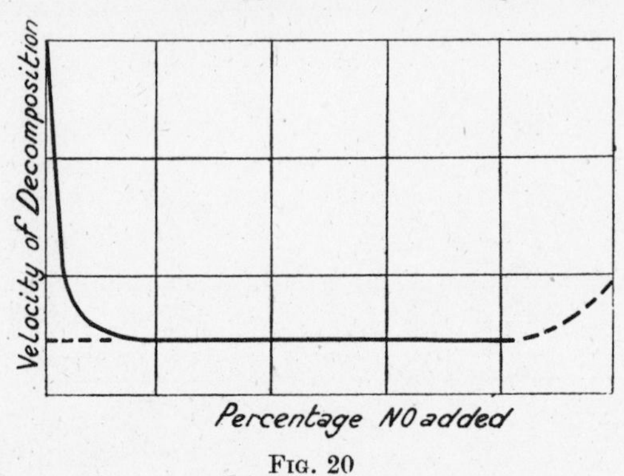

Fig. 20

radicals in the same way, giving unstable nitroso-methyl, which subsequently decomposed:

$$CH_3\cdot + \cdot NO \xrightarrow[\text{fast}]{} CH_3{-}NO \longrightarrow CH_2{=}NOH \longrightarrow HCN + H_2O.$$

They established that the inhibition process occurred exclusively in the gaseous phase and not on the walls of the reaction vessel.† In confirmation of this view, it was shown that a minute amount of nitric oxide, when added to diethyl ether at 800° C., completely inhibited the removal of tellurium mirrors by the radicals usually formed from the ether. More recent experiments by Forsyth‡ have shown that the bimolecular gas reaction between free methyl and nitric oxide proceeds easily at room temperature and has the low activation energy of 6·5 k.cals.

Ethylene and propylene have been shown to inhibit the thermal decomposition of organic vapours in the same way,§ whilst alkyl nitrites can be used as a source of nitric oxide.

Staveley and Hinshelwood regard inhibition of decomposition by nitric oxide as a diagnostic test for demonstrating whether or not a thermal decomposition involves a chain reaction of free alkyl radicals. It is significant that nitric oxide does not reduce the rate of a thermal decomposition to zero, but lowers it to a finite limit, which often remains constant for at least a tenfold variation in the nitric oxide concentration.

† Smith and Hinshelwood, *Proc. Roy. Soc.* 1939, A **179**, 131.

‡ Forsyth, *Trans. Faraday Soc.* 1941, **37**, 312.

§ Rice and Polly, *J. Chem. Phys.* 1938, **6**, 273; Fletcher and Rollefson, *J.A.C.S.* 1936, **58**, 2129.

As the nitric oxide concentration is still further increased the reaction velocity rises again, and in very high concentrations nitric oxide must be regarded as a positive catalyst. In the region of maximum inhibition it may be assumed that the nitric oxide acts by combining instantly with free alkyl radicals, and consequently in a decomposition sequence such as

$$CH_3\text{—}O\text{—}CH_3 \longrightarrow CH_3\cdot + \cdot OCH_3 \quad (\longrightarrow CH_2O + H\cdot, \text{ etc.}),$$

$$\left.\begin{array}{rl} CH_3\cdot + CH_3\text{—}O\text{—}CH_3 & \longrightarrow CH_4 + \cdot CH_2\text{—}O\text{—}CH_3 \\ \cdot CH_2\text{—}O\text{—}CH_3 & \longrightarrow CH_2O + CH_3\cdot \end{array}\right\} \text{chain sequence,}$$

the number of reaction chains produced in unit time by the self-decomposition of an ether molecule will be balanced by the number destroyed by the nitric oxide.

Consequently the *apparent chain-length* of the decomposition process will be given by the ratio

$$\frac{\text{velocity of uncatalysed decomposition}}{\text{velocity of reaction in presence of nitric oxide}}.$$

Table XVIII gives data for ethers, from which it can be seen (*a*) that the apparent chain-length is relatively short, and decreases rapidly as the molecule increases in complexity, and (*b*) that the chain-breaking effected by nitric oxide interferes with the reactions requiring the lowest activation energy, presumably the reactions of the free alkyl radicals.

TABLE XVIII

Thermal Decompositions of Ethers at 540° C.†

Ether	*Mean chain-length*	*Activation Energies*‡	
		With NO	*Without* NO
CH_3—O—CH_3	17	62 k. cals.	58·5 k. cals.
CH_3—O—C_2H_5	8·4	62	54·5
C_2H_5—O—C_2H_5	4·4	67	53·0
C_3H_7—O—C_3H_7 (*n*)	2·7	60·5	53·0
C_3H_7—O—C_3H_7 (*iso*)	1·4	65·5	63·0

‡ Average of whole process.

However, from the postulated mechanism for the reaction of nitric oxide it follows that one nitric oxide molecule should be consumed, as nitrosomethane, etc., for each reaction chain which is broken, and since during the decomposition of dimethyl ether only one molecule of nitric oxide is used up for the decomposition of at least 400 molecules of the

† Staveley and Hinshelwood, *Proc. Roy. Soc.* 1937, A **159**, 192.

ether, it is evident that the radical chain process cannot account for more than a small fraction of the whole decomposition. The higher ethers seem to consume a still lower percentage of nitric oxide.

This finding accords with the work of Patat and Sachsse,† who used the catalysis of the interconversion of the *ortho* and *para* forms of hydrogen (p. 86) to determine the concentration of free radicals present during the thermal decompositions of ethers, aldehydes, and ketones, and concluded that though alkyl radicals were certainly present in each case their concentration was so small that they could account for only from 0·1 to 1 per cent. of the whole decomposition.

Thus it is evident that most thermal decompositions are kinetically complex, and include a few *long-chain* reaction processes involving free alkyl radicals, together with many reactions which either do not produce free radicals at all, or which yield higher organic radicals which have far less available energy than methyl or ethyl and are unable to decompose other organic molecules (compare the photochemical decompositions of the higher aldehydes and ketones, pp. 118–21).‡

This subject is of great technical importance in connexion with the chemistry of the internal-combustion engine. Thus lead alkyls have valuable *anti-knock* properties,§ whilst many other compounds, such as the alkyl nitrites, have the opposite effect. Compounds of the former type promote the formation of chain reactions at low temperatures, and thus favour gradual combustion, whilst the latter, by acting as chain-breakers, inhibit the occurrence of smooth reaction at moderate temperatures. Combustion is thus delayed until there are reached those high temperature and pressure conditions in which violent *branched chain* oxidations can occur (compare pp. 95–6).

In this connexion it is significant to note that the branched chain paraffins, such as *iso*-octane (2 : 4 : 4-trimethyl-pentane), which are much more easily decomposed into methyl radicals than are the *normal* paraffins, have the best *knock-resisting* properties, and are consequently in the greatest demand for high-compression engines.

Reactions involving Free Alkyl Radicals in Solution

Though it is possible to prepare free alkyl radicals in solution by most of the methods indicated in Chapter I, very few of the ordinary reactions of alkyl groups involve electrically neutral radicals. The common alkylating agents, such as alkyl halides and dialkyl sulphates react via

† Patat and Sachsse, *Zeit. phys. Chem.* 1935, B **31**, 105; 1936, B **32**, 294.

‡ For a discussion, see Hinshelwood, *The Kinetics of Chemical Change*, Oxford, 1940.

§ Midgley and Boyd, *J. Ind. Eng. Chem.* 1922, **14**, 894.

alkyl cations, whilst alkyl anions can be formed from Grignard reagents and analogous metallic alkyls. The more unusual reactions which undoubtedly involve neutral radicals are discussed below.

1. Photochemical decomposition of ketones. In Chapter VI an account was given of the work of Bamford and Norrish, who showed in 1937 that the normal photochemical decomposition of acetone to yield carbon monoxide and ethane,

$$CH_3—CO—CH_3 \longrightarrow CH_3\cdot + \cdot COCH_3 \longrightarrow C_2H_6 + CO,$$

did not occur in solution in paraffin hydrocarbons. Instead of ethane there was produced *methane*, whilst the solvent lost an equivalent of hydrogen through the sequence of reactions

$$CH_3\cdot + C_nH_{2n+2} \longrightarrow CH_4 + \cdot C_nH_{2n+1},$$
$$2C_nH_{2n+1} \longrightarrow C_nH_{2n} + C_nH_{2n+2},$$

which is exactly similar to that which is believed to occur whenever the vapours of higher aliphatic compounds are decomposed (p. 129, above).

These experiments provided the first definite substantiation for the view that free alkyl radicals in solution undergo displacement reactions with solvent molecules in preference to dimerization,† and showed that in this respect the previously encountered free aryl radicals, such as phenyl (Chapter VIII) were not unique.‡

2. Thermal decomposition of lead tetra-ethyl. Lead tetra-ethyl is not as convenient a reagent for preparing free ethyl radicals in solution as it is for vapour phase reactions since it does not decompose below 200° C. However, by working in stainless steel bomb-tubes, Cramer§ has been able to examine the reactions of free ethyl with liquid hydrocarbons at temperatures of 200–270° C. He found that the reactions which occurred were exactly the same in the liquid and vapour phases. The ethyl radicals are converted to ethane by hydrogenation and to ethylene by disproportionation, though much of the ethylene is thereafter converted to a high-boiling hydrocarbon oil by chain polymerization.

Both paraffin hydrocarbons, including cycloparaffins, and olefinic hydrocarbons seem to be dehydrogenated quite easily, but aromatic hydrocarbons, such as benzene and naphthalene, are not attacked by ethyl groups at temperatures below 300° C.‖ Secondary and tertiary C—H groups give up their hydrogen atoms more easily than do CH_3

† Compare pp. 19, 130, 144–5.
‡ Compare Hey and Waters, *Chemical Reviews*, 1937, **21**, 169.
§ *J.A.C.S.* 1934, **56**, 1234; 1938, **60**, 1406.
‖ Compare the action of phenyl radicals, pp. 147 *et seq.*

groups. Even olefinic compounds, such as *cyclo*hexene or heptene react more easily to lose hydrogen than to form addition compounds. Evidently the exposed hydrogen atoms of CH_2 groups are more easily attacked by ethyl radicals than are the shielded carbon atoms of olefinic bonds (compare pp. 241–3, Chapter XI).

3. Thermal decomposition of diacyl peroxides. Just as aldehydes and ketones decompose, both thermally and photochemically, to give carbon monoxide and free alkyl radicals, so the diacyl peroxides, R—CO—O—O—CO—R, decompose slowly at moderate temperatures with elimination of the stable molecule carbon dioxide, to yield both free alkyl (or aryl) radicals and also free carboxylate groups which again are capable of a further similar decomposition; i.e.

$$R—CO—O—O—CO—R \longrightarrow R\cdot + CO_2 + \cdot O—CO—R, \quad (i)$$

$$R—CO—O\cdot \longrightarrow R\cdot + CO_2. \quad (ii)$$

Benzoyl peroxide was the first compound of this series to be studied in detail (see Chapter VIII); it yields the free phenyl radical. Alkyl radicals can, however, be made in the same way from the peroxides of aliphatic acids. Diacetyl peroxide, CH_3—CO—O—O—CO—CH_3, is the simplest compound of this type. Its photochemical decomposition both in the vapour phase and in solution was examined carefully by Walker and Wild in 1937.† They found that whereas photochemical decomposition of diacetyl peroxide vapour gave ethane and carbon dioxide together with just a little methane, the photochemical decomposition of the pure liquid peroxide, or of its solutions in cyclohexane or ethyl alcohol gave much more methane than ethane.

The thermal decomposition of diacetyl peroxide in solution is very slow below 70° C., but becomes rapid though still controllable at temperatures above 80° C. Higher diacyl peroxides of the aliphatic series are much more stable, and can be boiled in solvents for several hours before their decomposition is complete. Walker and Wild found that when diacetyl peroxide was boiled in toluene about 50 per cent. of the evolved gas consisted of methane. Thus methyl radicals must have abstracted hydrogen from the solvent. Under similar conditions, 2:3-diphenylbutane has been isolated from the decomposition of diacetyl peroxide in ethyl benzene.‡ The decomposition of dibenzoyl peroxide in chlorinated solvents was examined by Boeseken and Gelissen in 1924,§ but it was not until 1941 that the same reaction

† *J.* 1937, p. 1132.

‡ Kharasch, McBay, and Urry, *J. Organic Chem.* 1945, **10**, 401.

§ *Rec. trav. chim.* 1924, **43**, 869; see p. 169.

was studied with aliphatic peroxides by Kharasch, Kane, and Brown,† who showed that the free alkyl groups abstracted chlorine from carbon tetrachloride, leaving the radical $\cdot CCl_3$, which was isolated in the form of its dimeride hexachloroethane, C_2Cl_6:

$$R\cdot + CCl_4 \longrightarrow R{-}Cl + \cdot CCl_3; \qquad 2\cdot CCl_3 \longrightarrow C_2Cl_6.$$

Since *n*-butyryl peroxide yielded exclusively *n*-propyl chloride, and *iso*-butyryl peroxide exclusively *iso*-propyl chloride, Kharasch and his colleagues concluded that at moderate temperatures the free alkyl radicals preserve their identities and do not isomerize by hydrogen migration, a reaction which evidently can occur at higher temperatures.‡ They pointed out, too, that though there is evidence that a neutral radical, $R_1R_2R_3C\cdot$, when free probably has a planar and not a tetrahedral structure (p. 175), even this stereochemical change can be prevented by making the radical part of a rigid ring system.§

If glacial acetic acid is used as the solvent for diacetyl peroxide, then the acetate radical, $CH_3{-}CO{-}O\cdot$, which is one of the products of the primary decomposition, can have an abnormally long free life on account of regeneration by solvent exchange (p. 19):

$$\mathit{CH_3{-}CO{-}O}\cdot + H{-}O{-}CO{-}CH_3 \rightleftarrows \mathit{CH_3{-}CO{-}O}{-}H + \cdot O{-}CO{-}CH_3.$$

Kharasch and Gladstone‖ have shown that after prolonged boiling in glacial acetic acid, or in acetic anhydride, diacetyl peroxide yields methane, carbon dioxide and *succinic acid*, in 50 per cent. yield, together with about 5 per cent. of *methyl acetate*.

The formation of this ester substantiates the view that the primary decomposition of a diacyl peroxide involves the liberation of only 1 mol. of carbon dioxide, since methyl acetate is the obvious product of direct union of free methyl and acetate radicals:

$$CH_3{-}CO{-}O{-}O{-}CO{-}CH_3 \longrightarrow CH_3\cdot + CO_2 + \cdot O{-}CO{-}CH_3,$$
$$CH_3\cdot + \cdot O{-}CO{-}CH_3 \longrightarrow CH_3{-}O{-}CO{-}CH_3.$$

Esters of this same type are always very definite reaction products in thermal decompositions of dibenzoyl peroxide and its substitution derivatives.

Kharasch and Gladstone ascribe the formation of succinic acid to attack of free methyl on acetic acid, and subsequent dimerization of the

† *J.A.C.S.* 1941, **63**, 526.
‡ Glazebrook and Pearson, *J.* 1936, p. 1777.
§ Kharasch, Engelmann, and Urry, *J.A.C.S.* 1943, **65**, 2428.
‖ *J.A.C.S.* 1943, **65**, 15. See also *J. Organic Chem.* 1945, **10**, 386, 394.

$\cdot CH_2$—COOH radical, which they regard as a structure to some degree stabilized by resonance between the structures

$$\cdot CH_2{-}C{\overset{\large O}{\underset{OH}{\diagdown}}} \quad \text{and} \quad CH_2{=}C{\overset{\large O\cdot}{\underset{OH}{\diagdown}}}$$

and therefore of comparatively long free life:†

$$CH_3\cdot + CH_3{-}COOH \longrightarrow CH_4 + \cdot CH_2{-}COOH,$$

$$2\cdot CH_2{-}COOH \longrightarrow HOOC{-}CH_2{-}CH_2{-}COOH.$$

Subsequent work has shown that similar reaction products can be obtained by the decomposition of diacetyl peroxide in many other aliphatic acids, esters, and acid chlorides.

Though free alkyl radicals do not appear to react easily with benzene (p. 137) they can substitute some aromatic ring systems. In 1942 Fieser. Clapp, and Daudt‡ showed that trinitro-*m*-xylene (II) can be obtained in 10 per cent. yield by boiling diacetyl peroxide for a long time with trinitrotoluene (I) in glacial acetic acid.

$$\text{(I)} \xrightarrow[\text{in HOAc.}]{(CH_3COO)_2} \text{(II)}$$

CH₃ | NO₂ | NO₂ | NO₂ — (I)

CH₃ | NO₂ | NO₂ | CH₃ | NO₂ — (II)

Similarly, *m*-dinitrobenzene gives a mixture of 2:4-dinitrotoluene and 2:4-dinitro-*m*-xylene.

Quinones can be alkylated quite easily by this method. Thus Fieser and Oxford§ have shown that the reaction

$$\text{(2-methyl-1,4-naphthoquinone; O, O, CH}_3\text{, H)} + (RCOO\cdot)_2 \longrightarrow \text{(O, O, C–CH}_3\text{, C–R)} + CO_2 + RCOOH$$

can be carried out with a wide range of diacyl peroxides, including those of acetic, palmitic, stearic, chaulmoogric, and undecenoic acids, by boiling the reactants together for a long time in a suitable solvent such as acetic acid or ligroin. Since even unsaturated alkyl groups can

† Compare pp. 160, 231. ‡ *J.A.C.S.* 1942, **64**, 2053. § Ibid. 2060.

be introduced into the quinone ring system by this means it is evident that unsaturated alkyl radicals are capable of transient existence.

4. Decomposition of lead tetra-acetate. The successful alkylation of quinones by means of diacetyl peroxide was actually discovered by Fieser and his colleagues as a logical outcome of an investigation into a rather surprising reaction of lead tetra-acetate, $Pb(OCOCH_3)_4$. This substance, which is most useful as a specific, and controllable, oxidizing agent (pp. 227–32), was used by Fieser and Chang† in an attempt to effect the direct oxidation of (III), the Diels condensation product of butadiene and toluquinone, to the methylnaphthaquinone (IV), but the product was found to be the quinone (V), which contained two methyl groups in the quinonoid ring. Subsequent examination of this unexpected methylation process showed that whilst quinones could, in time, be methylated merely by heating with lead tetra-acetate, the reaction could be catalysed by adding a small amount of a promoter such as malonic acid, or an alcohol, and then could be carried out in boiling glacial acetic acid solution.

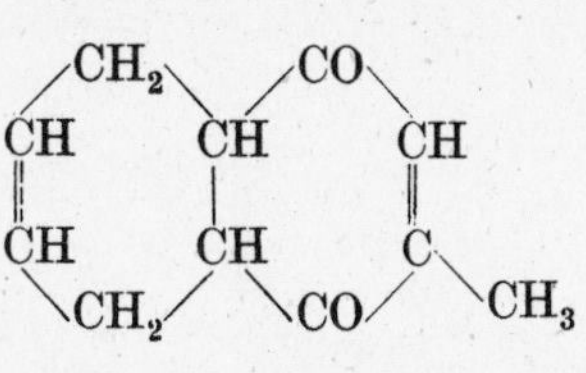

(III) 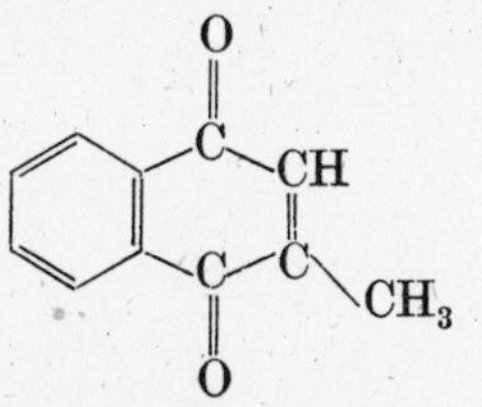 (IV) 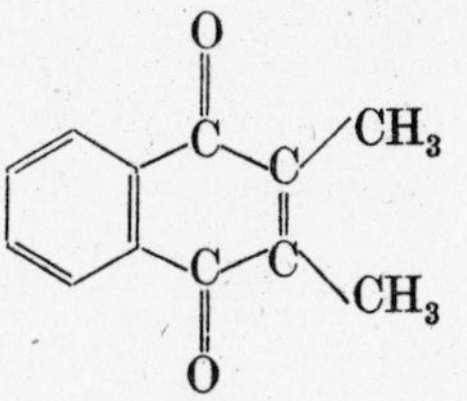 (V)

Under these circumstances both nitrobenzene and *m*-dinitrobenzene could be methylated to give nitrated toluenes, or xylenes, whilst benzene and chlorobenzene yielded benzyl acetate and chlorobenzyl acetate respectively.‡ Toluene yielded only benzyl acetate, as previously reported by Dimroth,§ whilst naphthalene, anthracene, and benzpyrene also gave acetoxy derivatives (i.e. the expected direct oxidation products).

To explain this methylation process Fieser suggested that lead tetra-acetate decomposes thermally to yield free acetate radicals (perhaps via diacetyl peroxide), and it was to confirm this hypothesis that he showed that diacetyl peroxide would also methylate:

$$Pb(OCOCH_3)_4 \longrightarrow Pb(OCOCH_3)_2 + 2\cdot O{-}COCH_3,$$
$$\cdot O{-}CO{-}CH_3 \longrightarrow CO_2 + \cdot CH_3.$$

† Fieser and Chang, *J.A.C.S.* 1942, **64**, 2043.
‡ Fieser, Clapp, and Daudt, ibid. 2053.
§ See p. 228.

Alkylation with other salts of tetravalent lead can of course be carried out in a similar manner. The alkylation processes seem to be autocatalytic, and the promoter may act as a hydrogen carrier which converts one carboxylate group to free carboxylic acid, or, as suggested by Hey,† facilitates the initial breakdown of the lead tetra-acetate.

5. The Kolbe Reaction. It is obvious that a neutral carboxylate radical must be the initial product of the electrolytic discharge of a carboxylate anion at an anode; e.g.

$$(CH_3CO{-}O:)^- \longrightarrow CH_3CO{-}O\cdot + e,$$

and hence the discovery of Kolbe, in 1849, that ethane and carbon dioxide were both liberated in good yield at the anode on electrolysis of a concentrated solution of potassium acetate, was for a long time interpreted‡ as anion discharge followed immediately by loss of carbon dioxide and *instantaneous* dimerization of the resulting methyl radicals.

Kolbe's anodic synthesis of ethane has been applied successfully in many synthesis of paraffin chains. Higher hydrocarbons can very easily be made in this way, and by the electrolysis of the half ester of a dibasic acid one can obtain the ester of a longer chain acid, with which the electrolytic process can, if required, be again repeated after partial hydrolysis,§

$$2EtOOC{-}CH_2{-}CH_2{-}COO^-K^+ \longrightarrow EtOOC{-}CH_2{-}CH_2{-}CH_2{-}CH_2{-}COOEt.$$

However, the Kolbe reaction cannot be used to convert aromatic acids to compounds of the diphenyl series, whilst aliphatic acids containing halogen or hydroxyl groups are oxidized quite differently.

Both methane and methyl acetate are regular by-products of the electrolysis of potassium acetate, and, as shown by Hofer and Moest,|| electrolyses in the presence of bicarbonate, sulphate, or perchlorate yield methyl alcohol in preference to ethane. The simple ionic discharge and dimerization theory is thus inadequate to account fully for the mechanism of the Kolbe reaction, and as an alternative it has been suggested that the electrolysis of strong aqueous solutions of acetates yields both diacetyl peroxide and peracetic acid,¶ following chemical oxidation in the solution in the vicinity of the anode. Both atomic oxygen¶

† Hey, *Annual Reports of the Chemical Society*, 1944, **41**, 191.

‡ Crum Brown, and Walker, *Annalen*, 1891, **261**, 107.

§ A detailed account is given in Glasstone and Hickling's monograph, *Electrolytic Oxidation and Reduction*, 1935, London (Chap. VIII).

|| *Annalen*, 1902, **323**, 284.

¶ Fichter, *et al.*, *Helv. Chim. Acta*, 1918, **1**, 146; 1923, **6**, 329; 1927, **10**, 869.

and hydrogen peroxide have been suggested as probable oxidizing agents:†

$$CH_3COOH + O \longrightarrow CH_3CO{-}OOH,$$
$$2(CH_3COO:)^- + H_2O_2 \longrightarrow (CH_3CO{-}O{-})_2 + 2(OH)^-,$$
$$CH_3COOH + H_2O_2 \longrightarrow CH_3CO{-}OOH + H_2O,$$
$$CH_3CO{-}OOH \longrightarrow CO_2 + CH_3OH.$$

Whilst there is strong electrochemical evidence to suggest that both hydrogen peroxide and active oxygen may easily be formed at anodes by the preferential discharge of hydroxyl anions, unfortunately hydrogen peroxide itself is not a good oxidizer for acetates, and Glasstone and Hickling, the originators of the hydrogen peroxide theory, had to suppose that the metals forming the anodes were essential contact catalysts. They had to admit, too, that carboxylate anion discharge could account satisfactorily for the facts concerning electrolysis in non-aqueous solutions.

At that time, however, the behaviour of free neutral radicals in solution was not fully understood, and it can be seen to-day that *all* features of the Kolbe reaction can be explained as natural reactions of carboxylate radicals. Firstly, an initial acetate radical in a solution containing abundant acetate anions will have a long life on account of regenerative exchange, and so dimerization to diacetyl peroxide will be favoured. Secondly, decomposition will give the short-life radical methyl which may (*a*) dimerize to ethane, (*b*) react with acetate radical to give methyl acetate or (*c*) react with water to give methyl alcohol,

$$CH_3\cdot + H_2O \longrightarrow CH_3{-}OH + \cdot H.$$

Fieser, Clapp, and Daudt‡ have recently shown that trinitrotoluene can be methylated at the anode compartment of an electrolytic cell containing sodium acetate and acetic acid, and hence there can now be no doubt of the production of free neutral alkyl radicals by the Kolbe reaction. The extent to which the free hydroxyl also participates in this reaction cannot easily be gauged, since the exchange process

$$\cdot OH + (CH_3CO{-}O:)^- \rightleftharpoons (:OH)^- + CH_3{-}CO{-}O\cdot$$

must also occur in all electrolyses in aqueous solution. One can of course explain the Hofer–Moest reaction as a direct union of methyl and hydroxyl radicals.

In substantiation of the free radical theory it is also significant that when electrolyses are carried out in pyridine solution substitution of the pyridine ring occurs.§

† Glasstone and Hickling, *J.* 1934, p. 1878.

‡ *J.A.C.S.* 1942, **64**, 2053.

§ Fichter and Stenzl, *Helv. Chim. Acta*, 1939, **22**, 970.

6. The electrolysis of organo-metallic compounds. Free alkyl radicals are liberated at anodes when metallic alkyls are electrolysed. Hein and his colleagues,† by using zinc diethyl as the solvent, have measured the conductivities of the alkyls of the alkali metals, such as sodium ethyl, and have shown that when lead anodes were used lead tetra-ethyl was formed. Both ethane and ethylene were gaseous products of this electrolysis.

Very similar results have been obtained by W. V. Evans and his colleagues in studies of the electrolysis of Grignard reagents in ether solution.‡ In this case there can be no doubt that the free alkyl radicals liberated at the anode of the electrolytic cell react very largely with the solvent. Thus when propyl magnesium bromide is electrolysed in diethyl ether the gaseous products include propane, propylene, ethylene, and carbon dioxide, whilst hexane, ethyl alcohol, *n*-propyl alcohol, and *sec*-amyl alcohol can be detected in the residual electrolyte. The formation of these diverse products can only be explained by presuming that the neutral propyl radical abstracts hydrogen from ether:

$$C_3H_7\cdot + C_2H_5{-}O{-}C_2H_5 \longrightarrow C_3H_8 + CH_3{-}\dot{C}H{-}O{-}C_2H_5$$

$$CH_3{-}\dot{C}H{-}O{-}C_2H_5 \longrightarrow CH_3{-}CHO + \cdot C_2H_5 \longrightarrow C_2H_6 + C_2H_4$$

$$CH_3{-}CHO \xrightarrow{C_3H_7MgBr} CH_3{-}CHOH{-}C_3H_7$$

A very similar instance of the abstraction of an α-hydrogen atom from ether by a free radical, with consequent production of acetaldehyde is described in Chapter VIII (p. 157).

Similarly when methyl magnesium iodide is electrolysed in di-*n*-butyl ether, the methyl radical abstracts hydrogen from both the α- and the β-positions in the solvent, but not apparently from the γ- or δ-positions, for the reactions can all be represented by the following sequences:

(*a*) $$CH_3\cdot + nBuO{-}CH_2{-}CH_2CH_2CH_3 \longrightarrow CH_4 + nBuO{-}\dot{C}H{-}CH_2CH_2CH_3$$

$$nBuO{-}\dot{C}H{-}CH_2CH_2CH_3 \longrightarrow nC_4H_9\cdot + CH_3CH_2CH_2{-}CHO$$

$$nC_4H_9\cdot \longrightarrow C_4H_8 + C_4H_{10}$$

$$CH_3CH_2CH_2{-}CHO \xrightarrow{(CH_3MgI)} CH_3CH_2CH_2CH(OH){-}CH_3$$

† *Z. anorg. Chem.* 1926, **141**, 161.

‡ Evans and Lee, *J.A.C.S.* 1934, **56**, 654; Evans and Field, ibid. 1936, **58**, 720, 2284; Evans and Braithwaite, ibid. 1939, **61**, 898.

$$(b)\ CH_3\cdot + nBuO{-}CH_2{-}CH_2CH_2CH_3 \longrightarrow CH_4 + nBuO{-}CH_2{-}\dot{C}H{-}CH_2CH_3$$

$$nBuO{-}CH_2{-}\dot{C}H{-}CH_2CH_3 \longrightarrow nC_4H_9{-}O\cdot + CH_2{=}CH{-}CH_2CH_3$$

$$nC_4H_9{-}O{-}MgI \longrightarrow nC_4H_9{-}OH.$$

From electrolyses carried out with *n*-butyl, *iso*-butyl, *tert*-butyl, and *n*-hexyl magnesium bromides† it became evident that as the length of the hydrocarbon chain in the free alkyl radical is increased the tendency to dimerize increases and reactions with the solvent become negligible.

7. Cathodic reduction. A wide range of organic compounds can be reduced, either in acid or in alkaline solution, if placed in the cathode compartment of an electrolytic cell. The reduction is brought about either by the *nascent hydrogen* liberated at the cathode, or by the release of electrons from the latter, and in many cases the whole reduction process is a surface reaction, and not one in which one can be sure of the formation of free neutral radicals in the electrolyte (compare Chapter X).

A number of investigators‡ have shown that organo-metallic derivatives of mercury and of lead can be obtained in good yield by the electrolytic reduction of ketones and of a few aldehydes. Thus the reduction of acetone has yielded both mercury di-*iso*-propyl and lead tetra-*iso*-propyl, $Pb(C_3H_7)_4$, and it is therefore highly probable that transient free hydrocarbon radicals have been formed by the electrolysis.

Again pinacones are regular electrolytic reduction products of ketones, whilst aldehydes similarly yield glycols; these products can be regarded as the dimers of intermediate neutral radicals having structures similar to those of the metallic ketyls (Chapter X):

$$CH_3{-}CO{-}CH_3 + \cdot H \longrightarrow CH_3{-}\dot{C}(CH_3){-}O{-}H \longrightarrow \begin{array}{c} CH_3 \\ | \\ CH_3{-}C{-}O{-}H \\ | \\ CH_3{-}C{-}O{-}H \\ | \\ CH_3 \end{array}$$

Few, if any, of the consequent reactions in solution of alkyl radicals produced by cathodic reduction have as yet been studied in great detail.

† Evans, Braithwaite, and Field, *J.A.C.S.* 1940, **62**, 534.

‡ Tafel, *Ber.* 1906, **39**, 3626; 1911, **44**, 323; Schall and Kirst, *Z. Elektrochem.* 1923, **29**, 537; Haggerty, *Trans. Amer. Electrochem. Soc.* 1929, **56**, 421.

VIII

FREE ARYL RADICALS AND THEIR REACTIONS IN SOLUTION

FROM modern theories of free radical stability (pp. 57–60) it would be expected that the phenyl radical (I) would have at least as high an energy level, and as short a free life, as the methyl radical, for the odd electron cannot be distributed throughout the whole of the benzene ring in the way that is possible in the mesomeric benzyl radical (II):

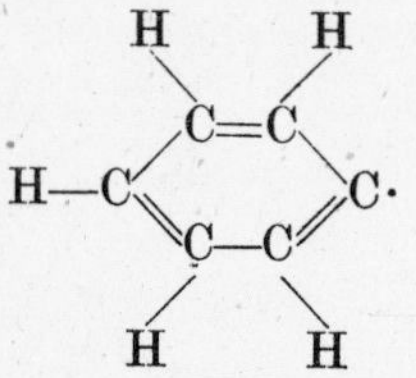

(I) 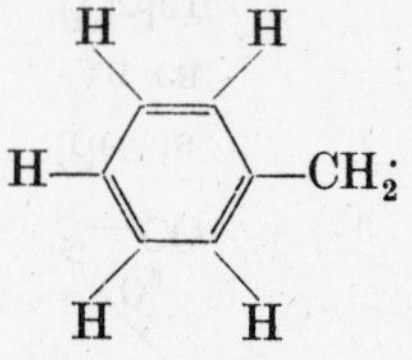 (II *a*) 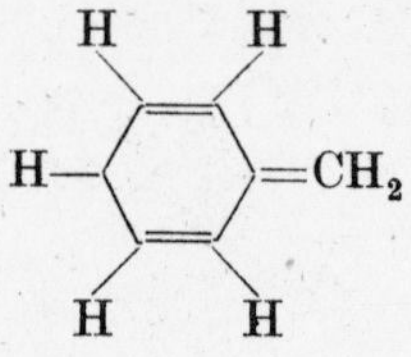 (II *b*)

It is not surprising, therefore, that Paneth and Lautsch† failed to detect the presence of phenyl radicals on pyrolysis of tin tetraphenyl, though they easily identified free benzyl from tin tetrabenzyl. Glazebrook and Pearson's success‡ in establishing that the free phenyl radical is formed upon photochemical decomposition of acetophenone shows, however, that free neutral aryl radicals can exist in the gas phase, though their mean free lives must be very brief indeed.

Whilst evidence for the existence of free aryl radicals in the vapour phase is very scanty, there is now on record a considerable amount of self-consistent evidence for their participation in reactions in solution.

As the study of gas reactions has shown, neutral aryl radicals are most likely to be formed from molecules which undergo thermal self-decomposition at comparatively low temperatures. Molecules of this type have one structural characteristic in common: the heat of formation of certain of their covalent bonds must be small, and invariably there can be eliminated either the stable atoms of an element such as lead or mercury, or a simple molecule of high stability, such as nitrogen, carbon monoxide, or carbon dioxide.

DECOMPOSITIONS OF AZO AND DIAZO COMPOUNDS

In 1933 Leermakers§ showed that azomethane, $CH_3—N=N—CH_3$, decomposes at about 400° C. to give nitrogen and free methyl radicals.

† *J.* 1935, p. 380. ‡ *J.* 1939, p. 589.

§ *J.A.C.S.* 1933, **55**, 3499; compare Rice and Evering, ibid. 3898.

Its aromatic equivalent, azobenzene, $C_6H_5—N=N—C_6H_5$, which has a completely conjugated structure, is stable at quite high temperatures, but azo compounds, Ar—N=N—X, containing only one aryl group, are very much less stable. As will be shown below, free neutral aryl radicals can readily be formed by the thermal decompositions of several types of compounds with this same general structure.

1. Aryl-azo-triarylmethanes. In 1897 Gomberg,† whilst engaged upon the study of steric hindrance which eventually led to the discovery of triphenylmethyl (p. 3), prepared the stable hydrocarbon tetraphenylmethane, $(C_6H_5)_4C$. One of his processes involved the condensation of triphenylchloromethane with phenyl-hydrazine, followed by oxidation of the product to phenyl-azo-triphenylmethane, which, on heating, lost nitrogen, and gave the desired product, though in very poor yield (about 5 per cent.):

$$Ph_3C—Cl + H_2N—NH—Ph \longrightarrow Ph_3C—NH—NH—Ph,$$
$$Ph_3C—NH—NH—Ph + HgO \longrightarrow Ph_3C—N=N—Ph + H_2O + Hg,$$
$$Ph_3C—N=N—Ph \longrightarrow Ph_4C + N_2.$$

In 1922 Wieland, Popper, and Seefried‡ studied this same reaction in greater detail and found that solutions of phenylazotriphenylmethane in light petroleum, xylone, or ethyl benzoate, evolved nitrogen at about 80° C. with the liberation of free triphenylmethyl radicals, which were identified spectrographically. The greater part of the triphenylmethyl was isolated as the peroxide. Wieland and his colleagues therefore suggested that the decomposition involved the formation of both the triphenylmethyl and phenyl free radicals,

$$Ph_3C—N=N—Ph \longrightarrow Ph_3C\cdot + N\equiv N + \cdot Ph,$$

but they were unable to isolate from their reaction product any diphenyl, which, as they thought, should have been produced from the phenyl radicals by dimerization. They established, however, that the phenyl radical was partly converted to benzene and that a little of the triphenylmethyl was converted to triphenylmethane.

In 1934 Hey§ showed that when this same decomposition was allowed to occur in benzene solution, diphenyl was formed in quantity, and that 4-chlorodiphenyl was produced by using chlorobenzene as the solvent. It was, therefore, evident that the free phenyl radicals reacted with the solvent, and did not survive long enough to meet and dimerize. Thus

$$Ph\cdot + C_6H_5Cl \longrightarrow Cl—C_6H_4—Ph + \cdot H$$

is a very rapid reaction. This conclusion has been fully substantiated

† *Ber.* 1897, **30**, 2043; 1903, **36**, 1085; *J.A.C.S.* 1898, **20**, 773.
‡ *Ber.* 1922, **55**, 1816.
§ *J.* 1934, p. 1966.

by Wieland and his collaborators,† who obtained a mixture of methyl-diphenyls by using toluene as solvent and a mixture of phenyl-pyridines by using pyridine as the solvent. Moreover, by carrying out the decomposition in carbon tetrachloride solution, they obtained both chlorobenzene and triphenylmethyl chloride, and also showed that the naphthylazotriphenylmethanes decomposed in the same way.

Acylazotriphenylmethanes, such as acetyl- and benzoylazotriphenylmethane, decompose in a similar manner.‡ Thus when acetylazotriphenylmethane is allowed to decompose in an atmosphere of oxygen both triphenylmethyl peroxide and diacetyl peroxide are formed:

$$CH_3—CO\dot{—}N=N—CPh_3 \longrightarrow CH_3—CO\cdot + N\equiv N + \cdot CPh_3$$

$$\xrightarrow{O_2} CH_3—CO—O—O—CO—CH_3 \qquad \xrightarrow{O_2} Ph_3C—O—O—CPh_3$$

whilst some benzoyl chloride is formed by the decomposition of benzoylazotriphenylmethane in carbon tetrachloride solution.

These investigations of Wieland provided the first experimental evidence for the existence of short-lived aryl and acyl radicals in solution, and in the years 1934 to 1937 his conclusions received ample confirmation from investigations of many other cognate thermal decompositions.

2. Diazo-acetates. Nitrogen is easily eliminated from all aromatic diazo-compounds, but, as explained in Chapter I, it is to be anticipated that free radicals would be produced most easily from those decompositions which can easily be carried out in non-dissociating solvents of low dielectric constant. Consequently it is not surprising that the most conclusive evidence for the production of free aryl radicals in solution has been obtained by the study of the decomposition of benzene-diazoacetate, Ph—N=N—O—$COCH_3$, a substance which can easily be prepared in the pure solid state, and which is readily soluble in most organic solvents.

Benzene-diazoacetate has been prepared by acetylating sodium benzene diazotate with acetic anhydride,§ but it is tautomeric with nitrosoacetanilide,

$$Ph—\underset{\displaystyle COCH_3}{\underset{|}{N}}—N=O \rightleftharpoons Ph—N=N—O—COCH_3,$$

and is easily made by passing nitrous fumes into a solution of acetanilide

† *Annalen*, 1934, **514**, 145. ‡ Wieland *et al.*, ibid. 1927, **452**, 1; 1926, **446**, 31.
§ Pechmann and Frobenius, *Ber.* 1894, **27**, 651; Bamberger, ibid. 1895, **28**, 403; Hantzsch and Wechsler, *Annalen*, 1902, **325**, 226.

in glacial acetic acid† or by adding nitrosyl chloride to a solution of acetanilide in a mixture of acetic acid and acetic anhydride containing potassium acetate.‡ It is a yellow crystalline solid, of melting-point about 50° C., which can be preserved in the cold when dry, but which evolves nitrogen slowly when in solution.

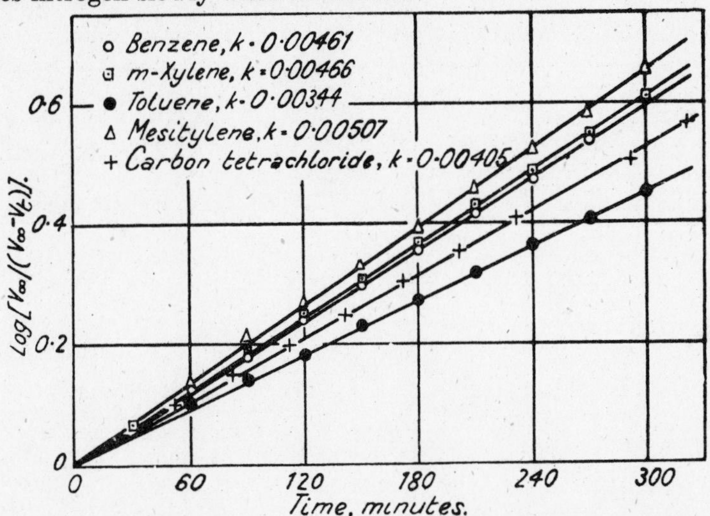

FIG. 21. Rate of decomposition of nitrosoacetanilide in various solvents. (From Grieve and Hey, *J.* 1934, p. 1800.)

In 1934 Grieve and Hey§ showed that benzene-diazoacetate decomposed unimolecularly at a constant rate in a wide range of solvents, such as benzene, toluene, xylene, chlorobenzene, nitrobenzene, anisole, and carbon tetrachloride, and that *para*-substituted diphenyl derivatives could be isolated as products of the decomposition in every aromatic solvent which was examined.

This is shown by Figs. 21 and 22 in which $\log\{V_\infty/(V_\infty - V_t)\}$ is plotted against t, where V_∞ is the final observed volume of nitrogen, measured over alkali, V_t the volume at time t, and k is the unimolecular velocity constant.

It was therefore evident, firstly, that the rate-determining reaction is the unimolecular evolution of nitrogen from benzene-diazoacetate,

$$\mathrm{Ph{-}N{=}N{-}O{-}COCH_3 \longrightarrow Ph\cdot + N_2 + \cdot O{-}COCH_3},$$

a process in which the solvent molecules are not involved, and secondly, that the phenyl radicals produced thereby substitute aromatic solvents of all types in a uniform manner,

$$\mathrm{Ph\cdot + C_6H_5}R \longrightarrow pR\mathrm{{-}C_6H_4{-}Ph + \cdot H},$$

† Grieve and Hey, *J.* 1934, p. 1803.

‡ France, Heilbron, and Hey, ibid. 1940, p. 370.

§ *J.* 1934, p. 1797.

which does not depend upon the polar nature of the substituent *R* already present in the benzene ring. Since the orientation of the product obtained by substituting an aromatic compound either with a cationoid reagent, such as nitric acid or bromine, or with an anionoid reagent such as sodamide in presence of air, depends upon the polar nature of the initial substituent group *R*, there being produced *either* a mixture of the

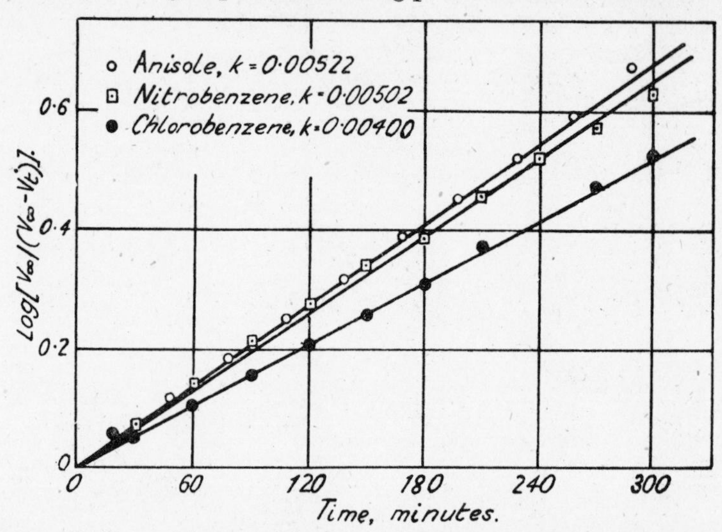

FIG. 22. Rate of decomposition of nitrosoacetanilide in various solvents. (From Grieve and Hey, *J.* 1934, p. 1800.)

ortho- and *para*-disubstituted derivatives, *or* preponderatingly the *meta*-disubstituted derivative as alternative possibilities, it was concluded that the phenyl radicals produced by the initial decomposition of benzene-diazoacetate molecules were non-polar, or in other words, that they behaved as *neutral* organic radicals.†

Confirmation of this deduction was provided in 1937 by Waters,‡ who showed that the aryl radicals liberated from benzene-diazo-acetate had an extraordinary degree of reactivity, similar to that of the free alkyl radicals which had previously been prepared by Paneth and his colleagues (Chapter I). Organic solvents of all types were found to be attacked by the decomposition products of benzene-diazo-acetate. From decompositions in anhydrous *n*-hexane, *cyclo*-hexane, ether, dioxane, acetone, ethyl acetate, acetonitrile, and acetic anhydride the products in each case were *benzene* and acetic acid. Evidently, there-

† For a theoretical, quantum mechanical, discussion of orientation rules for free radical substitution in aromatic nuclei, see Wheland, *J.A.C.S.* 1942, **64**, 900.

‡ Waters, *J.* 1937, p. 113.

fore, both the phenyl and the acetate radicals are capable of abstracting hydrogen from aliphatic substances:

$$Ph\cdot + H{-}R \longrightarrow Ph{-}H + \cdot R,$$

$$CH_3COO\cdot + H{-}R \longrightarrow CH_3COOH + \cdot R.$$

In a similar way halogen atoms were abstracted from solvents such as methyl iodide, bromoform, chloroform, and carbon tetrachloride, and the sulphur atom from carbon disulphide:

$$Ph\cdot + Hal{-}R \longrightarrow Ph{-}Hal + \cdot R,$$

$$Ph\cdot + CS_2 \longrightarrow Ph{-}S{-}S{-}Ph.$$

The decompositions in acetic anhydride, carbon tetrachloride, and carbon disulphide yielded carbon dioxide in quantity. This can only be attributed to the transient formation of the neutral acetate radical, $CH_3COO\cdot$, since an acetate anion, CH_3COO^-, never loses carbon dioxide at room temperature except on discharge at an anode:†

$$\cdot O{-}COCH_3 \longrightarrow CO_2 + \cdot CH_3\ (\rightarrow CH_3{-}CH_3).$$

Moreover, it was shown that, during the decomposition of benzene-diazo-acetate in the non-polar solvents carbon disulphide and carbon tetrachloride, metallic elements may be attacked. Water-soluble salts were produced from zinc, iron, copper, tin, lead, mercury, and antimony. Even in the presence of an excess of chalk, the elements zinc, iron, copper, and lead were attacked, so that the solution of the metal is not to be explained as an attack by acetic acid molecules in presence of air, but must be due to the free neutral acetate radicals.

The reaction with mercury in carbon tetrachloride solution yielded not only mercurous and mercuric salts but also phenyl mercuric chloride, Ph—Hg—Cl. This is decisive evidence for the formation of free phenyl radicals.

Later work by Hey and his colleagues, who have studied a number of aryl diazo-acetates, has fully substantiated the fact that the aryl radicals liberated in these decompositions substitute aromatic ring systems in a uniform manner in which polar orienting forces cannot be operating. In some cases it has been established‡ that hydrogenation of the aryl radical (the normal reaction in aliphatic solvents) can occur simultaneously with the formation of biaryl derivatives:

$$Ar{-}N{=}N{-}OCOCH_3 + H{-}Ph \longrightarrow Ar{-}H + Ph\cdot,$$

$$Ar{-}N{=}N{-}OCOCH_3 + Ph{-}H \longrightarrow Ar{-}Ph + H\cdot.$$

† Compare pp. 142–3.

‡ Haworth and Hey, *J.* 1940, p. 364.

For instance, both diphenyl and *p*-terphenyl are formed when dinitroso-diacetyl-*p*-phenylene diamine,

$$CH_3CO-\underset{\displaystyle NO}{\underset{|}{N}}-C_6H_4-\underset{\displaystyle NO}{\underset{|}{N}}-COCH_3,$$

decomposes in dry benzene, though this replacement of the diazo-acetate (= N-nitroso-acyl) group by hydrogen does not occur to any appreciable extent.

The mono-nitroso derivatives of carbanilide (III) and of diphenyl-guanidine are somewhat anomalous in that they yield both diphenyl and phenyl-*iso*-cyanate, the latter product evidently resulting from the self-stabilization of the free acyl group.

$$Ph-\underset{\displaystyle NO}{\underset{|}{N}}-CO-NH-Ph \rightleftharpoons Ph-N=N-O-CO-NH-Ph \quad \text{(III)}$$

$$Ph-N=N-O-CO-NHPh + C_6H_6 \longrightarrow C_6H_5-C_6H_5 + Ph-NCO + N_2 + H_2O.$$

The reaction of benzene-diazoacetate with pyridine,†

$$C_6H_5-N=N-OCOCH_3 + C_5H_5N \longrightarrow C_6H_5-C_5H_4N + N_2 + CH_3COOH,$$

has special theoretical significance. Phenyl-pyridines are produced in a total yield of about 60 per cent., and the mixture has been shown to contain all three possible (α, β, and γ) isomers. Only neutral phenyl radicals could possibly react in this way. A phenyl cation, Ph^+, would yield a phenyl-pyridinium salt, $C_5H_5N^+-C_6H_5\ X^-$, and even were this pyridinium salt to undergo subsequent molecular rearrangement then there would be formed only the α- and γ-phenyl-pyridines, but no β-phenyl-pyridine.

3. Diazo hydroxides. Diazonium salts in neutral aqueous solution exist in equilibrium with derivatives of benzenediazo hydroxide, which are capable of existing in isomeric forms:

$$\left[\begin{matrix}Ar-N \\ \quad\ \ \| \! | \\ \quad\ \ N\end{matrix}\right]^+ Cl^- + H_2O \rightleftharpoons \left[\begin{matrix}Ar-N \\ \quad\ \ \| \! | \\ \quad\ \ N\end{matrix}\right]^+ OH^- + HCl$$

Diazonium salt — Diazonium hydroxide

$$\underset{\text{sodium-}iso\text{-diazotate}}{\begin{matrix}Ar-N \\ \| \\ N-ONa\end{matrix}} \xleftarrow{NaOH} \underset{anti\text{-diazo hydroxide}}{\begin{matrix}Ar-N \\ \| \\ N-OH\end{matrix}} \rightleftharpoons \underset{syn\text{-diazo hydroxide}}{\begin{matrix}Ar-N \\ \| \\ HO-N\end{matrix}} \xrightarrow{NaOH} \underset{\text{sodium-}normal\text{ diazotate}}{\begin{matrix}Ar-N \\ \| \\ NaO-N\end{matrix}}$$

(The *syn*-diazo hydroxide is in equilibrium ($\downarrow\uparrow$) with the diazonium hydroxide.)

† Haworth, Heilbron, and Hey, *J.* 1940, p. 372.

Of these, the compound with the *syn*-diazo structure was supposed by Hantzsch to be the more unstable, owing to the ease with which it might eliminate a molecule of nitrogen, thus

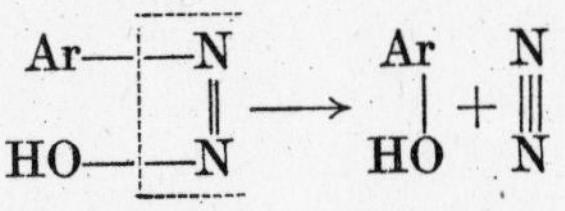

$$\begin{matrix} Ar—N \\ \| \\ HO—N \end{matrix} \longrightarrow \begin{matrix} Ar \\ | \\ HO \end{matrix} + \begin{matrix} N \\ ||| \\ N \end{matrix}$$

As yet, however, the structures that should be assigned to the isomeric diazo-hydroxides, or to their salts the diazotates, have not been established experimentally by physical methods, and in addition to those suggested by Hantzsch (above) two others must be taken into consideration, viz.

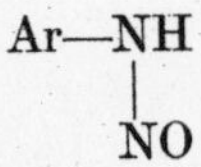

$$\begin{matrix} Ar—NH \\ | \\ NO \end{matrix}$$

due to Bamberger, and

$$\begin{matrix} Ar—\overset{+}{N}—\overset{-}{O} \\ \| \\ NH \end{matrix}$$

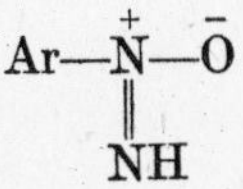

due to Angeli.†

In 1924 Gomberg and his colleagues‡ discovered that the diazo-hydroxides could be used for the preparation of unsymmetrically substituted biaryls, $XC_6H_4—C_6H_4Y$. They stirred a neutral aromatic liquid, such as benzene or nitrobenzene, with a cold concentrated diazonium salt solution, which they then neutralized with caustic soda. When the aqueous solution became alkaline, nitrogen was evolved, and there was formed, in the non-aqueous layer, a diphenyl derivative:

$$Ar—N_2—OH + C_6H_5R \longrightarrow Ar—C_6H_4R + N_2 + H_2O.$$

The success of the reaction depends upon the ability of the non-aqueous aromatic liquid to extract from the watery layer the *covalent* diazo-hydroxide as fast as it is formed. Since the diazo-hydroxides are very weak acids their sodium salts are hydrolysed to a considerable extent in alkaline solution, but in acid solution diazonium salts are formed. These do not hydrolyse appreciably for they are ammonium salts. Consequently reactions involving diazo-hydroxides take place only under alkaline, or well-buffered conditions.

When biaryl derivatives are made by the Gomberg reaction from an aromatic liquid C_6H_5R, the ordinary laws which govern aromatic

† For a review see Hodgson and Marsden, *J.* 1945, p. 207.

‡ Gomberg and Bachmann, *J.A.C.S.* 1924, **46**, 2339; Gomberg and Pernert, ibid. 1926, **48**, 1372.

substitution are not obeyed, for *ortho-* and *para*-substitution occurs irrespective of the nature of the 'directing group' R. For example, reaction between benzenediazo-hydroxide and nitrobenzene yields 4-nitrodiphenyl. A similar result had been obtained many years before by Kühling† and by Kliegl and Huber,‡ who worked with solid sodium and potassium diazotates. Hey and his colleagues§ have pointed out that, as too in the case of the diazo-acetates, this is indicative of substitution in the aromatic liquid by an electrically neutral aryl radical. Waters‖ has substantiated this conclusion by showing that benzenediazo-hydroxide can abstract hydrogen from aliphatic liquids and that it reacts with carbon disulphide to give diphenyl disulphide, whilst Hey has shown that it reacts with carbon tetrachloride to give chlorobenzene.

Hey's extension of the Gomberg reaction has proved to be of great synthetic value for effecting the union of aryl nuclei.¶ Phenylnaphthalenes have been made by Hey and Lawton†† by decomposing nitroso-acetyl-naphthalides in benzene, whilst the same reaction when carried out in naphthoic esters affords an easy route to the synthesis of dibenzofluorenones of carcinogenic interest.‡‡ An isomer of the drug cannabinol, found in hashish, has been made by a similar method.§§

Pyridyl-quinolines of known structure can be made by decomposing the diazo-hydroxides of aminoquinolines in pyridine solution, or alternatively by preparing nitrophenyl-pyridines by Hey's method from a diazo-hydroxide in pyridine, reducing the nitro group and then carrying out a Skraup reaction.‖‖ Aminophenyl-pyridines are also useful starting materials for the synthesis of pyridyl-acridines and other complex heterocyclic compounds of therapeutic interest.¶¶

Again pyridyl-phthalocyanines can be made both from amino-phthalocyanines and from 4-aminophthalonitrile by decomposing their diazo-hydroxides in pyridine.††† These are bright green, and can give rise to water-soluble quaternary salts which, unlike blue phthalocyanine which is a most insoluble pigment, are useful dyestuffs for cotton and viscose fibres.

† *Ber.* 1895, **28**, 41; 1896, **29**, 165.
‡ Ibid. 1920, **53**, 1646.
§ *J.* 1932, pp. 1888, 2245; 1934, pp. 1797, 1966.
‖ Ibid. 1937, p. 2014. Compare Jolles, *Atti Accad. Lincei*, 1932, **15**, 292.
¶ For a review see *Organic Reactions*, vol. ii, chapter vi (edited by Roger Adams, New York, 1944).
†† Hey and Lawton, *J.* 1940, p. 374.
‡‡ Swain and Todd, ibid. 1941, p. 674.
§§ Ibid. 1940, p. 1118.
‖‖ Hey, Cook, Heilbron, *et al.*, ibid. 1943, pp. 401, 403, 406.
¶¶ Cook, Heilbron, and Spinks, ibid. 1943, p. 417.
††† Hey *et al.*, U.S.P. 2277629; *J.* 1945, 409.

Elks and Hey† have shown that 1-aryl-3:3-dimethyltriazens, $Ar{-}N{=}N{-}N(CH_3)_2$, which are easily prepared by adding an aqueous solution of a diazotized aromatic base to aqueous dimethylamine in the presence of sodium carbonate, are stable compounds insoluble in water but soluble in organic solvents. Their solutions in hot aromatic solvents can easily be decomposed by leading in dry hydrogen chloride, when nitrogen is evolved and unsymmetrical diaryls are formed in good yields. This method of preparing a stabilized derivative of a diazo-hydroxide and then decomposing it in an aromatic solvent is obviously capable of many extensions, and many forms of stabilized diazo compounds are known products of technical value to the dyestuffs industry.‡ From the triazens instanced above the active agent is probably a covalent diazo-chloride (see later, pp. 156–62):

$$Ar{-}N{=}N{-}N(CH_3)_2 + 2HCl \longrightarrow Ar{-}N{=}N{-}Cl + (CH_3)_2\overset{+}{N}H_2Cl.$$

4. Diazo-cyanides are the only aromatic diazo-compounds which have received detailed physical examination. Dipole moment measurement§ shows that the stable isomeride is the *anti*-diazocyanide (IV), and that the labile isomeride is the *syn*-diazocyanide (V). This has been confirmed by studies of infra red spectra,|| and magnetic properties,¶ which show that the *iso*-cyanide structure (VI) is not a possible alternative for any known labile isomerides.

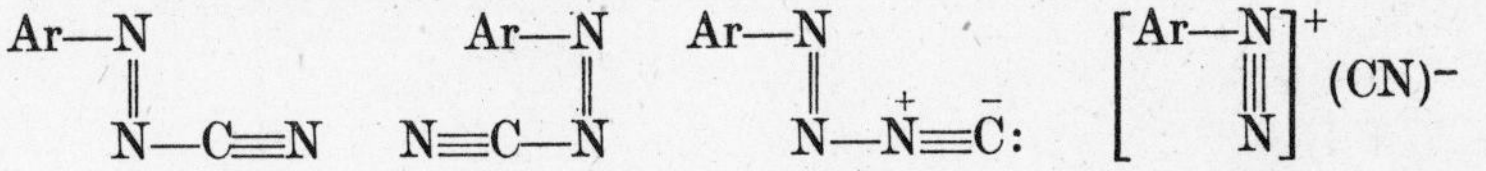

$$\begin{array}{cccc} \begin{array}{l} Ar{-}N \\ \quad\| \\ \quad N{-}C{\equiv}N \end{array} & \begin{array}{r} Ar{-}N \\ \| \\ N{\equiv}C{-}N \end{array} & \begin{array}{l} Ar{-}N \\ \quad\| \\ \quad N{-}\overset{+}{N}{\equiv}\overset{-}{C}: \end{array} & \left[\begin{array}{r} Ar{-}N \\ ||| \\ N \end{array}\right]^{+}(CN)^{-} \\ (IV) & (V) & (VI) & (VII) \end{array}$$

The *anti*-diazocyanides are red crystalline substances, analogous to stable *trans*-azobenzene, and do not liberate nitrogen on keeping, but the (*syn*)-diazocyanides can easily be decomposed. Their reactions have been studied by Stephenson and Waters,†† who showed that decompositions in non-ionizing solvents were catalysed by copper powder and appeared to involve the production of both free aryl and free cyanide radicals, since reactions typical of the diazo-acetates occur in solutions in ether, benzene, and carbon tetrachloride.

In ionizing solvents the mechanism of decomposition is complicated by the fact that some tautomerization to diazonium cyanides, (VII),

† Elks and Hey, *J.* 1943, p. 441.

‡ Compare Saunders, *The Aromatic Diazo-compounds*, chapter ii (Arnold, London, 1936).

§ Le Fèvre and Vine, *J.* 1938, p. 431.

|| Anderson, Le Fèvre, and Savage, ibid. 1947, p. 445; Sheppard and Sutherland, ibid. 1947, p. 453.

¶ Anderson, Bedwell, and Le Fèvre, ibid. 1947, p. 457.

†† Stephenson and Waters, ibid. 1939, p. 1796.

occurs. Even the *syn*-diazocyanides appear to be much more stable than the diazo-acetates, and this can be attributed to intramolecular resonance between the N=N and C≡N groups.

Since it was shown conclusively that, on decomposition, the *syn*-diazocyanides reacted with the surrounding solvent molecules, Hantzsch's theory for their decomposition, involving the liberation of nitrogen followed *immediately* by the union of the vicinal radicals left thereby cannot be correct. The radicals Ar· and ·CN, when liberated must have a sufficiently long free life to intermingle with solvent molecules.

5. Diazonium chlorides. The aromatic diazo compounds react with mineral acids to form diazonium salts, $(Ar—N_2)^+ X^-$, which are structurally analogous to ammonium chloride, and markedly different both in physical and in chemical properties from the covalent diazo-compounds, Ar—N=N—X, which have been considered in sections 2–4 above.

Free neutral radicals are not, in general,† produced in acidic aqueous solutions of aromatic diazo-compounds, but their formation does seem to be possible in certain non-aqueous solvents in which ionic dissociation is less favoured.

In 1926 Pray‡ found that dry benzenediazonium chloride decomposed in a whole series of aliphatic alcohols at an identical rate, although two different types of overall reaction occurred, viz.

$$C_6H_5N_2Cl + CH_3OH \longrightarrow C_6H_5—OCH_3 + N_2 + HCl,$$
$$C_6H_5N_2Cl + C_2H_5OH \longrightarrow C_6H_6 + CH_3CHO + N_2 + HCl.$$

As Hey first pointed out, this indicates that the rate-determining stage of the decomposition is independent of the solvent, and therefore is probably the elimination of nitrogen from a molecular form of benzenediazonium chloride. This supposition was followed up by Waters,§ who found that decomposition of the free radical type occurred in alcohol, acetone, ethyl acetate, acetonitrile, and, to a limited extent, in ether, in each of which liquids benzenediazonium chloride had some slight solubility.

Waring and Abrams|| have developed Pray's work by carrying out more detailed kinetic studies of the rate of decomposition of benzenediazonium chloride in a number of aliphatic alcohols, and have confirmed that the decomposition process is invariably a unimolecular

† See, however, Waters, *J.* 1942, p. 266. ‡ *J. Phys. Chem.* 1926, **30**, 1477.

§ *J.* 1937, p. 2007; 1938, p. 1077; 1939, p. 864; Hanby and Waters, ibid. 1939, p. 1792. || Waring and Abrams, *J.A.C.S.* 1941, **63**, 2757.

reaction. Curiously enough, though the overall reaction velocity constant, $k = PZe^{-E/RT}$, is constant, both the activation energies E and the collision constants PZ vary from alcohol to alcohol. This compensating effect must be due to the way in which the dissociable benzenediazonium chloride molecules gain the necessary activation energy by solvent collisions.

Decompositions of benzenediazonium chloride under benzene or carbon tetrachloride,† in which the salt appears to be quite insoluble, are uncontrollable, but resemble the thermal decompositions of solid diazonium chlorides, and of double salts such as $2PhN_2Cl,PtCl_4$, which have been studied by Griess‡ and later by Schwechten.§ The chief product is the corresponding aryl chloride.

Some of the decomposition reactions studied by Waters were strikingly novel, and their special character was made more evident by adding chalk in excess so as to keep the reaction mixture neutral throughout.

The reaction in acetone was as follows:

$$C_6H_5—N_2—Cl + CH_3—CO—CH_3 \longrightarrow C_6H_5—H + Cl—CH_2—CO—CH_3 + N_2;$$

the phenyl group was hydrogenated, whilst the acetone was chlorinated. Evidently, therefore, the benzenediazonium chloride did not react in the form of a salt, containing the inert chloride anion, but in the form of a compound containing covalent chlorine, such as a N-chloro-amine, or, more probably, by production of phenyl radicals and of free reactive chlorine atoms.

Ethyl acetate and diethyl ether were both degraded to acetaldehyde, so they too presumably undergo initial chlorination:

$$C_6H_5—N_2—Cl + CH_3—CH_2—O—COCH_3 \longrightarrow C_6H_5—H + CH_3—CHCl—O—COCH_3,$$

$$CH_3—CHCl—O—COCH_3 + H_2O \longrightarrow CH_3CHO + HCl + HO—COCH_3,$$

$$C_6H_5—N_2—Cl + CH_3—CH_2—OC_2H_5 \longrightarrow C_6H_5—H + CH_3—CHCl—OC_2H_5,$$

$$CH_3—CHCl—OC_2H_5 + H_2O \longrightarrow CH_3CHO + HCl + HOC_2H_5.$$

In all probability the oxidation of alcohols to aldehydes by diazonium salts, which are thereby reduced to aromatic hydrocarbons, involves a similar chlorination at an α-hydrogen atom of the carbinol group.

† Waters, *J.* 1937, p. 2007.
‡ Griess, *Annalen*, 1866, **137**, 52.
§ Schwechten, *Ber.* 1932, **65**, 1605.

By investigating the decomposition of solid aryl-diazonium chlorides under acetonitrile, Hanby and Waters† obtained some evidence of the addition of radicals to the CN group, since anilides could be isolated from the reaction products in up to 10 per cent. yield. The reaction may be formulated as

$$\mathrm{Ar\cdot + \cdot Cl + CH_3{-}CN \longrightarrow CH_3{-}CCl{=}N{-}Ar},$$
$$\mathrm{CH_3{-}CCl{=}N{-}Ar + H_2O \longrightarrow CH_3{-}CO{-}NH{-}Ar + HCl}.$$

Similar addition reactions have been described by Meerwein, Büchner, and Van Emster,‡ who found that aromatic diazonium chlorides in aqueous acetone, acetonitrile, or pyridine will add on to $\alpha\beta$ unsaturated compounds such as coumarin, methyl cinnamate, and methyl fumarate, but that the reaction does not occur in other solvents, such as alcohol or dioxane. The products easily lose hydrogen chloride, forming an unsaturated compound containing an aryl substituent in the α-position to the original carbonyl, or similar group; thus

$$\mathrm{C_6H_5{-}CH{=}CH{-}COOCH_3 + ClC_6H_4{-}N_2Cl}$$
$$\longrightarrow \mathrm{C_6H_5{-}\underset{}{CH(Cl)}{-}CH(C_6H_4Cl){-}COOCH_3 + N_2}$$
$$\longrightarrow \mathrm{C_6H_5{-}CH{=}C(C_6H_4Cl){-}COOCH_3 + HCl}$$

The yield of the addition product is increased by the addition of sodium acetate, or other buffer salt, and consequently a covalent diazo-acetate (section 2 above), diazo-hydroxide, or diazo-halide, may be the active agent.

It is significant that the addition only takes place when diazonium chlorides or diazonium bromides are used. Their sulphates and nitrates do not act in this way. Cupric salts strongly catalyse the reaction, but cuprous salts have scarcely any catalytic effect.

Meerwein and his colleagues consider that the reaction is a polar coupling process, in which the direction of addition is controlled by the ester, carbonyl, or nitrile group, as in the Michael reaction

$$\mathrm{Ph{-}\overset{\delta+}{CH}{=}\overset{\delta-}{CH}{-}\overset{\delta+}{C}({=}\overset{\delta-}{O}){-}OEt} \;\; (\overset{-}{Cl} \rightarrow \overset{\delta+}{CH};\; \overset{+}{N}{=}N{-}Ph \rightarrow \overset{\delta-}{CH}) \longrightarrow \mathrm{Ph{-}CH(Cl){-}CH(N{=}N{-}Ph){-}CO{-}OEt}$$

† *J.* 1939, p. 1792.

‡ *J. prakt. Chem.* 1939, (ii) **152**, 237.

followed by elimination of nitrogen, as occurs in many cases of addition of diazomethane to olefines:

$$\text{Ph—CH(Cl)—CH(N=N—Ph)—CO—OEt} \longrightarrow \text{Ph—CH(Cl)—CH(Ph)—CO—OEt} + N_2$$

and suggested that the direct phenylation of quinones by diazonium salts, discovered by Kvalnes,† was another reaction of the same type:

$$\text{O=C}\lt\text{(CH=CH)}_2\gt\text{C=O} + PhN_2Cl \longrightarrow \text{O=C}\lt\text{(CH=C(Ph))(CH=CH)}\gt\text{C=O} + N_2 + HCl \longrightarrow \text{HO—C}\lt\text{(C(Ph)=CH)(CH=CH)}\gt\text{C—OH}$$

More recently, however, Koelsch‡ showed that benzenediazonium chloride, in a buffered acetone solution containing a little cupric chloride, added on to acrylonitrile to give α-chloro-dihydrocinnamonitrile (VIII), in which the phenyl group is in the β-position to the nitrile group:

$$CH_2\text{=CH—CN} + \text{Ph—N=N—Cl} \longrightarrow CH_2\text{(Ph)—CH(Cl)—CN} + N_2$$

(VIII)

and subsequently Koelsch and Boekelheide§ found that aryl diazonium chlorides add on to crotonic acid and its esters to give the β-aryl derivatives, though with cinnamates the α-aryl derivatives are formed:

$$CH_3\text{—CH=CH—COOH} + \text{Ph—}N_2\text{—Cl} \longrightarrow CH_3\text{—CH(Ph)—CH(Cl)—COOH} + N_2$$

$$\text{Ph—CH=CH—COOEt} + \text{Ar—}N_2\text{—Cl} \longrightarrow \text{Ph—CH(Cl)—CH(Ph)—COOEt} + N_2$$

whilst cinnamalacetic acid gave a 1:4-addition product:

$$\text{Ph—CH=CH—CH=CH—COOH} + \text{Cl—N=N—Ph} \longrightarrow \text{Ph—CH(Cl)—CH=CH—CH(Ph)—COOH}$$

$$\longrightarrow \text{Ph—CH=CH—CH=CH—Ph}$$

† Kvalnes, *J.A.C.S.* 1934, **56**, 2478.
‡ Koelsch, ibid. 1943, **65**, 57.
§ Koelsch and Boekelheide, ibid. 1944, **66**, 412.

They point out that this reversal in the mode of addition to unsaturated acids does not accord with a polar reaction, but is strongly indicative of the presence of *neutral* aryl radicals, for the following reason:

Addition of a neutral aryl group to acrylonitrile, or any similar $\alpha\beta$ unsaturated aliphatic compound, can give either (IX) or (X):

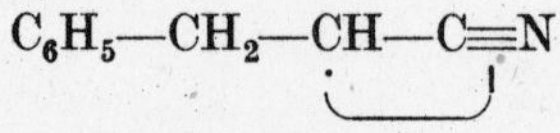

$$C_6H_5—CH_2—\dot{C}H—C{\equiv}N \qquad (IX)$$

$$\cdot CH_2—CH(C{\equiv}N)(C_6H_5) \qquad (X)$$

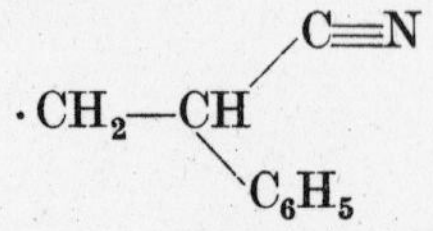

Of these two radicals (IX), but not (X), is internally stabilized by resonance of the odd electron with the adjacent unsaturated C≡N group. Consequently (IX) will have the lower energy content, and will therefore be the more easily formed. In the case of addition to cinnamic acid, however, the alternative radicals are (XI) and (XII),

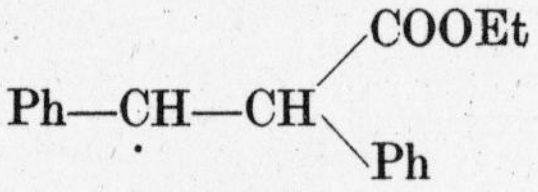

$$Ph—\dot{C}H—CH(COOEt)(Ph) \qquad (XI)$$

$$(Ph)_2CH—\dot{C}H—COOEt \qquad (XII)$$

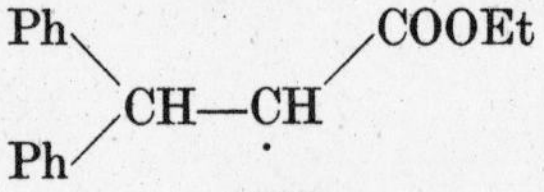

of which (XI) will be the more stable, since mesomerism of the odd electron with the aromatic ring can occur, as in the case of the benzyl radical (p. 146).

Further, Koelsch suggests that the function of the cupric salt is to abstract *one* electron from the radical formed by the addition of the aryl group, leaving a cation to which a halide or acetate anion might subsequently become attached:

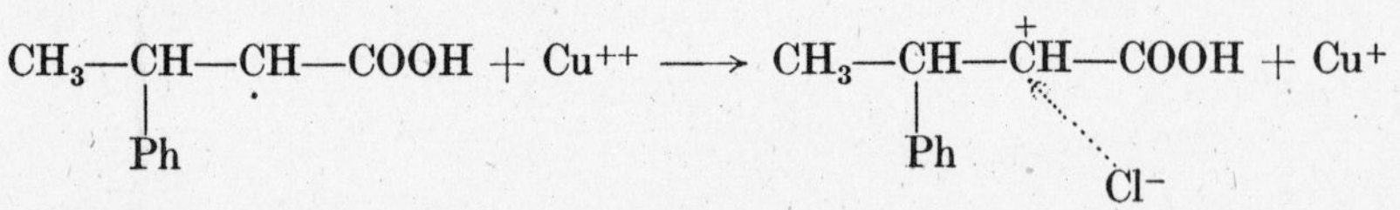

$$CH_3—CH(Ph)—\dot{C}H—COOH + Cu^{++} \longrightarrow CH_3—CH(Ph)—\overset{+}{C}H—COOH + Cu^{+} \quad (\cdots Cl^{-})$$

The chlorine atom liberated by the initial dissociation of the diazo-chloride will then reoxidize the cuprous ion. This catalytic effect is comparable with that suggested by Waters for the mechanism of the Sandmeyer reaction (p. 163).

In contrast to this addition of diazonium chlorides to unsaturated acids, Waters in 1939† found that both benzene-diazoacetate and benzene

† Waters, *J.* 1939, p. 1805.

diazonium chloride in acetone substitute *cyclo*-hexene in the α-position, adjacent to the double bond:

$$\text{Ph—N=N—O—COCH}_3 + \begin{array}{c} \text{CH}_2 \\ \text{CH} \quad \text{CH}_2 \\ \| \qquad | \\ \text{CH} \quad \text{CH}_2 \\ \text{CH}_2 \end{array} \longrightarrow \begin{array}{c} \text{CH}_3\text{CO—O} \\ \text{CH} \\ \text{CH} \quad \text{CH}_2 \\ \| \qquad | \\ \text{CH} \quad \text{CH}_2 \\ \text{CH}_2 \end{array}$$

giving Δ^2-*cyclo*-hexenyl acetate and Δ^2-*cyclo*-hexenyl chloride respectively. Whilst this reaction may be explained as an addition and elimination process, subsequent investigations by Farmer and Michael† (p. 168) indicate that this reaction is a direct substitution in the α-methylene position by a free neutral radical.

The most remarkable feature of the decomposition of aryl-diazonium chlorides in solvents such as acetone and ethyl acetate is the fact that most metals, such as zinc, copper, mercury, antimony, silver, and even gold can be attacked by the reacting mixture, even when an excess of chalk has been added to prevent the production of any free acid.‡ Metallic chlorides are formed, and in many cases organo-metallic compounds also. Consequently new syntheses have been developed for the production of aromatic derivatives of mercury, antimony, arsenic, and tellurium.§ These reactions are explicable only on the assumption that the diazonium chlorides eliminate nitrogen and yield two active radicals:

$$ArN_2Cl \longrightarrow Ar\cdot + N_2 + \cdot Cl.$$

The production of organo-metallic compounds indicates the presence of active aryl groups, whilst the formation of chlorides from metals such as silver and gold indicates the production of the extremely reactive atomic form of chlorine, and not the inert chloride anion.

Obviously by using massive solid metals the optimum yields of organo-metallic compounds cannot be obtained, and finely pulverized metals, or still better free metals, formed by reduction *in situ* should be employed. Nesmejanow, Kozeschkow, and Klimowa‖ have shown that by reduction of a metallic double salt of a diazonium chloride with tin, copper powder, or stannous chloride, aryl derivatives of tin (Ar_2SnCl_2) and lead (Ar_2PbCl_2, Ar_3PbCl) can be produced, e.g.

$$(ArN_2Cl)_2,SnCl_4 + Sn \longrightarrow Ar_2SnCl_2 + SnCl_4 + 2N_2,$$

† Farmer and Michael, *J.* 1942, p. 513.
‡ Waters, ibid. 1937, p. 2007; 1939, p. 864.
§ Ibid. 1937, p. 2007; 1938, pp. 843, 1077; 1939, p. 867.
‖ *Ber.* 1935, **68**, 1877; *J. Gen. Chem. Russia*, 1936, **6**, 164.

whilst Gilman† has applied the same reaction in the preparation of organo-bismuth compounds of the types Ar_2BiCl and $ArBiCl_2$. The production of mercury diaryls by this process was discovered by Nesmejanow in 1929:‡

$$2ArN_2Cl,HgCl_2 + 6Cu \longrightarrow Ar_2Hg + 2N_2 + 3Cu_2Cl_2.$$

All these reactions can be carried out most efficiently in organic solvents and do not occur in water. Naturally the reaction conditions vary somewhat, and acetone, ethyl acetate, and alcohol have been found to give optimum yields according to the exact process involved.

The Sandmeyer Reaction

Free radical mechanisms for many reactions of diazonium chlorides have been illustrated above, but it is erroneous to infer therefrom that all non-aqueous reactions of diazo-compounds are necessarily of this same type. In many organic solvents (e.g. acetic acid) the reactions of diazonium compounds are, like the majority of those in water, reactions of diazonium cations, $(ArN_2)^+$, and not those of neutral radicals or of unionized ArN_2Cl molecules.

A survey of the decomposition reactions of aromatic diazo-compounds in aqueous solution§ indicates that three distinct types of reaction processes are known.

Type I: Decompositions in acid solution, leading to the formation of phenols:

$$ArN_2X + H_2O = Ar—OH + N_2 + H—X.$$

These are undoubtedly decompositions of diazonium cations, $(ArN_2)^+$, since it has been shown that the rate of evolution of nitrogen is independent of the nature of the radical X.||

Type II: Non-ionic decompositions of aryl diazo-hydroxides, which are present in neutral and slightly alkaline solutions. These have been considered in section 3 above. Heilbron and Hey and their co-workers have shown that reactions in aqueous pyridine are of this type.¶

Type III: Reactions such as $ArN_2Halogen \rightarrow Ar—Halogen + N_2$ *which usually need a special catalyst*, such as a cuprous salt (*Sandmeyer reaction*) or metallic copper (*Gattermann reaction*). Two alternative interpretations of the mechanism of the Sandmeyer reaction have been

† *J.A.C.S.* 1939, **61**, 3586; 1941, **63**, 949.
‡ *Ber.* 1929, **62**, 1010, 1018.
§ Waters, *J.* 1942, p. 266.
|| Cain, *Ber.* 1905, **38**, 2511; Cain and Nicoll, *J.* 1902, **81**, 1412; 1903, **83**, 206, 470; Moelwyn-Hughes and Johnson, *Trans. Faraday Soc.* 1940, **36**, 948.
¶ *J.* 1940, pp. 349, 358.

put forward, though it is probable that the essential features of both hypotheses should be incorporated in any complete explanation of these important preparative processes.

(*a*) Hodgson and his colleagues† have suggested that Sandmeyer reactions are ionic reactions (Type I) of complex double salts, and that the high yields of aryl halides are attributable to their stability, and to the high local halide concentrations of their complex anions, e.g. (Cu_2Cl_4), whereby the competing action of water molecules can become negligible. This is a rational explanation in view of the fact that good yields (over 60 per cent.) of aryl chlorides can be obtained by decomposing diazonium chlorides both in concentrated hydrochloric acid‡ and in concentrated aqueous solutions of many metallic chlorides.† On the other hand, it is difficult to understand why the cuprous halides should be so much more efficient than those of other metals in dilute solution or in weak acid, and why metallic copper, but not other metals, should again be an efficient catalyst in the analogous Gattermann reaction.

The view that double salt formation is involved is substantiated by the fact that complex diazonium cobaltinitrites when decomposed in the presence of copper salts give good yields of aromatic nitro-compounds,§ whilst excellent yields of aromatic nitriles are obtainable by decomposing nickel diazonium cyanides even without addition of any copper compound.||

(*b*) Waters¶ has suggested that both the Sandmeyer and the Gattermann reactions are non-ionic decompositions of diazonium cations brought about by a single-electron transference from a catalyst, and that several analogous reactions are of the same character. It is suggested that the following cyclic electron transference occurs:

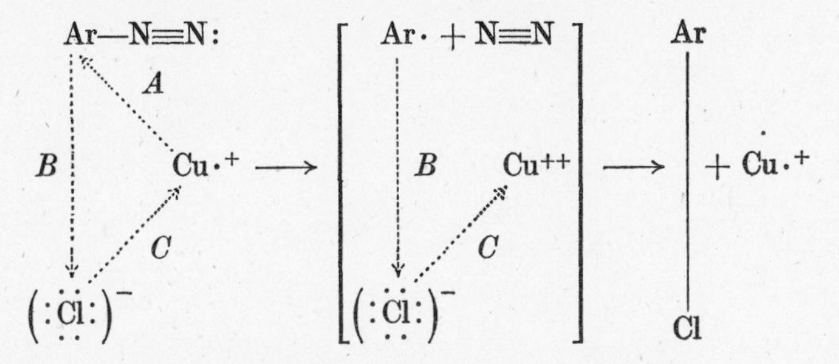

† Hodgson, Birtwell, and Walker, *J.* 1941, p. 770; 1942, p. 720; 1944, p. 18; Hodgson and Sibbald, ibid. 1944, p. 394; *Chem. Reviews*, 1947, **40**, 251.

‡ Hantzsch, *Ber.* 1900, **33**, 2525.

§ Hodgson and Marsden, *J.* 1944, p. 22.

|| Korczynski and Fandrich, *Compt. rend.* 1926, **183**, 421; Korczynski, Mrozinski, and Vielau, ibid. 1920, **171**, 182.

¶ Waters, *J.* 1942, p. 266.

In the initial phase (*A*) an electron from the cuprous cation converts the diazonium cation to a neutral aryl radical and molecular nitrogen:

$$Cu\cdot^{+} \longrightarrow Cu^{++} + e,$$
$$(Ar{:}N{:}{:}{:}N{:})^{+} + e \longrightarrow Ar\cdot + {:}N{:}{:}{:}N{:}$$

then, in phase (*B*), the aryl radical reacts with the adjacent halogen anion to give an aryl halide molecule, thereby setting free another electron, which can at once be picked up (*C*) by the cupric cation resulting from reaction (*A*):

$$Ar\cdot + (Cl)^{-} \longrightarrow Ar{-}Cl + e,$$
$$e + Cu^{++} \longrightarrow Cu\cdot^{+}.$$

In the Gattermann reaction, metallic copper is thought to act as the primary electron source.

The single-electron transfer mechanism, which may well occur intramolecularly within the molecule of a double salt, does explain why cuprous salts are almost unique in promoting the Sandmeyer reaction in solutions of moderate concentration. Metallic cations of constant valency, such as Na^{+}, Ca^{++}, Al^{+++}, cannot act as electron sources, and, without initial partial reduction (phase *C*), neither can cations in their highest state of oxidation, such as Fe^{+++}, Cu^{++}, Au^{+++}, and Pt^{++++}. Moreover, the oxidation potential for the release of an electron from the cation of any other of the transition elements is far too high for the change to occur easily in acid media, as the following figures indicate:

contrast	$Mn^{++} \longrightarrow Mn^{+++}$	oxidation potential about $+1{\cdot}5$ volts
	$Ni^{++} \longrightarrow Ni^{+++}$	,, ,, very high
	$Co^{++} \longrightarrow Co^{+++}$	,, ,, about $+1{\cdot}8$ volts
	$Fe^{++} \longrightarrow Fe^{+++}$	,, ,, ,, $+0{\cdot}75$ volt
with	$Cu^{+} \longrightarrow Cu^{++}$	,, ,, ,, $+0{\cdot}2$ volt
and	$Cu^{0} \longrightarrow Cu^{+}$	,, ,, ,, $-0{\cdot}13$ volt

The stannous cation (oxidation potential *c.* $-0{\cdot}4$ volt) is too powerful a reducing agent in acid solution, and converts diazonium cations into aryl-hydrazines. As^{+++} and Sb^{+++} are too feeble reducing agents in acid solution, but in neutral solution they do react with aromatic diazo-compounds and undergo a valency change. The Bart and Schmidt reactions,

$$ArN_2OH + Na_2HAsO_3 \longrightarrow Ar{-}AsO(ONa)_2 + N_2 + H_2O,$$
$$ArN_2OH + ArAs{=}O \longrightarrow Ar_2AsO(OH) + N_2,$$
$$ArN_2OH + Na_2HSbO_3 \longrightarrow Ar{-}SbO(ONa)_2 + N_2 + H_2O,$$

which occur under these circumstances are most probably non-polar reactions of the diazo-hydroxides (Type II reactions).

It is significant that these reactions, and all analogues of the Sandmeyer reaction which can be effected without the use of a copper salt, involve ions having oxidation/reduction potentials of very closely similar values, so that the energy requirements for the cyclic reaction processes will all be very much the same. Thus the replacement of the diazo group by iodine can be represented by the cyclic sequence (XIII).

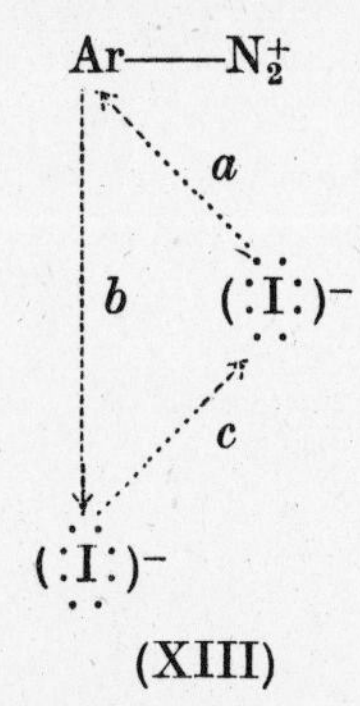

(XIII)

It is facilitated by the presence of free iodine or of copper salts. The decompositions of diazonium perbromides, and the reactions of diazo-compounds with thiols, xanthates, and dithiocarbamates are probably similar, involving, in the latter instance, thiol radicals R—S· (compare pp. 188–9).

The fact that symmetrical di-aryls, and azo-compounds, are often formed as side-products in Sandmeyer and Gattermann reactions is in full accord with the radical mechanism given above, for these substances are obvious products of dimerization of free neutral radicals. As would be expected, the diaryls are formed in high yield when cuprous salts are added gradually to aqueous solutions of diazonium salts, whereas aryl halides are best made by adding diazonium salts to solutions of the cuprous halides.†

The Pschorr reaction‡ for preparing phenanthrene derivatives from *o*-amino-α-phenyl-cinnamic acids is of this type, and has obvious similarities with the non-ionic decompositions of the diazo-hydroxides.

Decompositions of Diaroyl Peroxides, Ar—CO—O—O—CO—Ar

Dibenzoyl peroxide, like other diacyl peroxides (pp. 138–40), decomposes, often explosively, when heated or when exposed to ultra-violet

‡ Compare Saunders and Waters, *J.* 1946, p. 1154.
† Pschorr, *Ber.* 1898, **29**, 496.

light, liberating the simple stable molecule carbon dioxide. Its self-decomposition can be expressed by the equations:

$$\text{Ph—CO—O—O—CO—Ph} \longrightarrow \text{Ph—Ph} + 2CO_2,$$
$$\text{Ph—CO—O—O—CO—Ph} \longrightarrow \text{Ph—CO—O—Ph} + CO_2;$$

the chief product is diphenyl, but some phenyl benzoate and a little benzene are also formed.†

The decompositions of all diacyl peroxides in solution are more complex, since reactions with solvent molecules are involved. Thus the decomposition of dibenzoyl peroxide in boiling benzene gives carbon dioxide, diphenyl, and benzoic acid, together with smaller quantities of phenyl benzoate, terphenyl, and quaterphenyl.‡ Its decomposition in toluene solution yields a mixture of 2- and 4-methyl-diphenyls, in chlorobenzene 4-chlorodiphenyl is produced, in nitrobenzene a mixture of 2- and 4-nitrodiphenyls, and in ethyl benzoate a mixture of the 2-, 3-, and 4-carboxylic esters of diphenyl.§ Moreover, a mixture of α-, β-, and γ-phenyl-pyridines results from the decomposition of dibenzoyl peroxide in pyridine solution.|| Substitution derivatives of dibenzoyl peroxide act similarly.¶

The formal resemblance between these reactions and those of benzenediazo-acetate (pp. 148–52) or benzenediazo-hydroxide (pp. 152–5) is so close that the initial decomposition processes are evidently reactions of similar types. Just as benzenediazo-acetate eliminates the very stable molecule nitrogen and leaves free phenyl and acetate radicals, so dibenzoyl peroxide eliminates the stable molecule carbon dioxide and leaves free phenyl and benzoate radicals, the reaction probably occurring in two stages, of which (ii) may be the more rapid:

$$\text{Ph—CO—O—O—CO—Ph} \longrightarrow \text{Ph}\cdot + CO_2 + \cdot\text{O—CO—Ph}, \qquad \text{(i)}$$
$$\text{Ph—CO—O}\cdot \longrightarrow \text{Ph}\cdot + CO_2. \qquad \text{(ii)}$$

The free radicals, by subsequent reactions with each other, or with solvent molecules, then give rise to stable final products such as hydrocarbons, acids, and esters, by three main reactions:††

$$\text{Ar}\cdot + C_6H_5X \longrightarrow \text{Ar—}C_6H_4X + \cdot\text{H}, \qquad \text{(iii)}$$
$$\text{Ar}\cdot + \text{H—R} \longrightarrow \text{Ar—H} + \cdot\text{R}, \qquad \text{(iv)}$$
$$\text{Ar—CO—O}\cdot + C_6H_5X \longrightarrow \text{Ar—CO—O—H} + \cdot C_6H_4X. \qquad \text{(v)}$$

† Erlenmeyer and Schoenauer, *Helv. Chim. Acta*, 1936, **19**, 338.

‡ Gelissen and Hermans, *Ber.* 1925, **58**, 285.

§ Hey, *J.* 1934, p. 1966; Wieland, Schapiro, and Metzger, *Annalen*, 1934, **513**, 93.

|| Overhoff and Tilman, *Rec. trav. chim.* 1929, **48**, 993; Hey, *Annual Reports of the Chemical Society*, 1940, **37**, 283. ¶ Gelissen and Hermans, *Ber.* 1925, **58**, 285, 476, 764; Wieland and Razuvaiev, *Annalen*, 1930, **480**, 157. †† For a fuller discussion see Hey and Waters, *Chemical Reviews*, 1937, **21**, 186. For kinetic studies see Nozaki and Bartlett, *J.A.C.S.* 1946, **68**, 1686.

Whilst the aryl radicals produced from diaroyl peroxides react with aromatic solvents chiefly by process (iii), as evidenced above, reaction (iv) occurs preferentially in all aliphatic solvents. The radicals (H·, R·) produced from the solvent can again undergo reactions of all three types, and this increases the complexity of the resultant products.

Definite evidence of the production of free aryl radicals from aromatic solvent molecules by reactions (iv) and (v) has been obtained by Wieland and his colleagues.†

Some tetraphenylmethane is produced by the action of dibenzoyl peroxide on triphenylmethyl in benzene solution, but the reaction is not simply

$$\text{Ar—CO—O—O—CO—Ar} \longrightarrow \text{Ar}\cdot + CO_2 + \text{Ar—CO—O}\cdot,$$
$$\text{Ar}\cdot + \cdot CPh_3 \longrightarrow \text{Ar—}CPh_3,$$

but includes also the solvent reaction

$$\text{Ar—CO—O}\cdot + C_6H_6 \longrightarrow \text{Ar—CO—OH} + C_6H_5\cdot,$$

since tetraphenylmethane is still produced when di-*p*-phenyl-benzoyl peroxide, $(Ph—C_6H_4—CO—O\cdot)_2$, replaces dibenzoyl peroxide.

When di-*p*-toluoyl peroxide is decomposed in toluene containing triphenylmethyl the products include *p*-toluic acid and triphenylmethyl-*p*-toluate, Tol—COO—CPh_3, indicating that the radical Tol—CO—O· must be a primary reaction product. When chlorobenzene is used as a solvent in place of toluene, another reaction product is $Cl—C_6H_4—CPh_3$, whilst in methyl benzoate $Ph_3C—C_6H_4—COOMe$ is formed.

Many investigations have shown that dibenzoyl peroxide can dehydrogenate aliphatic solvents, and often the fate of the consequent solvent radicals can be traced, for they can, like aryl radicals, substitute in aromatic rings.

The decomposition of dibenzoyl peroxide in *cyclo*-hexane yields benzene (reaction iv), benzoic acid (reaction v), and small quantities of both *cyclo*-hexyl benzoate and phenyl-*cyclo*-hexane.‡ If triphenylmethyl is added to this reaction mixture, then triphenylmethane is also formed, indicating that atomic hydrogen must have been present (reaction iii).§

Dibenzoyl peroxide oxidizes ethyl alcohol to acetaldehyde, whilst from its decomposition in *iso*-butyl alcohol Gelissen and Hermans||

† Wieland, Ploetz, and Indest, *Annalen*, 1937, **532**, 166; Wieland and A. Meyer, ibid. 1942, **551**, 249.

‡ Gelissen and Hermans, *Ber*. 1926, **59**, 662.

§ Wieland and Meyer, loc. cit., p. 249.

|| Gelissen and Hermans, *Ber*. 1925, **58**, 765.

isolated, besides benzene and *iso*-butyraldehyde, *iso*-butyl benzoate and both *o*- and *p*-iso-butoxybenzoic acids, $C_4H_9O—C_6H_4COOH$, which indicates that the butoxyl radical, $C_4H_9—O\cdot$, must be able to substitute in the aromatic ring. Similarly, from the decomposition of dibenzoyl peroxide in acetic acid they isolated benzoic acid, benzene, phenyl acetate, and salicylic acid.†

Most complicated mixtures are obtained when diacyl peroxides decompose in the presence of olefines. Thus Farmer and Michael‡ have shown that the decomposition of dibenzoyl peroxide in *cyclo*-hexene yields benzene, benzoic acid, Δ^2-*cyclo*-hexenyl benzoate, phenyl-Δ^2-*cyclo*-hexene, Δ^2-*cyclo*-hexenyl-Δ^2-*cyclo*-hexene, *cyclo*-hexyl benzoate, 2-Δ^2-*cyclo*-hexenyl-*cyclo*-hexyl benzoate, and traces of many other substances. Hence the following reactions of free radicals must all occur:

(*a*) [cyclohexene] + PhCOO· (Ph·) ⟶ [cyclohexenyl radical, H] + Ph—COO—H (Ph—H)

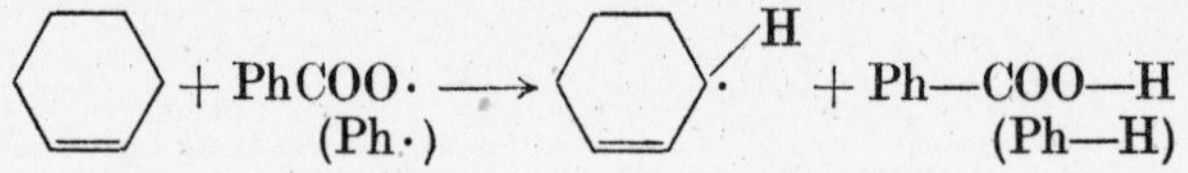

(*b*) [cyclohexene] + PhCOO· (Ph·) ⟶ [cyclohexene, H, OCOPh (Ph)] + ·H

(*c*) [cyclohexenyl radical, H] + [cyclohexene] ⟶ [cyclohexenyl, H H, cyclohexenyl] + ·H

(*d*) [cyclohexene] + PhCOO· (Ph·) ⟶ [cyclohexyl radical, H, OCOPh (Ph), H]

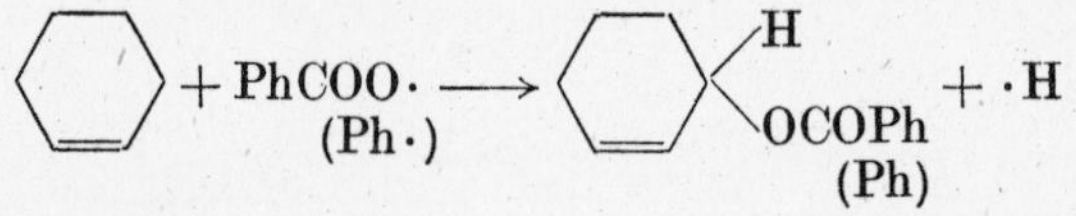

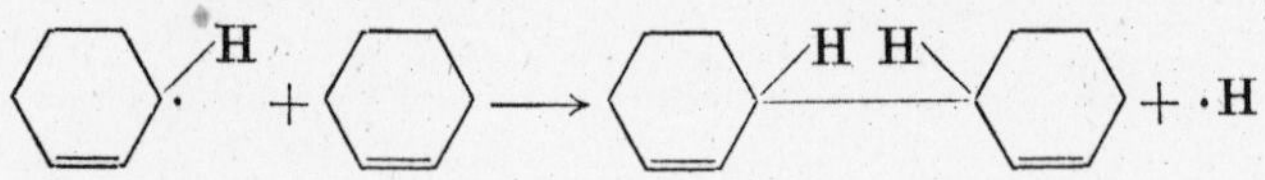

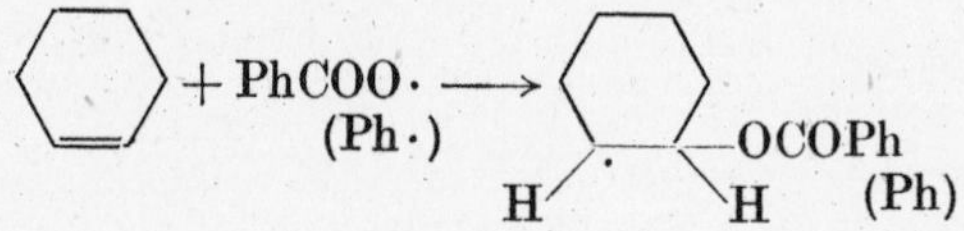

(*e*) [cyclohexyl radical, H, OCOPh, H] + [cyclohexene] ⟶ [cyclohexenyl—cyclohexyl, H, OCOPh] etc.

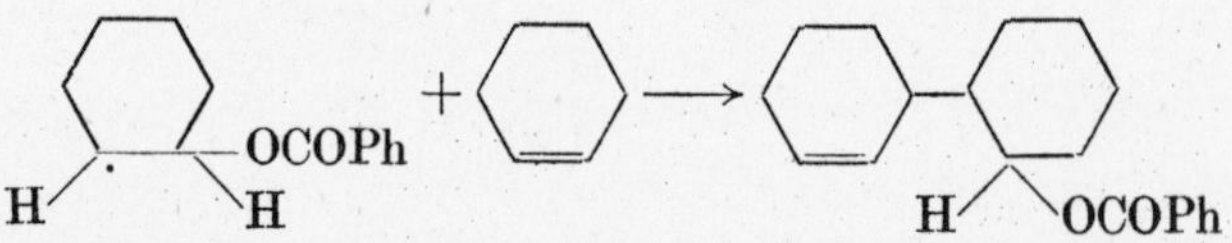

Farmer and his colleagues have pointed out that the α-methylene group of the system, —CH_2—CH=CH—, and not the double bond, is the preferential point of attack by free radicals (compare p. 161), and in a series of papers have shown the bearing of this fact upon the chemistry of oxidation and polymerization processes.§ Thus when dibenzoyl peroxide is heated with raw rubber to 140° a species of vulcanization

† Gelissen and Hermans, loc. cit., p. 770.

‡ *J.* 1942, p. 513.

§ Farmer, *Trans. Faraday Soc.* 1942, **38**, 348, 341, 356; *J.S.C.I.* 1947, **66**, 86.

occurs,† and, presumably by acting in the same way, many diazo compounds are active vulcanizers.‡

Decompositions in chlorinated solvents are also extremely interesting. Boeseken and Gelissen§ found that when dibenzoyl peroxide was boiled in carbon tetrachloride it yielded chlorobenzene, ω-trichloro-*p*-toluic acid, and hexachloroethane, whilst in chloroform solution benzene, ω-trichloro-*p*-toluic acid, and phosgene were the principal products. These results indicate that the radical $\cdot CCl_3$ has been liberated from the solvent:

$$Ph\cdot + CCl_4 \longrightarrow Ph{-}Cl + \cdot CCl_3,$$

$$Ph\cdot + CHCl_3 \longrightarrow Ph{-}H + \cdot CCl_3.$$

Reynhart|| was unable to isolate any ω-trichloro-*p*-toluic acid from decompositions carried out at 0° C., but, from the decomposition in chloroform, isolated benzoyl chloride and benzoic acid, and found that more and more benzene was formed as the reaction temperature was raised. He showed, however, that both chlorobenzene and αββ-trichlorostyrene, $Ph{-}CCl{=}CCl_2$, were formed when dibenzoyl peroxide was boiled in tetrachloro-ethylene, so that the formation of reactive fragments from chlorinated hydrocarbons has been well substantiated.

Kharasch and Dannley have shown that the dinaphthoyl peroxides react similarly.¶

Decompositions of Organo-metallic Compounds

Since the covalent bonds of organic compounds of heavy metals, such as lead, tin, and mercury, are all relatively weak it is but to be expected that free aryl radicals should be formed by their thermal decompositions. The small amount of experimental evidence as yet available substantiates this view.

Whilst aryl-mercuric halides are stable up to 300° C., mercury di-aryls, Ar_2Hg, decompose rather more easily. Razuvaiev and Koton†† have shown that when mercury-diphenyl is heated in alcohols it yields free mercury and benzene, not diphenyl, whilst the alcohols are oxidized to aldehydes or ketones. Again, when mercury-diphenyl and hydrazobenzene are heated together in ligroin at 150°, benzene and azobenzene are formed.‡‡ Mercury-dibenzyl decomposes somewhat more easily. Tin-tetraphenyl can also act as a phenylating agent.§§ It reacts with

† Ostromislensky, *J. Russ. Phys. Chem. Soc.* 1915, **47,** 1885.

‡ Buizov, ibid. 1921, **53,** 166; Levi, *Gomma*, 1937, **1,** 4; Fisher, *Ind. Eng. Chem.* 1939, **31,** 1381. § *Rec. trav. chim.* 1924, **43,** 869. || Ibid. 1927, **46,** 72. ¶ *J. Organic Chem.* 1945, **10,** 406. †† Razuvaiev and Koton, *J. Gen. Chem. Russia*, 1931, **1,** 864. ‡‡ Idem, 1935, **5,** 361. §§ Bost and Borgstrom, *J.A.C.S.* 1929, **51,** 1922.

alkyl halides to give unsaturated hydrocarbons and tin-triphenyl halides and with acetyl chloride to give acetophenone. On heating with sulphur, however, it yields diphenyl sulphide and diphenyl disulphide. Lead-tetraphenyl decomposes in a similar way,† and when heated with metallic mercury yields mercury-diphenyl.‡

Hein and his colleagues§ consider that the neutral phenyl radical is eliminated in the decomposition reactions of pentaphenyl chromium salts, $(C_6H_5)_5CrX$, which are marked reducing agents and easily lose one phenyl group.

Neutral hydrocarbon radicals may also be concerned in the random 'redistribution reactions' which have recently received detailed study by Calingaert and his colleagues,‖ though these reactions are all catalysed by the corresponding metallic halides, and there is, as yet, no evidence of reaction with solvent molecules.

OTHER THERMAL DECOMPOSITIONS

Iodonium salts. Diphenyl iodonium iodide, (XIV), easily changes on heating into iodobenzene, but the molecular rearrangement is not a simple shift of a phenyl cation, as might be supposed,

$$\underset{\text{(XIV)}}{\overset{\displaystyle C_6H_5-\overset{+}{I}-C_6H_5}{I^-}} \longrightarrow \left[\begin{matrix} C_6H_5^+ \; I-C_6H_5 \\ I^- \end{matrix}\right] \longrightarrow \begin{matrix} C_6H_5 \\ \diagdown \\ I \end{matrix} + I-C_6H_5,$$

since the ease of rearrangement of iodonium salts is not independent of the initial anion. Thus *p*-tolyl-iodonium iodide decomposes at 178°, the chloride decomposes at 155°, whilst tolyl-iodonium sulphide decomposes at room temperature. Sandin, McClure, and Irwin¶ have shown that when diphenyl-iodonium iodide is boiled in *n*-propyl alcohol in the presence of mercury some phenyl-mercuric iodide is formed. The reaction even occurs to some extent in boiling water in the presence of chalk. When boiled in *n*-propyl alcohol in presence of powdered tellurium, diphenyl-iodonium iodide yielded diphenyl telluride, which was identified as its dibromide, whilst in sodium sulphide solution containing antimony powder diphenyl-iodonium iodide yielded triphenylstibine sulphide. *p*-Tolyl-iodonium iodide and sulphide reacted similarly. These reactions so strongly indicate the production of neutral phenyl and tolyl radicals, rather than of their cations, that Sandin, McClure,

† Razuvaiev and Koton, *J. Gen. Chem. Russia*, 1935, **5**, 361.
‡ Dull and Simons, *J.A.C.S.* 1933, **55**, 3898.
§ Hein *et al.*, *Ber.* 1921, **54**, 2711; 1928, **61**, 730; 1929, **62**, 1157.
‖ See Gilman, *Organic Chemistry*, vol. ii (1943 ed.), article by Calingaert, pp. 1806–20.
¶ Sandin, McClure, and Irwin, *J.A.C.S.* 1939, **61**, 2944.

and Irwin suggest that the iodonium salts must exist in equilibrium with a covalent complex in which the iodine atom holds more than an octet of valency electrons,

$$\begin{matrix} C_6H_5-\overset{+}{\ddot{\underset{..}{I}}}-C_6H_5 \\ :\ddot{\underset{..}{Cl}}:^- \end{matrix} \quad \text{mesomeric with} \quad \begin{matrix} C_6H_5:\ddot{I}:C_6H_5 \\ :\ddot{\underset{..}{Cl}}: \end{matrix}$$

(XV)

and that part at least of the decomposition follows the non-polar course. Acceptance of this view implies that *d* electrons must be concerned in the valency bonds.

Benzyl ethers. Some phenyl ethers, such as phenyl allyl ether, $CH_2{=}CH{-}CH_2{-}O{-}C_6H_5$, and benzyl phenyl ether,

$$C_6H_5{-}CH_2{-}O{-}C_6H_5,$$

and most phenyl esters, can be made to undergo molecular rearrangement (the Claisen rearrangement) into alkyl or acyl phenols, substituted in the *ortho* position chiefly, when heated with acidic catalysts such as anhydrous zinc or aluminium chlorides. It is usually considered that this is an intramolecular process involving the migration of an electropositive alkyl or acyl group.

Hickinbottom† has shown, however, that when phenyl benzyl ether is heated in quinoline at 250° C. free benzyl is produced, for reaction with the solvent occurs yielding both benzyl-quinoline and toluene,

$$C_6H_5{-}CH_2\cdot + C_9H_7N \longrightarrow C_6H_5{-}CH_2H + \cdot C_9H_6N,$$
$$C_6H_5{-}CH_2\cdot + C_9H_7N \longrightarrow C_6H_5{-}CH_2{-}C_9H_6N + \cdot H,$$

together with hydroxyphenyl-quinolines which are obviously derived from alkoxy groups. This attack on the solvent is consistent only with the hypothesis that some thermal dissociation into free neutral radicals occurs.

The reaction is catalysed by metals such as zinc and copper. These may act by facilitating the formation of neutral benzyl by a single electron transference:

$$C_6H_5{-}CH_2{-}O{-}C_6H_5 + Cu^0 \longrightarrow C_6H_5{-}CH_2\cdot + Cu^+ + (:O{-}C_6H_5)^-.$$

The same activation process may well be concerned also in the catalysed substitution reactions of aryl halides (Ullmann's reactions), which can be effected by a mere trace of copper or of a copper salt,‡ e.g.

$$Ar{-}Cl + Cu^0 \longrightarrow Ar\cdot + Cu^+ + Cl^-,$$

† Hickinbottom, *Nature*, 1938, **142**, 830; 1939, **143**, 520.

‡ Compare Koelsch and Whitney, *J. Org. Chem.* 1941, **6**, 795. See also Chapter X, p. 210.

and should be represented as the initial stage (*A* of p. 163) of an oxidation/reduction cycle of the type suggested on previous pages for the Sandmeyer and Gattermann reactions. The activation by metallic copper of the decomposition of the unstable *syn*-diazo-cyanides (p. 155) may be explained similarly:

$$Ar—N_2—CN + Cu^0 \longrightarrow Ar\cdot + N_2 + Cu^+CN^-.$$

Hyponitrites. Harris, Marshall, and Jarrett† have recently suggested that, in solution, benzyl hyponitrite,

$$C_6H_5—CH_2—O—N{=}N—O—CH_2—C_6H_5,$$

decomposes in a similar manner to the aliphatic diazo-compounds, giving nitrogen and free benzoxy radicals, $C_6H_5—CH_2—O$. In support of this view they have shown that benzyl hyponitrite is a much more effective polymerization catalyst than is dibenzoyl peroxide (compare p. 195).

Production of Aryl Radicals by Electrolysis

Just as free alkyl radicals can be formed in ether solution by electrolysing alkyl magnesium halides (pp. 144–5) so free aryl radicals can be formed by the electrolysis of aryl magnesium halides,‡ though in the examples as yet examined the current efficiency is very low. The electrolysis of phenyl magnesium bromide in dry ether yields mainly benzene and styrene, together with traces of diphenyl, *p*-terphenyl, higher hydrocarbons, and a small amount of ethyl alcohol. *p*-Tolyl magnesium bromide similarly yields *p*-methyl-styrene, and *p*-chlorophenyl magnesium bromide *p*-chloro-styrene but scarcely any diphenyl derivatives as side-products. Evidently, therefore, the aryl radicals, when liberated at the anode, react almost exclusively with the solvent by the following sequence of changes:

$$Ph^-{:}Mg^{++}{:}Br^- \longrightarrow Ph\cdot \ (\textit{at anode})$$

$$Ph\cdot + CH_3—CH_2—O—C_2H_5 \longrightarrow Ph—H + CH_3—CH—O—C_2H_5$$

$$CH_3—\dot{C}H—O—C_2H_5 \longrightarrow C_2H_5\cdot + CH_3—CH{=}O$$

$$C_2H_5\cdot \longrightarrow C_2H_6 + C_2H_4 \quad (\textit{disproportionation})$$

$$CH_3—CH{=}O + PhMgBr \longrightarrow CH_3—CH\begin{matrix}\diagup Ph \\ \diagdown OMgBr\end{matrix}$$

$$\downarrow$$

$$CH_2{=}CH—Ph + H_2O \longleftarrow CH_3—CH\begin{matrix}\diagup Ph \\ \diagdown OH\end{matrix}$$

† *Nature*, 1947, **159**, 843.

‡ Evans, Pearson, and Braithwaite, *J.A.C.S.* 1941, **63**, 2574.

In contrast to phenyl magnesium bromide, benzyl magnesium bromide on electrolysis gives a good yield of dibenzyl. This is but to be expected, since the benzyl radical is a resonance-stabilized system which therefore has a much lower free energy than the phenyl radical. Consequently it does not attack the solvent so readily, but persists in the solution until dimerization occurs.

Evans, Pearson, and Braithwaite† conclude that free aryl radicals such as phenyl must have even higher energy contents, and consequently a greater degree of reactivity than free alkyl radicals, such as ethyl, for whilst reaction with the solvent is the chief characteristic of aryl radicals produced by electrolysis, disproportionation and dimerization are the chief characteristics of alkyl radicals in solution, and this view accords with evidence derived from studies of gas reactions (compare p. 129).

† Evans, Pearson, and Braithwaite, loc. cit.

IX

REACTIONS CATALYSED BY FREE RADICALS

Reactions initiated by Halogen Atoms

1. Halogen substitution. Gaseous substitution and addition processes initiated by halogen atoms have been described on pp. 97–100, in which it was pointed out that atomic chlorine and atomic bromine, but not atomic iodine, can set up reaction chains in which substitution of C—H links and addition to C=C links can both be effected. The resemblance between the gas-phase chlorination of methane and the chlorination of most liquid paraffins in sunlight is so close† that it can safely be inferred that both processes have the same atomic chain mechanism. Moreover, substances which can generate free radicals, such as lead tetra-ethyl or hexaphenylethane, can catalyse the chlorination of liquid paraffins.‡

The kinetics of substitution reactions of liquid bromine are often more complex, in that both atomic and ionic reactions may proceed simultaneously. Aliphatic bromination generally takes the atomic course, except in polar solvents of high dielectric constant (see p. 14) or on polar surfaces, whilst aromatic substitution is usually an ionic process, favoured by salt-like catalysts. Toluene is a good example of a molecule in which each type of reaction can occur according to the experimental circumstances, and the hypothesis that halogenation of its aliphatic side chain proceeds by the atomic mechanism, favoured by high temperatures, and initiated photochemically,

$$Br_2 + h\nu \rightleftharpoons 2Br\cdot,$$

$$Br\cdot + C_6H_5{-}CH_3 \longrightarrow Br{-}H + C_6H_5{-}CH_2\cdot,$$

$$C_6H_5{-}CH_2\cdot + Br_2 \longrightarrow C_6H_5{-}CH_2{-}Br + \cdot Br,$$

which accords with kinetic evidence,§ has been substantiated by the fact that other generators of free radicals, such as diacyl peroxides,|| are able to effect rapid and exclusive side-chain substitution in the dark at room temperatures, whilst substances such as nitrites, or alcohol, which promptly destroy free bromine atoms, inhibit side-chain substitution.

By measuring heats of reaction Magee and Daniels¶ have shown that

† Waters, *Proc. Durham Phil. Soc.* 1932, **8**, 459.

‡ Vaughan and Rust, *J. Org. Chem.* 1940, **5**, 449.

§ Waters, *Trans. Faraday Soc.* 1941, **37**, 778.

|| Kharasch, Margolis, White, and Mayo, *J.A.C.S.* 1937, **59**, 1405; Kharasch, White, and Mayo, *J. Org. Chem.* 1938, **3**, 33.

¶ Magee and Daniels, *J.A.C.S.* 1940, **62**, 2825.

photochemical brominations of toluene, diphenylmethane, and triphenylmethane in carbon tetrachloride solution are chain reactions which are inhibited by oxygen. Since more heat is evolved when oxygen is present there must also occur a competing photo-oxidation reaction which has a much shorter chain-length, and thus reduces the equilibrium concentration of such active radicals as $Ph—CH_2\cdot$

Brown, Kharasch, and Chao† have pointed out that it is possible for the atomic halogenation of a paraffin hydrocarbon to proceed by either of two alternative routes:

Route I.

$$Cl\cdot + H—CR_3 \longrightarrow H—Cl + \cdot CR_3 \qquad (a)$$

$$\cdot CR_3 + Cl_2 \longrightarrow Cl—CR_3 + \cdot Cl \qquad (b)$$

Route II.

$$Cl\cdot + H—CR_3 \longrightarrow Cl—CR_3 + \cdot H \qquad (a)$$

$$H\cdot + Cl_2 \longrightarrow H—Cl + \cdot Cl \qquad (b)$$

and, by the following method, proved that Route I—i.e. hydrogen abstraction and formation of a free hydrocarbon radical—and not Route II is that actually followed:

Route I (a) yields the free radical $\cdot CR_3$, which should have a planar configuration (compare p. 56), and consequently the subsequent reaction I (b) should give a *racemic* product even when an optically active hydrocarbon, $HCR_1R_2R_3$, has been taken.

On the other hand, Route II (a) should proceed, via the complex (I), through a Walden inversion, to give an optically active product.

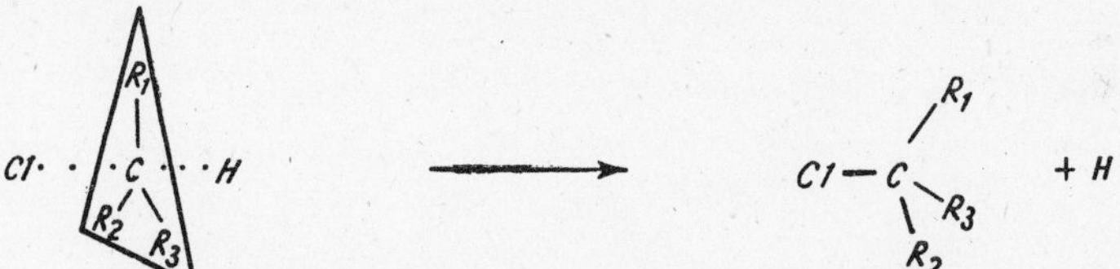

$$Cl\cdot\ \cdot\ \cdot\ C(R_1)(R_2)(R_3)\ \cdot\ \cdot\ \cdot H \longrightarrow Cl—C(R_1)(R_2)(R_3) + H$$

(I) (II)

They chlorinated active amyl chloride (III) to 1:2-dichloro-2-methyl butane (IV), both photochemically, and by the use of sulphuryl chloride and dibenzoyl peroxide (see p. 185), and, in each case, found that their product was *not* optically active.

$$Cl—CH_2—\overset{*}{C}(CH_3)(H)—C_2H_5 \longrightarrow Cl—CH_2—\overset{*}{C}(CH_3)(Cl)—C_2H_5$$

(III) (IV)

† Brown, Kharasch, and Chao, *J.A.C.S.* 1940, **62**, 3435.

This is a particularly valuable demonstration of the general principle that whenever a free radical attacks a saturated molecule it reacts only with one of the peripheral atoms (compare p. 130).

2. Halogen addition. On pp. 99–100 it was indicated that the photochemical additions of both chlorine and bromine to the isomeric dichloroethylenes, and to tetrachloroethylene, have proved to be chain reactions both in the vapour phase and in carbon tetrachloride solution.† The addition of chlorine to benzene to give benzene-hexachloride, $C_6H_6Cl_6$, is also a reaction of this type.‡ It is significant that the overall rate of these liquid phase reactions is proportional to the square root of the intensity of the absorbed light, showing that each quantum of absorbed radiation generates two active particles,

$$Cl_2 + h\nu \longrightarrow 2Cl\cdot,$$

and thus sets up simultaneously two reaction chains.§

Since each quantum of light may bring about the combination of up to several thousand molecules, it is evident that free halogen atoms are not easily destroyed by collision with all solvent molecules. However, in a chlorinated solvent, such as carbon tetrachloride, the identity of the active atoms may change very rapidly, although their chemical type may persist for a very long time, due to the continual occurrence of exchange reactions such as

$$Cl\cdot + CCl_4 \rightleftharpoons Cl{-}Cl + \cdot CCl_3,$$

which may be compared with the reaction between atomic hydrogen and deuterium (p. 86; compare p. 19).

Just as in the chain reactions of chlorine with hydrogen, methane, or carbon monoxide (Chapter V), so in the photochemical additions of chlorine and bromine to olefines it has regularly been found that oxygen is a powerful inhibitor of reaction.‖ If oxygen is present in appreciable concentration, then it is often possible to isolate oxidation products of the olefine from the reaction mixture. Thus dichloroacetyl chloride, $CHCl_2{-}CO{-}Cl$, is formed during the course of chlorination of trichloroethylene, and trichloroacetyl chloride may be formed similarly from tetrachloroethylene.

Bockemüller and Pfeuffer¶ have found that when benzene solutions

† For discussion see Gwyn Williams, *Trans. Faraday Soc.* 1941, **37**, 749.

‡ Smith, Noyes, and Hart, *J.A.C.S.* 1933, **55**, 4444.

§ Müller and Schumacher, *Zeit. phys. Chem.* 1937, B **35**, 285, 455; 1937, B **37**, 365.

‖ Bauer and F. Daniels, *J.A.C.S.* 1934, **56**, 2014; Brown and F. Daniels, ibid. 1940, **62**, 2820.

¶ Bockemüller and Pfeuffer, *Annalen*, 1939, **537**, 178.

of unsaturated compounds such as styrene, allyl chloride, or allyl bromide are treated, in diffused light, with low concentrations of bromine, oxygen can be absorbed by the reacting mixture while, and only while, bromine is adding on to the double bond. In the product the absorbed oxygen can be titrated, almost quantitatively, as peroxidic oxygen. Unstable peroxides are probably formed, thus†

$$\mathrm{Br} + \mathrm{CH_2{=}CHPh} \longrightarrow \mathrm{Br{-}CH_2{-}\dot{C}H{-}Ph},$$

$$\mathrm{Br{-}CH_2{-}\dot{C}H{-}Ph} + \mathrm{O_2} \longrightarrow \mathrm{BrCH_2{-}CH(O{-}O\cdot){-}Ph},$$

and, by replacing the active radical by a much less active one, slow down the bromination reaction chain, but may initiate as an alternative an autoxidation of the olefine.

Again, in the complete absence of oxygen the rate of addition of bromine to cinnamic acid in cold carbon tetrachloride solution is too fast for kinetic measurement.‡ Even small quantities of oxygen retard the reaction considerably.§ As Table XIX shows, the quantum yield in this photo-bromination varies inversely with the oxygen concentration, though it increases almost directly with increase in the bromine concentration.

TABLE XIX

Photo-bromination of Cinnamic Acid in Carbon Tetrachloride at 35° C.

Oxygen concentration (millimoles/litre)	0·0	0·8	1·8	5·3
Quantum efficiency of bromine addition	180	50	20	15

The essential chain mechanism of the reaction

$$\left.\begin{aligned} \mathrm{Br_2} + h\nu &\rightleftharpoons \mathrm{2Br\cdot},\\ \mathrm{Br\cdot} + \mathrm{Ph{-}CH{=}CH{-}COOH} &\longrightarrow \mathrm{Ph{-}\dot{C}H{-}CHBr{-}COOH},\\ \mathrm{Ph{-}\dot{C}H{-}CHBr{-}COOH} + \mathrm{Br_2} &\longrightarrow \mathrm{Ph{-}CHBr{-}CHBr{-}COOH} + \mathrm{\cdot Br} \end{aligned}\right\}$$

is not altered, but other reactions are introduced in which oxygen is consumed, probably by the initial formation of a very unstable peroxide radical,

$$\mathrm{Ph{-}\dot{C}H{-}CHBr{-}COOH} + \mathrm{O{=}O} \longrightarrow \mathrm{Ph{-}CH(O{-}O\cdot){-}CHBr{-}COOH},$$

† Compare Chapter XI, pp. 240–5.

‡ Bauer and F. Daniels, *J.A.C.S.* 1934, **56**, 2014.

§ Brown and F. Daniels, ibid. 1940, **62**, 2820.

which rapidly breaks down to oxidation products of cinnamic acid, or brings about chain-breaking processes such as

$$\underset{\displaystyle\text{Ph—CH—CHBr—COOH}}{\overset{\displaystyle\text{O—O}\cdot}{|}} + \cdot\text{Br} \longrightarrow \text{Ph—CHBr—CHBr—COOH} + O_2.$$

Fig. 23† shows the way in which oxygen is taken up by an illuminated solution of cinnamic acid in carbon tetrachloride immediately following the additions of small quantities of bromine (these are added at the instants *A* and *B*), though there is no reaction between cinnamic acid and oxygen when the bromination chain process is not simultaneously occurring. Stilbene and triphenylethylene behave in the same way.

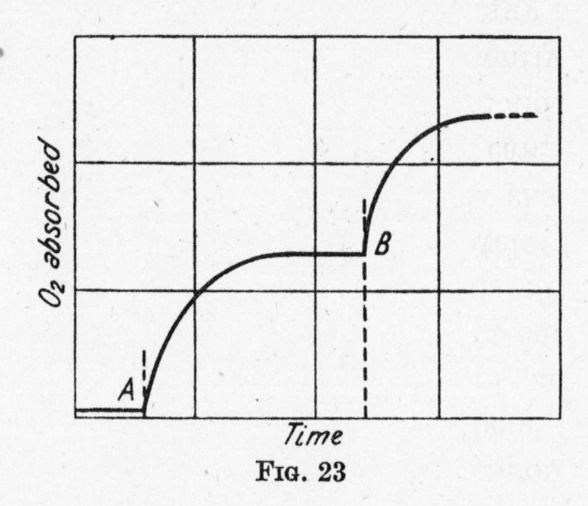

FIG. 23

Frequent accounts of the occurrence of induction periods, or of difficultly reproducible positive catalysis in the addition of halogens to olefines in non-ionizing solvents, seem to indicate that quite a number of *thermal* halogenations also proceed by the atomic mechanism. The addition of bromine to phenanthrene and its derivatives‡ can be cited as a reaction of this type.

The stereochemical aspect of atom-catalysed addition to olefines is an important one. It has provided satisfactory explanations (i) of the geometrical isomerization and (ii) of *trans* addition to olefines such as cinnamic and maleic acids.

Cis-trans isomerization of maleic acid to fumaric acid or of *allo*-cinnamic acid to cinnamic acid is most easily carried out in solution by addition of a little bromine, or iodine, and exposure to ultra-violet light. Under feeble illumination the transformation proceeds at a rate proportional both to the square root of the intensity of the light, and to the

† After Brown and Daniels, loc. cit., p. 2823.
‡ Price, *J.A.C.S.* 1936, **58**, 1835; Fieser and Price, ibid., p. 1838.

concentration of the halogen, but when more light energy is available than the solution can absorb, then the rate becomes proportional to the square root of the concentration of the halogen. Thus, in both limiting circumstances the rate-determining process is unquestionably the fission of the halogen molecule into two active fragments.†

Each atom then adds on to one end of the olefinic linkage, giving an intermediate radical having a single bond, with which free rotation is possible.

```
                                              Br
                                              |
Br· + Ph—C—H                            Ph—C—H
          ||          <——                    |
HOOC—C—H          ——>           HOOC—C—H   Radical (a)
                                              |
Allocinnamic acid                            ↓↑
                                             Br            free rotation
                                             |             about single bond
                                        Ph—C—H
                                    /        |
Ph—C—H                            /     H—C—COOH   Radical (b)
      ||                        ↙            |
 H—C—COOH                                   |
Cinnamic acid                                | Br·
                                             ↓
                                             Br
                                             |
                                        Ph—C—H
                                             |             trans Dibromocinnamic
                                        H—C—COOH                  acid
                                             |
                                             Br
```

Thus with *allo*cinnamic acid, if the radical in state (*a*) loses its bromine atom the original *allo*cinnamic acid is regenerated, but if it is in state (*b*) then cinnamic acid is obtained, whilst if a second bromine atom adds on to the radical (*b*) then the *trans* addition compound is produced. On account of the electrostatic repulsion between the similarly oriented dipolar groups Ph— and HOOC—, state (*b*) of the radical possesses slightly less energy, and is therefore of more probable occurrence, than state (*a*). Consequently, *allo*cinnamic acid is gradually converted into the more stable isomeride. Dimerization of the radicals before bromine elimination is also possible, and there is evidence to indicate that it is

† Wachholtz, *Zeit. phys. Chem.* 1927, **125**, 1; Berthoud *et al.*, *J. Chim. Phys.* 1927, **24**, 213; 1928, **25**, 40; 1930, **27**, 291; *Helv. Chim. Acta*, 1927, **10**, 289; 1930, **13**, 385. The effects due to dissolved oxygen (above) do not invalidate these conclusions, though undoubtedly the stereochemistry of bromine addition could not have been elucidated in rapidly reacting, oxygen-free, systems.

in this way that the various truxillic and truxinic acids are formed from the cinnamic acids.†

In addition to atomic halogens, other catalysts for effecting geometrical isomerization are metallic atoms such as potassium, nitric oxide, and dibenzoyl peroxide. The latter compound rapidly brings about the isomerization of *iso*-stilbene to stilbene in the dark,‡ but if 'anti-oxidants', such as quinol or thiophenol, are added then the isomerization cannot be brought about in direct sunlight, even in the presence of hydrochloric or hydrobromic acids. Undoubtedly these reaction-inhibitors act by combining immediately with free bromine atoms, and with radicals, and thereby become 'chain-breakers'.§

The photochemical isomerization of olefines can, in many cases, be brought about by ultra-violet light without the aid of a catalyst, provided that the wave-length of the light is sufficiently low for activation of the double bond. Though, in theory, the energy increment required to permit the occurrence of free rotation in an olefine may not be quite as great as that needed to sever one carbon-to-carbon link, it has been found that, in general, radical-catalysed isomerization of olefines requires less activation energy than does the uncatalysed photochemical change. Thus for maleic acid the wave-lengths of the light needed to effect the bromine-catalysed and the uncatalysed processes are about 4,360 A and 3,130 A respectively.||

3. Substitution of paraffins by thiol groups. Kharasch and Eberly¶ have shown that alkyl radicals obtained by the photochemical action of chlorine on paraffin hydrocarbons will react with carbon disulphide, giving products from which thiols can be obtained by reduction. They represent the reaction sequence as

$$Cl_2 + h\nu \longrightarrow 2Cl\cdot, \qquad R{-}H + Cl\cdot \longrightarrow R\cdot + H{-}Cl,$$

$$R\cdot + CS_2 \longrightarrow R{-}S{-}\dot{C}S, \qquad R{-}S{-}\dot{C}S + Cl_2 \longrightarrow R{-}S{-}CS{-}Cl + \cdot Cl.$$

In this way *cyclo*-hexane was converted in good yield to *cyclo*-hexylthiol. These reactions resemble in every way the reaction which occurs between carbon disulphide and free phenyl radicals (p. 151).

Peroxide Catalysed Reactions

1. Addition of hydrogen bromide to olefines. The addition of halogen acids to olefines is, most frequently, a polar reaction, and

† Berthoud, *Helv. Chim. Acta*, 1930, **13**, 385.
‡ Kharasch, Mansfield, and Mayo, *J.A.C.S.* 1937, **59**, 1155.
§ Compare Price, ibid. 1936, **58**, 1835; Brown and Daniels, ibid. 1940, **62**, 2822.
|| For a discussion see Rollefson and Burton, *Photochemistry*, chap. ix.
¶ Kharasch and Eberly, *J.A.C.S.* 1941, **63**, 625.

Markownikow's rule, stating that *the negative constituent attaches itself to the carbon atom which carries the smaller number of hydrogen atoms*, which is in accordance with the electronic theory of 'general polarity',† usually gives a correct prediction of the structure of the addition product. Thus

$$CH_3—CH=CH_2 + H—Br \longrightarrow CH_3—CHBr—CH_3.$$

In 1933, however, Kharasch and Mayo‡ showed that, for the addition of hydrogen bromide to allyl bromide, the nature of the reaction-product depended upon the exact experimental conditions under which the reaction was carried out.

When freshly purified reagents were mixed, in complete absence of air, the addition reaction required several days for completion, and the chief product was 1:2-dibromopropane, just as one would have predicted:

$$CH_2=CH—CH_2Br + H—Br \longrightarrow CH_3—CHBr—CH_2Br. \quad (A)$$

In the presence of air an alternative reaction, yielding 1:3-dibromopropane, also occurred:

$$CH_2=CH—CH_2Br + H—Br \longrightarrow CH_2Br—CH_2—CH_2Br. \quad (B)$$

A careful study of the experimental conditions showed that peroxides were essential catalysts for the formation of the 1:3-dibromo compound, and peroxidic substances were evidently produced when allyl bromide, and most other olefines, were exposed to air, since stored samples oxidized ferrous thiocyanate, giving a characteristic pink colour.

In the absence of oxygen, or of peroxides, this same 'catalysed' addition to olefines can be brought about by dissociating a little of the hydrogen bromide photochemically, or by adding, and then irradiating photochemically, dissociable substances such as aldehydes and ketones.§

By adding traces of organic peroxides the abnormal reaction (B) could be accelerated to such an extent that the complete addition of hydrogen bromide to give 1:3-dibromopropane could be carried out in a few hours. In contrast, when substances such as quinol, diphenylamine, or thiocresol, which destroy peroxides, were added the formation of the 1:3-dibromopropane was inhibited, though the 1:2-dibromopropane was still formed slowly.

Further investigations indicated that whilst the rate of hydrogen

† For a detailed discussion, see Waters, *Physical Aspects of Organic Chemistry*, 1935, chaps. viii and xi.

‡ Kharasch and Mayo, *J.A.C.S.* 1933, **55**, 2468.

§ Vaughan, Rust, and Evans, *J. Org. Chem.* 1942, **7**, 477.

bromide addition was dependent upon the nature of the solvent in which the reaction was carried out, solvents affected the structure of the reaction product only in so far as they promoted, or inhibited, the existence of peroxides. Again the degree of illumination of the reaction mixture affected only the reaction velocity.

Subsequently Kharasch and Mayo and their colleagues found that the 'peroxide effect' regularly influenced the mode of addition of hydrogen bromide to olefines, acetylenes, and di-olefines, and their results, which are frequently of great synthetic importance, have been substantiated by many other workers.†

The most powerful catalysts for promoting the 'peroxide effect' are benzoyl and lauryl peroxides, perbenzoic acid, and ascaridole (menthene peroxide from wormseed oil). When used in amounts of up to 1 per cent. they will bring about a complete reversal of the mode of addition of hydrogen bromide to the double bond, except with such strongly polar molecules as acrylic or cinnamic acids. Thus it is evident that the polar activation of the double bond, which is depicted below,

$$\overset{\longmapsto}{R}—\overset{\delta+}{CH}=\overset{\delta-}{CH_2} \quad \text{or} \quad \overset{\longmapsto}{R}—CH=CH_2$$

$$\underset{\delta-}{Br}—\underset{\delta+}{H} \qquad\qquad Br—H$$

can be superseded by a more facile substitution process.

By 1937 it was realized independently, both in England‡ and America§ that the peroxide-catalysed addition occurred by the following atomic chain process:

Stage 1. The peroxide radical (or possibly oxygen) reacts with hydrogen bromide, giving a trace of atomic bromine:

$$Ph—CO—O\cdot + H—Br \longrightarrow Ph—CO—O—H + \cdot Br.$$

Stage 2. Atomic bromine adds on to the double bond *at the point of higher electron density*, since it is an electrophilic reagent, thus giving the radical of least free energy (see below):

$$Br\cdot + CH_3—CH=CH_2 \longrightarrow CH_3—\dot{C}H—CH_2Br.$$

Stage 3. The carbon radical, produced by stage 2, then reacts with a molecule of hydrogen bromide, abstracting hydrogen and leaving a further bromine atom:

$$CH_3—CH—CH_2Br + H—Br \longrightarrow CH_3—CH_2—CH_2Br + \cdot Br.$$

† For reviews of the subject see Smith, *Annual Reports of the Chemical Society*, 1939; Mayo and Walling, *Chemical Reviews*, 1940, **27**, 351.

‡ Hey and Waters, ibid. 1937, **21**, 202.

§ Kharasch, Engelmann, and Mayo, *J. Org. Chem.* 1937, **2**, 288.

Stages 2 and 3 then continue as a recurrent chain process until side reactions destroy either of the active radicals.

The inhibitors of the peroxide catalysed reaction are all substances which release hydrogen very easily, and so promptly reduce any of the free radicals to stable molecules, thus terminating the reaction chains, e.g.

$$\mathrm{Ph{-}CO{-}O\cdot + H{-}S{-}C_6H_5 \longrightarrow PhCOOH + \cdot S{-}C_6H_5}$$
$$\mathrm{\longrightarrow C_6H_5{-}S{-}S{-}C_6H_5.}$$

Typical side reactions have been traced out by Urushibara and Simamura,† who have found that, in presence of oxygen, hydrogen bromide reacts with stilbene in the dark to give stilbene dibromide, and with allyl bromide to give small quantities of free bromine, hydrogen peroxide, and 1:2:3-tribromopropane. All these products evidently result from the direct combination of two free radicals, and are indicative of the presence of atomic bromine in the reacting mixture.

The reversal of the normal mode of addition of hydrogen bromide to olefines is primarily due to the fact that *free halogen atoms*, unlike halogen anions, *are electrophilic reagents* which tend to acquire some control over an extra electron in order to gain octet stability. Free radicals have somewhat similar chemical characteristics to active cations, such as H^+ or CH_3^+, and therefore will react preferentially at points of high electron density. Moreover, of the two radicals (V) and (VI),

$$\underset{\text{(V)}}{\mathrm{Alkyl{-}\underset{\displaystyle Br}{\underset{|}{CH}}{-}CH_2\cdot}} \qquad \text{and} \qquad \underset{\text{(VI)}}{\mathrm{Alkyl{-}\dot{C}H{-}CH_2Br}}$$

the latter (VI) has the lower free energy, and thus is the more likely to be formed by atomic addition to $\mathrm{Alkyl{-}CH{=}CH_2}$.

In contrast to this, the halide anions, e.g. Br^-, or complex anions, e.g. Br_3^-, $FeBr_4^-$, which take part in the normal (polar) addition‡ react at points of low electron density, since they possess an unshared electron pair to which a cation can be co-ordinated.

The normal mode of addition to olefines of hydrogen fluoride, hydrogen chloride, or of hydrogen iodide is not reversed by the use of peroxide catalysts.§

† *Bull. Soc. Chem. Japan*, 1939, **14**, 323.

‡ Compare, Gwyn Williams, *Trans. Faraday Soc.* 1941, **37**, 749.

§ Kharasch and Hannum, *J.A.C.S.* 1934, **56**, 712, 1782; Kharasch, Kleiger, and Mayo, *J. Org. Chem.* 1939, **4**, 428; Gross and Linn, ibid. 1938, **3**, 26.

Thus the reactions

$$CH_2{=}CHCl + H{-}Cl \longrightarrow CH_3{-}CHCl_2 \text{ (requiring metallic salt catalysis)}$$

and

$$CH_2{=}CHCl + H{-}I \longrightarrow CH_3{-}CHClI$$

occur invariably, whereas both

$$CH_2{=}CHCl + H{-}Br \longrightarrow CH_3{-}CHClBr \quad \text{(polar)}$$

and

$$CH_2{=}CHCl + H{-}Br \longrightarrow CH_2Br{-}CH_2Cl \quad \text{(peroxide catalysed)},$$

can each be made to proceed with 100 per cent. efficiency.

The apparently unique sensitivity of hydrogen bromide to peroxide catalysis can be explained satisfactorily on thermochemical grounds,† for the heats of reaction of the component radical processes have the following approximate values:

TABLE XX

	Reaction	*Heat of reaction, ΔH, in k.cals.* X = F	Cl	Br	I
Stage 2	$RCH{=}CH_2 + \cdot X \longrightarrow R\dot{C}H{-}CH_2X$	+66	+26	+13	−1
Stage 3	$R\dot{C}H{-}CH_2X + HX \longrightarrow RCH_2{-}CH_2X + X\cdot$	−60	−15	0	+16
Stage 1	$R' + H{-}X \longrightarrow R'{-}X + H\cdot$	As for Stage 3.			

With both hydrogen fluoride and hydrogen chloride, stages 1 and 3 of the radical chain (p. 182) are endothermic, and require so high an activation energy that their occurrence is improbable.

With hydrogen iodide, in contrast, stage 2 may be endothermic, and certainly both stages 1 and 3 would yield inactive iodine atoms. Moreover, hydrogen iodide must be classed with the anti-oxidants which promptly destroy peroxide radicals, thus

$$Ph{-}CO{-}O\cdot + H{-}I \longrightarrow Ph{-}CO{-}O{-}H + I\cdot.$$

Nevertheless, peroxides greatly accelerate the rate of addition of hydrogen iodide to olefines by the normal polar process. This is due to the liberation of a little free iodine, which then forms complex anions, such as I_3^-. In accordance with this view it has been shown that the addition of iodine to allyl alcohol

$$CH_2{=}CH{-}CH_2OH + I_2 \rightleftharpoons CH_2I{-}CHI{-}CH_2OH$$

is a termolecular reaction, which proceeds with a velocity proportional to the square of the molecular concentration of the iodine.‡

† Mayo and Walling, *Chemical Reviews*, 1940, **27**, 375. (This is an excellent critical review of this whole subject.)

‡ Gwyn Williams, loc. cit.

2. Reactions of sulphuryl chloride. Sulphuryl chloride, SO_2Cl_2, which can be prepared catalytically from, and may be decomposed, both thermally and photochemically, into sulphur dioxide and chlorine,

$$SO_2Cl_2 \rightleftharpoons SO_2 + Cl_2,$$

is a simple and effective chlorinating agent. It was first used with polar catalysts such as antimony pentachloride for the chlorination of aromatic substances, but in the presence of organic peroxides it can be used for the chlorination of alkyl groups. Thus boiling toluene can be converted quantitatively into benzyl chloride in 15 minutes by treatment with an equivalent of sulphuryl chloride and a trace of either dibenzoyl peroxide or dilauryl peroxide.†

Substances which destroy atomic chlorine, such as iodine and molecular oxygen, are inhibitors of this reaction. Consequently chlorination with sulphuryl chloride is best carried out by boiling the desired reactant alone, or in a dry chlorinated solvent such as carbon tetrachloride, in a flask fitted with a reflux condenser, until the ebullient vapours have swept all the air out of the reaction vessel, and then adding a trace of a dried organic peroxide and finally running in dropwise the calculated quantity of freshly distilled sulphuryl chloride. Evolution of considerable quantities of sulphur dioxide and of hydrogen chloride indicates the occurrence of reaction, and, from time to time, as this slackens, a little more peroxide should be added. Successive addition of small quantities of the organic peroxide is more effective than one large initial addition, since the catalysed substitution proceeds only so long as fresh reaction chains can be started.

Kharasch and Brown interpret this reaction as follows:

$$\left.\begin{array}{lll} (PhCO{-}O{-})_2 & \longrightarrow & Ph\cdot + CO_2 + Ph{-}CO{-}O\cdot \\ Ph\cdot + SO_2Cl_2 & \longrightarrow & Ph{-}Cl + \cdot SO_2Cl \end{array}\right\} \text{chain starting} \qquad \begin{array}{r}(i)\\(ii)\end{array}$$

$$\left.\begin{array}{lll} \cdot SO_2Cl & \longrightarrow & SO_2 + \cdot Cl \\ Cl\cdot + H{-}R & \longrightarrow & H{-}Cl + \cdot R \\ R\cdot + SO_2Cl_2 & \longrightarrow & R{-}Cl + \cdot SO_2Cl \end{array}\right\} \text{reaction chain} \qquad \begin{array}{r}(iii)\\(iv)\\(v)\end{array}$$

but Schumacher and Stauff‡ consider that it is unnecessary to postulate the existence of the radical $\cdot SO_2Cl$, since they believe that the reversible molecular dissociation of sulphuryl chloride to sulphur dioxide and chlorine proceeds so rapidly that reaction mixtures always contain

† Kharasch and Brown, *J.A.C.S.* 1939, **61**, 2142; Kharasch, Brown, and Chao, ibid. 1940, **62**, 3435.

‡ Schumacher and Stauff, *Chemie*, 1942, **55**, 341.

free molecular chlorine. The reaction chain then becomes simply reaction (iv) above and the simple reaction

$$R\cdot + Cl_2 \longrightarrow R—Cl + \cdot Cl, \qquad (vi)$$

whilst the removal of molecular chlorine by this process then favours the dissociation of more sulphuryl chloride.

The fact that sulphuryl chloride can be used to bring about the addition of chlorine to olefines such as *cyclo*-hexene† accords with this view, for atomic chlorine is a hydrogen-substituting agent rather than an additive reagent with olefines of this type.‡

As one would anticipate for an atomic substitution process, only the aliphatic side-chains of hydrocarbons such as toluene and xylene are chlorinated by this peroxide-catalysed method, and purely aromatic compounds, such as benzene and chlorobenzene can be used as inert solvents for carrying out the chlorination of other substances. Aromatic nitro-compounds are not attacked, whilst some compounds which contain reactive hydrogen atoms, such as diphenylmethane, act as inhibitors.

By this method aliphatic carboxylic acids, and acid chlorides, can be chlorinated at points remote from the carboxyl group,§ principally in the β-position, whereas in the polar Hell-Volhard reaction (use of iodine or PCl_5 as catalysts) the α-position is attacked exclusively.

Sulphuryl chloride can also be used as a sulphonating agent, for if a mixture of sulphuryl chloride and a paraffin is refluxed and irradiated then sulphonation occurs. Concurrent chlorination can, under these circumstances, be suppressed by adding a little pyridine or quinoline. Since this process leads to the side-chain sulphonation of toluene, Kharasch and Reid‖ ascribe it to the action of the radical $\cdot SO_2Cl$, but alternatively it may be explained by the sequence

$$R\cdot + SO_2 \longrightarrow R—SO_2\cdot, \qquad R—SO_2\cdot + Cl_2 \longrightarrow R—SO_2—Cl + \cdot Cl.$$

Under normal circumstances peroxides catalyse the decomposition of sulphonic chlorides,

$$R—SO_2—Cl \longrightarrow R—Cl + SO_2,$$

and Schumacher and Stauff consider that the tertiary bases bring about the removal of the peroxide catalysts by favouring the accumulation of molecular chlorine in the reaction mixture, and in accordance with this

† Kharasch and Brown, *J.A.C.S.* 1939, **61**, 3433.
‡ Waters, *Nature*, 1944, **154**, 772.
§ Kharasch and Brown, *J.A.C.S.* 1940, **62**, 925.
‖ Kharasch and Reid, ibid. 1939, **61**, 3089.

view Kharasch, Chao, and Brown† have pointed out that whereas chlorination mixtures containing free peroxides remain colourless throughout the reaction, sulphonation mixtures soon become greenish yellow due to the presence of chlorine. Aliphatic acids may easily be sulphonated at 50–60° C. by this method. The sulphonyl group enters the aliphatic chain at positions distant from the carboxyl group, one of the regular reaction products being the cyclic anhydride of the β-sulphonated acid:

$$CH_3—CH_2—COOH + SO_2Cl_2 \xrightarrow{\text{light}} \begin{array}{l} CH_2—CH_2—COOH \\ | \\ SO_2—Cl \end{array} \longrightarrow \begin{array}{l} CH_2—CH_2 \\ |\qquad \quad \rangle CO \\ SO_2—O \end{array}$$

3. Addition of bisulphites to olefines. In 1925 Kolker and Lapworth‡ found that by working with emulsions, preferably stabilized by kieselguhr, ammonium bisulphite could be made to add on to simple olefines, such as ethylene, amylene, *cyclo*-hexene, pinene, and dipentene, and proved that saturated sulphonic acids, and not sulphites, were formed. Until then the only olefinic substances known to react with bisulphites were unsaturated aldehydes and ketones.

In 1938 Kharasch, May, and Mayo§ demonstrated that this reaction with olefines does not normally occur in the absence of oxygen. It could be inhibited either by evacuating all the air from the system, or more effectively, by adding anti-oxidants such as quinol, whilst in contrast both peroxides and nitrites were positive catalysts. They studied in detail the addition of ammonium bisulphite to styrene, and proved that their reaction product was the phenylethane-β-sulphonate,

$$Ph—CH_2—CH_2—SO_3NH_4,$$

and not the α-sulphonate as Ashworth and Burkhardt‖ had previously thought.

Consequently the mechanism of the bisulphite addition is the free-radical process shown below:

Stage 1. Abstraction of one electron by the catalyst:

$$\left[\begin{array}{c} H—O—\ddot{S}{=}O \\ \| \\ O \end{array}\right]^- + R\cdot \longrightarrow (R:)^- + \begin{array}{c} H—O—\dot{S}{=}O \\ \| \\ O \end{array}$$

† Kharasch, Chao, and Brown, ibid. 1940, **62**, 2393.

‡ Kolker and Lapworth, *J.* 1925, p. 307.

§ Kharasch, May, and Mayo, *J. Org. Chem.* 1938, **3**, 175; *Chem. and Ind.* 1938, **57**, 774.

‖ Ashworth and Burkhardt, *J.* 1928, p. 1791.

or, alternatively,

$$\left[\mathrm{H{-}O{-}\ddot{S}{=}O} \atop {\| \atop \mathrm{O}}\right]^{-} + \mathrm{R}\cdot \longrightarrow \mathrm{R{-}H} + \left[\mathrm{\bar{O}{-}\dot{S}{=}O} \atop {\| \atop \mathrm{O}}\right]\dagger$$

Stage 2. Addition to the olefine at the point of higher electron density:

$$\mathrm{PhCH{=}CH_2 + H\dot{S}O_3 \longrightarrow Ph\dot{C}H{-}CH_2SO_3H.}$$

Stage 3. Hydrogen abstraction with regeneration of the bisulphite radical:

$$\mathrm{Ph{-}\dot{C}H{-}CH_2SO_3H + (HSO_3)^- \longrightarrow Ph{-}CH_2{-}CH_2SO_3H + (\dot{S}O_3)^-.}$$

The active radicals are either the electrically neutral 'odd' molecule $\mathrm{H\dot{S}O_3}$ or else the 'radical-ion' $(\mathrm{\dot{S}O_3})^-$, according to the acidity of the solution:

$$(\mathrm{\dot{S}O_3})^- + \mathrm{H_2O} \rightleftharpoons \mathrm{H\dot{S}O_3} + (\mathrm{OH})^-;$$

and these same entities, are concerned in the metal-catalysed autoxidation of sulphites to sulphates (pp. 234–6).

The hydrogen donor in stage 3 above can be any available molecule, whilst alternatively the active radical $\mathrm{Ph\dot{C}H{-}CH_2SO_3H}$ may undergo disproportionation,

$$\mathrm{2Ph\dot{C}H{-}CH_2SO_3H \longrightarrow PhCH_2{-}CH_2SO_3H + PhCH{=}CHSO_3H,}$$

or combine with oxygen, and thereby become oxidized to the carbinol, $\mathrm{Ph{-}CH(OH){-}CH_2SO_3H}$, which is, it has been shown, one of the regular reaction products.‡

4. Addition of thiols to olefines. Isolated examples of the addition of thiols to olefines have long been noted,§ and it was pointed out by Ashworth and Burkhardt|| in 1928 that the reaction had the reverse course to that which would have been predicted by Markownikow's rule; thus

$$\mathrm{Ph{-}CH{=}CH_2 + Ph{-}S{-}H \longrightarrow Ph{-}CH_2{-}CH_2{-}S{-}Ph.}$$

Jones and Reid¶ have shown that traces of peroxides are necessary

† See p. 235.
‡ Kharasch, Schenck, and Mayo, *J.A.C.S.* 1939, **61**, 3092.
§ Posner, *Ber.* 1905, **38**, 646.
|| *J.* 1928, p. 1799.
¶ *J.A.C.S.* 1938, **60**, 2452.

for this addition, and thus, as Kharasch, Read, and Mayo† have pointed out, it must be a chain reaction involving neutral thiol radicals:

$$Ph—CO—O\cdot + H—S—Ph \longrightarrow Ph—CO—O—H + \cdot S—Ph,$$

$$Ph—CH{=}CH_2 + \cdot S—Ph \longrightarrow Ph—\dot{C}H—CH_2—S—Ph,$$

$$Ph—\dot{C}H—CH_2—S—Ph + H—S—Ph \longrightarrow Ph—CH_2—CH_2—S—Ph + \cdot S—Ph.$$

The great synthetic value of this peroxide-catalysed reaction has already become evident.‡ Ipatieff and his colleagues§ have shown that hydrogen sulphide, as well as many simple thiols, can be made to add on to higher aliphatic olefines by working at high temperatures and pressures, though in the absence of a catalyst there is scarcely any reaction below 180° C.

The addition of hydrogen sulphide to simple olefines, such as butylene, diallyl, and vinyl chloride, can also be brought about by irradiation with ultra-violet light, or in the presence of some acetone with light of slightly longer wave-length.|| Mercaptans and thio-ethers can both be prepared in this way, and in every case the sulphur atom adds on to the carbon atom which initially carries the larger number of hydrogen atoms, thus

$$CH_2{=}CHCl + H_2S \longrightarrow H—S—CH_2—CH_2Cl.$$

Thioacetic acid, CH_3—CO—S—H, is another reagent that can be added on to olefines;¶ upon subsequent hydrolysis a saturated thiol is formed. Some thiols, such as cysteine and glutathione can be added on to olefines such as maleic acid under biological conditions, and thus it is evident that this catalysed reaction must be reckoned with as a potential mode of bio-synthesis.††

5. Carboxylation with oxalyl chloride. Kharasch and Brown‡‡ have shown that just as paraffins can be sulphonated by means of sulphuryl chloride (p. 186), so they can be carboxylated by treatment with oxalyl chloride at room temperature and irradiation with light from a tungsten filament or mercury lamp; e.g.

$$C_6H_{12} + (COCl)_2 \longrightarrow C_6H_{11}—CO—Cl + CO + HCl.$$

Since oxalyl chloride decomposes photochemically to give carbon

† *Chem. and Ind.* 1938, **57**, 752.
‡ Cunneen, *J.* 1947, pp. 36, 134.
§ *J.A.C.S.* 1938, **60**, 2731; 1939, **61**, 71.
|| Vaughan and Rust, *J. Org. Chem.* 1942, **7**, 472.
¶ Holmberg, *J. prakt. Chem.* 1934, **141**, 93.
†† Morgan and Friedman, *J. Biol. Chem.* 1938, **32**, 733.
‡‡ Kharasch and Brown, *J.A.C.S.* 1942, **64**, 329.

monoxide and chlorine, the reaction is best represented as the following chain process:

$$\text{Cl—CO—CO—Cl} + h\nu \longrightarrow 2\cdot\text{CO—Cl},$$
$$\cdot\text{CO—Cl} \longrightarrow \text{CO} + \cdot\text{Cl},$$
$$\cdot\text{Cl} + \text{R—H} \longrightarrow \text{H—Cl} + \cdot\text{R},$$
$$\cdot\text{R} + (\text{CO—Cl})_2 \longrightarrow \text{R—CO—Cl} + \cdot\text{CO—Cl}, \quad \text{etc.}$$

The same reaction can be initiated in the dark by adding an organic peroxide as a catalyst:

$$(\text{PhCOO})_2 \longrightarrow \text{Ph}\cdot + \text{CO} + \cdot\text{OCOPh},$$
$$\text{Ph}\cdot + \text{Cl—CO—CO—Cl} \longrightarrow \text{Ph—Cl} + \text{CO} + \cdot\text{CO—Cl}.$$

This reaction can be carried out in liquid paraffins, and also in solution in chloroform or carbon tetrachloride, but it is not effective in benzene or other aromatic solvents, even though these substances are not opaque to light of the wave-length requisite for decomposition of the oxalyl chloride. Toluene, xylene, and mesitylene cannot be photochemically carboxylated in the side-chain, and even the peroxide-catalysed reaction gives a very poor yield.† In these cases the lack of reactivity may be due to resonance stabilization of the benzyl group, making it incapable of attacking oxalyl chloride molecules.

Diphosgene, which can also split off the ·CO—Cl group, has also been used as a carboxylating agent, but the yields are very poor.‡

Some unsaturated substances, such as styrene, can be carboxylated by means of oxalyl chloride in the absence of light or of a catalyst, but this reaction is considered to be a polar process:

$$\text{Ph—CH=CH}_2 + (\text{COCl})_2 \longrightarrow \text{Ph—CH=CH—COCl} + \text{CO} + \text{HCl}.$$

6. The Cannizzaro reaction and similar processes. In 1931 Haber and Willstätter§ suggested that the Cannizzaro reaction, whereby alkaline solutions of aromatic aldehydes may be converted to equivalent mixtures of the corresponding alcohol and acid, was a chain process, involving hydrogen transference, in which neutral organic radicals were involved,

$$\text{Ph—}\dot{\text{C}}\text{=O} + \text{Ph—CH=O} + \text{H}_2\text{O} \longrightarrow \text{Ph—CO—OH} + \text{Ph—}\dot{\text{C}}\text{H—O—H},$$
$$\text{Ph—}\dot{\text{C}}\text{H—O—H} + \text{Ph—CH=O} \longrightarrow \text{Ph—CH}_2\text{OH} + \text{Ph—}\dot{\text{C}}\text{=O},$$

and supposed that a catalyst, such as ferric cation, initiated the reaction by abstracting a hydrogen atom from a —CH=O group (see p. 267).

† Kharasch, Kane, and Brown, *J.A.C.S.* 1942, **64**, 333, 1621.
‡ Kharasch, Eberly, and Kleiman, ibid., p. 2975.
§ Haber and Willstätter, *Ber.* 1931, **64**, 2844.

This hypothesis has been supported by Kharasch and Foy,† who stated that the Cannizzaro reaction did not occur in the complete absence of oxygen or of peroxides. On this basis Weiss, in 1941,‡ suggested that the reaction should be represented essentially as a chain reaction involving atomic hydrogen and free organic radicals such as $Ph—\dot{C}=O$ and $Ph—\dot{C}H—OH$.

Careful work§ has shown, however, that the Cannizzaro reaction can proceed even with carefully purified reagents under an atmosphere of nitrogen. In dioxane, methyl alcohol and ethyl alcohol solutions, it proceeds at a rate which is proportional to the *square* of the concentration of the aromatic aldehyde, and to the first power of the concentration of the alkali, as is required by the equation

$$2ArCHO + NaOH = ArCH_2OH + ArCOONa.$$

Alexander|| has demonstrated that in dioxane solution the reaction velocity is affected neither by the addition of sodium peroxide or dibenzoyl peroxide, nor by the addition of peroxide inhibitors such as hydroquinone or diphenylamine. Again, Bonhoeffer and Fredenhagen¶ have carried out the Cannizzaro reaction in heavy water, and have shown that none of the hydrogen directly bound to carbon underwent isotope exchange. Thus initiation of the reaction is due neither to the removal of atomic hydrogen from an aldehyde molecule by a free radical, such as phenyl, nor to the removal of hydrogen cation by the alkali. Consequently the Cannizzaro reaction must be substantially a reaction between an aldehyde molecule and the anion (*a*) in which neither free ions nor free radicals are formed.

```
            H                  O⁻         ·O
            |                  |   .....   |
(a)   Ar—C—OH           Ar—C·       H—C—Ar   (b)
            |                  |           |
            O⁻                 OH          H
```

It may perhaps proceed bimolecularly by hydrogen atom transfer with the transient formation of a complex, such as (*b*), which would account for ester production under certain circumstances.

The true explanation of the Cannizzaro reaction, whatever it may be,

† Kharasch and Foy. *J.A.C.S.* 1935, **57**, 1510; compare Urushibara and Takebayashi, *Bull. Soc. Chem. Japan*, 1937, **12**, 328.

‡ Weiss, *Trans. Faraday Soc.* 1941, **37**, 782.

§ Molt. *Rec. trav. chim.* 1937, **56**, 233; Blanksma and Zaaijer, ibid. 1938, **57**, 727.

|| Alexander, *J.A.C.S.* 1947, **69**, 289.

¶ Bonhoeffer and Fredenhagen, *Zeit. phys. Chem.* 1938, A **138**, 379.

must be applicable also to many analogous disproportionation reactions between alcohols and aldehydes or ketones:

$$\begin{matrix} R^1 \\ R^2 \end{matrix}\!\!>\!C{=}O + \begin{matrix} R^3 \\ R^4 \end{matrix}\!\!>\!C\!\!<\!\!\begin{matrix} H \\ OH \end{matrix} \rightleftharpoons \begin{matrix} R^1 \\ R^2 \end{matrix}\!\!>\!C\!\!<\!\!\begin{matrix} H \\ OH \end{matrix} + \begin{matrix} R^3 \\ R^4 \end{matrix}\!\!>\!C{=}O$$

including the valuable Meerwein–Pondorff process for reducing ketonic groups by means of aluminium *iso*-propoxide and the Oppenauer process for oxidizing alcohols by means of acetone and a little aluminium *tert*-butoxide.

It should be borne in mind, however, that atomic mechanisms can be postulated for all reduction processes (compare Chapters III and X), but only in a very few cases is diagnostic experimental evidence available of the exact course of the reaction; moreover polarographic studies have given very little indication of the two-stage reduction of any aliphatic aldehydes or ketones.† Again the intermediate radicals in these homolytic reduction processes would have electronic structures analogous to those of the metallic ketyls (p. 203), which, in the aliphatic series, are most unstable, and have only been prepared, as yet, from di-tertiary ketones.

Chain Polymerization of Olefines‡

Reference has been made in Chapters V and VII to the gas-phase polymerization of ethylene to the valuable insulating material 'polythene'. This reaction, which may be catalysed both by atomic hydrogen and by free alkyl radicals, effects the formation of saturated molecules containing long hydrocarbon chains

$$\begin{aligned} R\cdot + CH_2{=}CH_2 &\longrightarrow R{-}CH_2{-}CH_2\cdot \\ &\longrightarrow R{-}CH_2{-}CH_2{-}(CH_2{-}CH_2)_n{-}R' \end{aligned}$$

and, since the molecular structure is of a simple linear type, many of the physical properties of the resultant polymer are primarily dependent upon its mean molecular weight.

The conversion of ethylene to polythene can be regarded as a representative model for many other syntheses of industrially important polymers, e.g.

$CH_2{=}CH{-}Cl$ (*Vinyl chloride*) ⟶ Polyvinyl chloride
⟶ Polyvinyl alcohol ⟶ Polyvinyl acetate,

$CH_2{=}C(CH_3){-}COOCH_3$ (*Methyl methacrylate*) ⟶ Polymethylmethacrylate,
('Perspex', 'Plexiglas', 'Lucite')

† Adkins and Cox, *J.A.C.S.* 1938, **60**, 1151. ‡ Compare *J.* 1947, 252–80.

$$CH_2{=}CH{-}Ph\text{: } (\textit{Styrene}) \longrightarrow \text{Polystyrene,}$$

$$CH_2{=}C(Cl){-}CH{=}CH_2\text{: } (\textit{Chloroprene}) \longrightarrow \text{'Neoprene',}$$

which are generally prepared by liquid phase reactions.

The study of vapour phase polymerization has, however, thrown an important light on the reaction mechanisms which may be involved in these catalysed changes. Thus Melville† has shown that the photochemical polymerizations of methyl methacrylate and of methyl acrylate vapours are complex, two reactions at least being involved.

One of these, which can be initiated by hydrogen atoms, is a rapid chain reaction propagated by active centres which disappear very soon after the source of illumination has been removed.

Another slower reaction, which may not require an independent catalyst, sets in after an induction period, during which active centres of polymerization form upon the surface of the reaction vessel, and can continue for a long time after the source of illumination has been removed. This reaction is inhibited at once by atomic hydrogen, and is slowly inhibited by iodine, whilst oxygen does not destroy the active centres of polymerization once they have been formed.

As Melville has pointed out, two types of mechanisms can be postulated for the chain polymerization of olefines:

Type A. Non-polar opening of the double bond, and subsequent addition of free radicals to the monomeric olefine; i.e.

Stage 1.

$$CH_2{=}\underset{\underset{Me}{|}}{\overset{\overset{COOMe}{|}}{C}} + h\nu \longrightarrow \cdot CH_2{-}\underset{\underset{Me}{|}}{\overset{\overset{COOMe}{|}}{C}}\cdot$$

or

$$R\cdot + CH_2{=}\underset{\underset{Me}{|}}{\overset{\overset{COOMe}{|}}{C}} \longrightarrow R{-}CH_2{-}\underset{\underset{Me}{|}}{\overset{\overset{COOMe}{|}}{C}}\cdot$$

Stage 2.

$$R{-}CH_2{-}\underset{\underset{Me}{|}}{\overset{\overset{COOMe}{|}}{C}}\cdot + CH_2{=}\underset{\underset{Me}{|}}{\overset{\overset{COOMe}{|}}{C}} \longrightarrow R{-}CH_2{-}\underset{\underset{Me}{|}}{\overset{\overset{COOMe}{|}}{C}}{-}CH_2{-}\underset{\underset{Me}{|}}{\overset{\overset{COOMe}{|}}{C}}\cdot \quad \text{etc.}$$

Stage 3.

Chain termination by union of two free radicals: $R_1\cdot + R_2\cdot \longrightarrow R_1{-}R_2$.

† Melville, *Proc. Roy. Soc.* 1937, A **163**, 511; 1938, A **167**, 99.

Type B. Hydrogen transfer, and polar addition.

This was represented by Melville as

$$CH_2{=}C(COOMe)(Me) + H{-}C(H){=}C(COOMe)(Me) \longrightarrow CH_3{-}C(COOMe)(Me){-}C(H){=}C(COOMe)(Me)$$

whereby the double bond was reproduced at the end of the growing polymer.

It is in better accord with polar theories of addition however to represent the change as

Stage 1. *Proton transfer.*

$$CH_2{=}C(COOMe){-}Me + H^+ \longrightarrow \overset{+}{C}H_2{-}CH(COOMe){-}Me$$

Stage 2. *Repeated Michael addition reactions.*

$$CH_2{=}C(COOMe)Me + \overset{+}{C}H_2{-}CH(COOMe)Me \longrightarrow \overset{+}{C}H_2{-}C(COOMe)Me{-}CH_2{-}C(COOMe)Me{-}H$$

dependent upon polarization of the double bond induced by the group COOMe, i.e. $C{=}C{-}C{=}O$. *Iso*-butene, however, probably adds on a proton to give a tertiary carbonium ion, rather than a primary carbonium ion,† i.e.

$$Me_2C{=}CH_2 + H^+ \longrightarrow Me_2\overset{+}{C}{-}CH_3, \quad \text{etc.}$$

It is reasonable to conclude that the rapid, hydrogen catalysed, reactions are of Type A, whilst the slower reactions, which can continue in the absence of light, are of Type B.

Chain polymerizations of olefines in the liquid phase can be brought about by catalysts belonging to two very distinct types. One can use either organic catalysts, such as dibenzoyl peroxide, which are capable of generating free neutral radicals in solution,‡ or else inorganic catalysts such as boron fluoride, aluminium chloride, or stannic chloride which are all reagents of electrophilic type, e.g.

$$R{-}X + BF_3 \longrightarrow R^+(XBF_3)^-,$$

which can also be used to bring about polar condensations, such as the Friedel–Crafts reaction, which frequently involve addition to olefinic links,§ and it is reasonable to consider that the organic catalysts pro-

† Evans and Polanyi, *J.* 1947, p. 252.

‡ Sodium metal is to be included as a catalyst of this type, see Chapter X, p. 206.

§ Compare Plesch, Polanyi, and Skinner, *J.* 1947, p. 257; Waters, *Physical Aspects of Organic Chemistry*, 1935, p. 231; G. Williams, *J.* 1940, p. 775.

mote olefine polymerizations of Type A whilst the inorganic catalysts favour polymerization of the polar Type B. Consideration of Type B polymerization is outside the scope of this book.

Chain polymerization by free neutral radicals. Dibenzoyl peroxide is the catalyst most frequently used for polymerizing liquid olefines such as styrene and methyl methacrylate, and as soon as it had clearly been recognized that solutions of dibenzoyl peroxide tended to decompose spontaneously to give neutral phenyl and benzoate radicals (Chapter VIII, pp. 165–9) it was suggested by Hey and Waters† that the true active catalyst was the neutral phenyl radical, which could add on to one end of an olefinic link, e.g.

$$Ph\cdot + CH_2{=}CH{-}Ph \longrightarrow Ph{-}CH_2{-}\dot{C}H{-}Ph.$$

This theory accords with kinetic evidence of the mechanism of chain polymerization in the liquid phase. Thus the polymerization itself is, after an induction period, a reaction of zero order,‡ although the concentration of the dibenzoyl peroxide diminishes unimolecularly,§ whilst again the average molecular weight of the resultant polymer is the greater the less the concentration of catalyst used.

Moreover, it has been proved conclusively that the free radical catalysts combine with the olefine in the polymeric molecule, for when substances such as di-*p*-bromobenzoyl peroxide,‖ di-3:4:5-tribromobenzoyl peroxide,¶ or di-chloroacetyl-peroxide‖ are used to bring about the polymerization of either styrene or methyl methacrylate then the resulting polymers contain some unsaponifiable halogen. Most decisive results have been obtained from polymerizations carried out in dilute solution in benzene under conditions favouring the formation of polymers of low molecular weight.

Free *p*-bromophenyl radicals obtained by the self-decomposition of *p*-bromobenzenediazo hydroxide (see p. 152) can also catalyse the polymerization of styrene emulsions.†† Again Blomquist, Johnson, and Sykes‡‡ have shown that when halogenated N-nitrosoacylarylamines (pp. 148–52) such as (VII), (VIII), and (IX), which, by decomposing as

† Hey and Waters, *Chemical Reviews*, 1937, **21**, 201.

‡ Flory, *J.A.C.S.* 1937, **59**, 241; Schulz and Husemann, *Zeit. phys. Chem.* 1936, B **34**, 187; Norrish and Brookman, *Proc. Roy. Soc.* 1939, A **171**, 147.

§ Kamenskaya and Medvedev, *Acta Physicochem. U.R.S.S.* 1940, **13**, 565; Price and Tate, *J.A.C.S.* 1943, **65**, 517. For a detailed review see Mark and Raff, *High Polymeric Reaction*, New York, 1941.

‖ Price, Kell, and Krebs, *J.A.C.S.* 1942, **64**, 1103; Price and Kell, ibid. 1941, **63**, 2798; Bartlett and Cohen, ibid. 1943, **65**, 543.

¶ Price and Tate, ibid., p. 517.

†† Price and Durham, ibid. 1942, **64**, 2508.

‡‡ Blomquist, Johnson, and Sykes, ibid. 1943, **65**, 2446.

aryldiazoacetates, can give rise to both free aryl and free carboxylate radicals, are used to bring about the polymerizations of styrene, methyl methacrylate, or acrylonitrile then only from catalyst (VII) did the resultant polymer contain combined bromine.

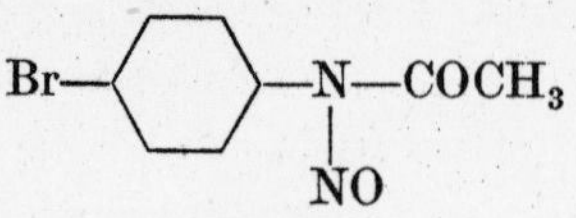

Br—C_6H_4—N(NO)—$COCH_3$
(VII)

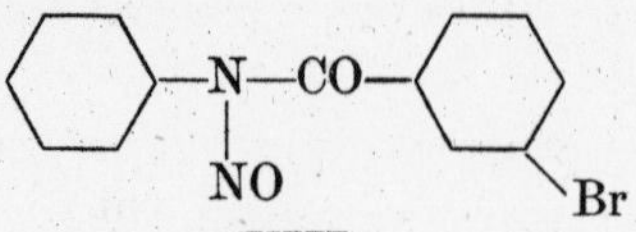

C_6H_5—N(NO)—CO—C_6H_4Br
(VIII)

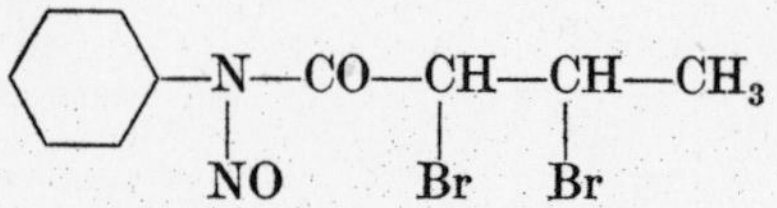

C_6H_5—N(NO)—CO—CH(Br)—CH(Br)—CH_3
(IX)

All this work indicates that only *active* free radicals, such as free aryl groups, and not more stabilized resonance systems, such as carboxylate groups, can add on directly to olefinic linkages.

It is evident, too, that solvents can play a significant part in controlling both the mechanism and the rate of these radical-catalysed polymerizations by taking part in exchange reactions, such as those described on pp. 167–9. Thus Cuthbertson, Gee, and Rideal† showed kinetically that toluene, when used as a solvent, participated in the peroxide-catalysed polymerization of vinyl acetate, whilst Price and Durham‡ showed that aromatic nitro compounds, such as nitrobenzene, not only tended to inhibit the polymerization of styrene, but actually became part of the resulting low molecular weight polymer. They pointed out that by reaction with the solvent there may, in this case, be formed a radical sufficiently stabilized by resonance to be unable to attack the monomeric olefine, with the result that the reaction-chain then ends by dimerization.

Thus the reaction of a radical R· with nitrobenzene gives the product (X) which is mesomeric with (XI):

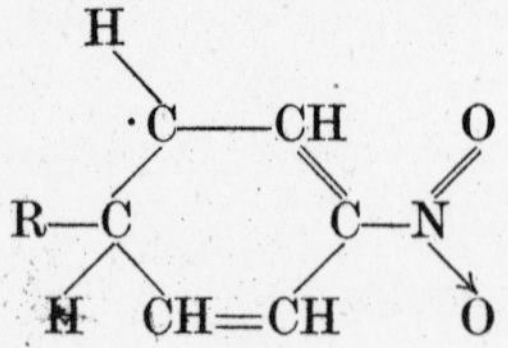

H
·C——CH O
R—C C—N
H CH=CH O
(X)

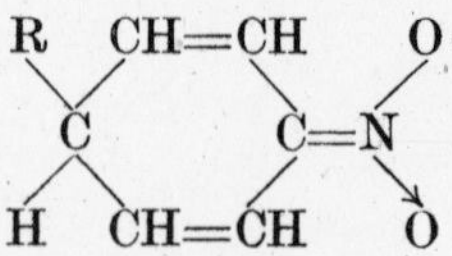

R CH=CH O·
C C=N
H CH=CH O
(XI)

† Cuthbertson, Gee, and Rideal, *Proc. Roy. Soc.* 1939, A **170**, 321.
‡ Price and Durham, *J.A.C.S.* 1943, **65**, 757.

in which, as in the carboxylate radical, $R—C\langle^{O\cdot}_{O}$, the 'odd electron' is distributed throughout a group of atoms.

Nitrothiophene is a still more effective retarder of polymerization, and again becomes incorporated into the final polymer molecule.†

In a somewhat similar manner, molecular oxygen (or air) tends to reduce the speed of catalysed olefine polymerization by combining to yield peroxide radicals which are less active than free hydrocarbon radicals, though in the absence of other catalysts one may usually attribute the spontaneous polymerization of several olefinic substances to catalysts consisting of organic peroxides formed by autoxidation (see pp. 240–5).

'Anti-oxidant' substances, such as quinol, pyrogallol, or naphthylamines, which, by releasing hydrogen easily, immediately combine with free radicals, can, even when present in traces, prevent olefine polymerization by destroying the active centres of the chain process. In technical operations they are regularly used to stabilize the organic monomers, and thereby ensure controllable synthesis.

Emulsion polymerization. The peroxide-catalysed polymerization of a liquid olefine is a process which is somewhat difficult to control, especially in the later stages when the percentage of residual monomer becomes low. Solvents, or involatile plasticizers, such as dibutyl phthalate, are often added to prevent the irregular separation of polymerized material, but even in these ways it is not easy to produce commercially valuable material of high molecular weight, such as that required for rubber substitutes.

Polymers of high molecular weight can however be obtained rapidly and uniformly by dispersing the monomeric olefine, by means of a soap, or a similar reagent, in the form of a fine emulsion in water, and then adding the catalyst in low concentration to the aqueous phase. On account of the dispersion of the reacting organic liquid in a large bulk of water, effective temperature control is possible. Moreover, the probability of more than one active radical forming at the same time in any one oil drop is so slight that the frequency of termination of the chain addition process is very low, and consequently polymers of very high molecular weight (*c.* 300,000–500,000) are obtainable.

Dibenzoyl peroxide is still a suitable catalyst to use for effecting emulsion polymerization, but it can be replaced by a number of inorganic peroxides, such as hydrogen peroxide, sodium perborate, or sodium

† Price, ibid., p. 2380, and *Reactions at Carbon-Carbon Double Bonds*, 1946.

perphosphate. Search of the patent literature reveals, however, that traces of other substances, both organic and inorganic, are often added to regulate the reaction.

M. G. Evans and his collaborators† have recently shown that small quantities of mild reducing agents, such as ferrous salts, sulphites, and arsenites can accelerate, and may even initiate, emulsion polymerization due to hydrogen peroxide, and other inorganic per-salts. In accordance with the theories of Haber and Weiss, they suggest that single electron transferences such as

$$Fe^{++} + H—O—O—H \longrightarrow Fe^{+++} + (:OH)^{-} + \cdot O—H,$$

$$Fe^{++} + (:\bar{O}—SO_2—O—O—SO_2—\bar{O}:) \longrightarrow Fe^{+++} + (SO_4)^{=} + (\cdot O—SO_2—\bar{O}:)$$

occur, giving free neutral radicals in the aqueous phase, which persist, by exchange with water molecules (see p. 19), until they reach the olefine and add on to one end of a double bond, thus setting up a polymerization chain. Since the experimental evidence in support of the free radical mechanism of olefine polymerization is now so abundant, this work may be regarded as giving decisive confirmation to the Haber–Weiss theory.

Since a wide range of reducing agents can be used to initiate the polymerization of olefines, such as acrylic nitrile, by hydrogen peroxide it is clear that the peroxide bond —O—O— can be broken to give a free radical by any one-electron donor, provided that its oxidation potential is high enough. Even ethylene gas is readily absorbed, and polymerized, by mixtures of hydrogen peroxide and ferrous salts. As would be expected, oxygen acts as an inhibitor of this change.

Structural features of olefine polymers. The radical-catalysed polymerization of olefines, and of di-olefines such as chloroprene and isoprene, always yields symmetrical chain products, in which the monomeric units have become linked together in regular head-to-tail arrangement. This fact, which has in many instances been established by oxidative or hydrolytic degradation, indicates that, as with the 'peroxide catalysed' additions of hydrogen bromide (p. 180), sulphites (p. 187), or thiols (p. 188) to olefines, the active radical always adds on to the more electro-negative end of the C=C double bond to give the free radical with the least possible free energy, i.e.

$$R\cdot + CH_2=CH—Ph \longrightarrow R—CH_2—\dot{C}H—Ph \quad \textit{not} \quad Ph—\underset{\cdot}{\overset{R}{\overset{|}{C}}}H—CH_2.$$

† *Trans. Faraday Soc.* 1946, **42**, 155–83; *J.* 1947, p. 266. See Chapter XI.

Since the resultant stable polymer is most probably formed by a chain-terminating union of two free radicals, one would expect to find that in any polymer the regular head-to-tail structure would, as in squalene or the carotenoid hydrocarbons, be broken once throughout the chain, but it is almost impossible by chemical means to detect this unique discordancy in the structure of a high polymer.

Only a few olefinic substances can be easily converted catalytically to long-chain polymers. These all have the general structure $CH_2{=}C\langle^{X}_{Y}$ in which group X (at least) has an unsaturated, or strongly polar, character, such as $COOCH_3$, CN, Cl, Ph.

This polar group X undoubtedly plays a vital part in facilitating both the polar (Type B) and the free radical (Type A) polymerization processes. Thus it is only because groups such as CO or CN can facilitate catio-enoid activation,† $C{=}C{-}C{=}O$, that one can get developed an electro-negative carbon centre to which the proton, or equivalent, polar catalyst can become attached, e.g.

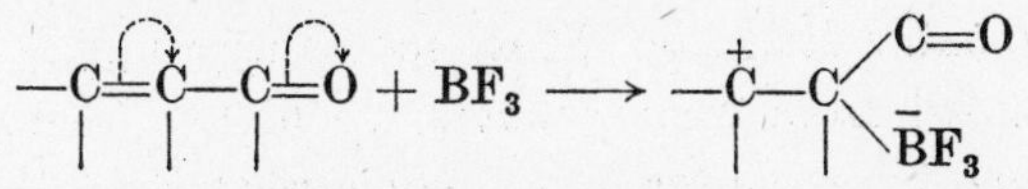

$$-\underset{|}{C}{=}\underset{|}{C}-\underset{|}{C}{=}O + BF_3 \longrightarrow -\underset{|}{\overset{+}{C}}-\underset{|}{C}\langle^{C=O}_{\bar{B}F_3}$$

Again, the non-polar activation, consequent upon free radical addition, invariably leads to the production of a mesomeric radical stabilized by resonance to such an extent that the activation energy needed for opening up the olefinic bond is reduced from about 50 k.cals. to 25 k.cals. or less.‡ For instance

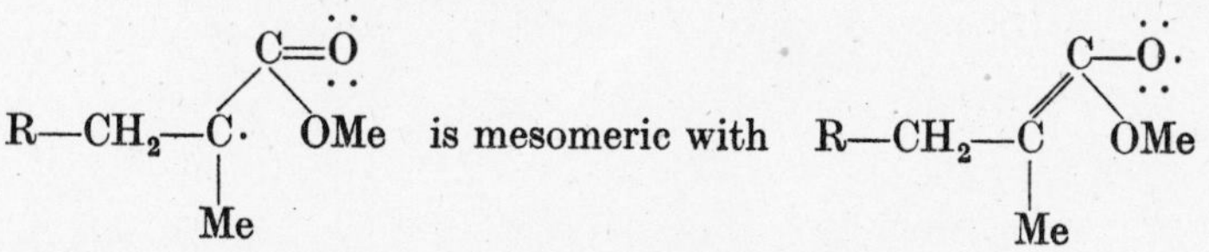

$$R{-}CH_2{-}\underset{\underset{Me}{|}}{C}\cdot\langle^{C=\ddot{O}}_{\ddot{O}Me} \text{ is mesomeric with } R{-}CH_2{-}\underset{\underset{Me}{|}}{C}{=}\langle^{C-\ddot{O}\cdot}_{\ddot{O}Me}$$

It should be noted that olefines containing the group

$$-CH_2{-}CH{=}CH-$$

do not yield chain polymers, since in this structure the hydrogen atoms of the α-methylene group are attacked by free radicals more easily than is the olefinic bond.§

Again substances of the general structure X—CH=CH—X, as for example maleic acid, in which there is 'discordant' or 'crossed' polarity,†

† Compare Waters, *Physical Aspects of Organic Chemistry*, 1935, chap. XV.
‡ Compare Flory, *J.A.C.S.* 1937, **59**, 241.
§ See pp. 168, 241–3.

do not themselves polymerize when treated with peroxide catalysts, though they undergo addition reactions very easily and can, in admixture with easily polymerized olefines, enter into 'co-polymers' in which they become distributed more or less at random along the paraffinic chain.

Co-polymerization of a mixture of olefines is the general technical route for preparing long-chain molecules in which the chemical structure can be adjusted at will to suit mechanical requirements. For instance co-polymers of vinyl chloride and vinyl acetate are much more valuable, as thermoplastic resins, than either polyvinyl chloride which is chemically inert, difficultly soluble, and of very high softening-point, or polyvinyl acetate which is easily soluble and softens at little above atmospheric temperatures. The co-polymers of olefines such as styrene, or acrylic nitrile, with conjugated di-enes, such as butadiene, are of outstanding technical importance as *synthetic rubbers*. Thus 'buna-S' (GR—S), the most favoured rubber substitute, is the co-polymer of styrene and butadiene, whilst 'buna-N' (GR—N) is the co-polymer of acrylic nitrile and butadiene, and 'butyl rubber' is the co-polymer of *iso*-butylene and butadiene. These substances, unlike the paraffinic polymers obtained from mon-olefines, are highly elastic, since their molecular forms can be altered by geometrical isomerizations which need not involve the fission of carbon-to-carbon bonds. They are all manufactured by the use of peroxide catalysts, emulsion polymerization being the most favoured general procedure.

X

REACTIONS INVOLVING METALS

THE CHEMICAL CHARACTER OF METALS

IN Chapters I and V it was pointed out that metallic atoms easily parted with electrons, and could be used in the vapour phase for the production of free radicals. However, whilst the reaction between sodium vapour and an organic halide can correctly be represented as a transference of a single electron from a metallic atom to the halogen atom, liberating a neutral organic radical,

$$Na\cdot + :\ddot{Cl}\cdot\,\cdot CH_3 \longrightarrow Na^+(:\ddot{Cl}:)^- + \cdot CH_3, \qquad (1)$$

it does not necessarily follow that the reaction between a solid, or molten, metal and a solution of an alkyl halide (i.e. the Wurtz–Fittig reaction, see pp. 207–10) occurs by the same mechanism.

Metals in bulk are electrical conductors, and consequently, when there is some source of current (see below, p. 202), are capable of providing a regular supply of electrons without being ionized. For instance, when a dilute acid is electrolysed between platinum electrodes the cathode continually parts with electrons to hydrogen ions, $2H^+ + 2e \rightarrow H{-}H$, but the platinum is not ionized. Even when a metal such as iron or zinc dissolves in a dilute acid the metallic ions are not liberated at the place where electrons are transferred to the liquid (a cathodic area), but elsewhere (at an anodic area).

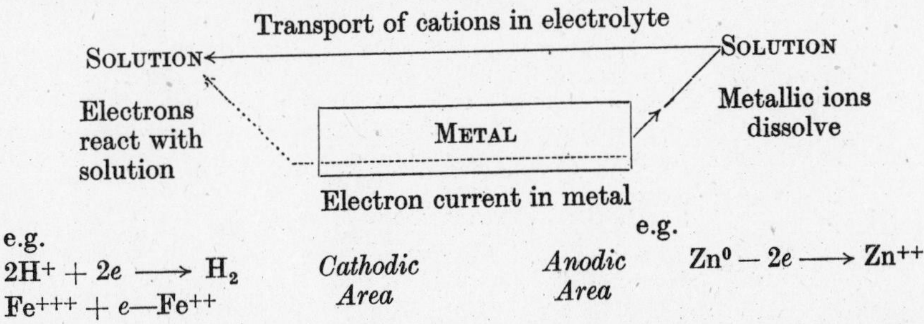

Since the cathodic area of the surface of any metal should be regarded merely as an abundant electron-source, it is impossible, when studying metallic reactions, to decide whether electrons are liberated singly (as in 1) or in pairs (as in 2),

$$CH_3I + 2Na\cdot \longrightarrow (CH_3)^-Na^+ + Na^+I^-, \qquad (2)$$

when the metal ionizes, except by identifying in the solution itself neutral radicals e.g. ($CH_3\cdot$) or anions [e.g. $(CH_3:)^-$] as *immediate* reaction products.

Both organic and inorganic reactions of metals should always be considered from the electrolytic standpoint, and analysed, wherever possible, into distinct cathodic and anodic processes.

It should be remembered, however, that though these two processes may occur at different localities on the surface of any piece of metal they must take place concurrently, for otherwise the metal will become inert on account of electrical polarization. Thus if at a cathodic area so many electrons enter the solution that the surface potential rises by V volts, then extra energy, eV electron volts, or $23{,}070V$ calories per gram-equivalent, must be provided to release any further electrons. Only by the loss of positive ions, or by inflow of electrons from elsewhere, as in electrolysis, can the metal be depolarized.

Again, the continuous solution of a metal at an anodic area can only occur if there is formed a soluble salt, in which form the metallic cations can diffuse away from the metallic surface. Otherwise an adherent anodic film will soon cover the metal and inhibit further reaction. This is particularly the case with reactions in organic solvents of little or no ionizing power, such as alcohol or benzene, in which most inorganic salts are insoluble. In a few cases, however, the solution of a metal may be brought about by the formation of a soluble organo-metallic compound, such as zinc ethyl, or of a co-ordination complex, such as a Grignard reagent (e.g. $CH_3MgI,2Et_2O$). It is to overcome this difficulty that recourse is made to reagents such as sodium powder, copper-bronze, or zinc dust.

Though the great majority of the reactions of metals, even in organic chemistry, are obviously electrolytic in character a direct reaction of another type can occur. Covalent organo-metallic compounds can be formed by direct addition of any reagent which can accept electrons, e.g.

$$2CH_3\cdot + \cdot Hg\cdot \longrightarrow CH_3:Hg:CH_3.$$

The latter process undoubtedly occurs under the conditions used by Paneth, Rice, and others (pp. 7–9) for identifying neutral radicals. It is also a process whereby substances such as carbon monoxide can be firmly adsorbed ('chemi-sorbed') on to metallic surfaces.

It will be seen, therefore, that the exact mechanism of any reaction involving a metal cannot be decided until a critical study of its exact course has been made. In the following sections of this chapter experimental evidence is set forward to show that the production of neutral radicals in reactions involving metals is by no means a rarity, and that many peculiarities of metallic reactions can be explained thereby.

REACTIONS OF THE ALKALI METALS

1. The metallic ketyls and their analogues. In 1891 Beckmann and Paul† found that metallic sodium dissolved, without evolution of hydrogen, in air-free solutions of aromatic ketones in dry ether, giving dark blue products, and in 1911 Schlenk and Weickel‡ concluded that these substances contained trivalent carbon, since, like triphenylmethyl, they reacted rapidly with both iodine and oxygen, regenerating the original ketone and not a dimeric product, and when decomposed by water gave mixtures of the original ketone and the corresponding hydrol, rather than the pinacol (A), which should have been formed quantitatively if the blue ketyls were normal quadrivalent carbon compounds.

$$Ph_2C{=}O + Na\cdot \longrightarrow Ph_2\dot{C}{-}O{-}Na$$

$$2Ph_2\dot{C}{-}O{-}Na + I_2 \longrightarrow 2Ph_2C{=}O + 2NaI$$

$$2Ph_2\dot{C}{-}O{-}Na + O_2 \longrightarrow 2Ph_2C{=}O + Na_2O_2$$

$$Ph_2\dot{C}{-}O{-}Na + H{-}OH \begin{cases} \nearrow Ph_2C\begin{smallmatrix}ONa\\OH\end{smallmatrix} \longrightarrow Ph_2C{=}O \\ \searrow Ph_2C\begin{smallmatrix}ONa\\H\end{smallmatrix} \longrightarrow Ph_2CH(OH) \end{cases}$$

not

$$\begin{matrix}Ph_2C{-}O{-}Na\\|\\Ph_2C{-}O{-}Na\end{matrix} + 2H_2O \longrightarrow \begin{matrix}Ph_2C{-}OH\\|\\Ph_2C{-}OH\end{matrix} \quad (A)$$

High yields of the pinacols (A) can however be obtained by hydrolysing metallic ketyls with dilute acid.§ Alkali, by stabilizing the oxygen as an anion, evidently hinders dimerization of the ketyl radical (compare the semi-quinones, p. 73).

Other reactions which are indicative of the free radical, rather than of the pinacol structure are the following:

$$Ph_2\dot{C}{-}O{-}Na + CH_3I \longrightarrow Ph_2C\begin{smallmatrix}ONa\\CH_3\end{smallmatrix} \longrightarrow Ph_2C\begin{smallmatrix}OH\\CH_3\end{smallmatrix}$$

$$Ph_2\dot{C}{-}O{-}Na + Ph_3C{-}Cl \longrightarrow Ph_2C{=}O + Ph_3\dot{C}\cdot + NaCl.$$

† *Annalen*, 1891, **266**, 1. ‡ *Ber.* 1911, **44**, 1182; compare ibid. 1913, **46**, 2840.
§ Bachmann, *J.A.C.S.* 1933, **55**, 1179.

Again, just as triphenylmethyl will react with metallic sodium to give an ionized salt, so, with an excess of sodium, the metallic ketyls slowly react to give violet *di*-sodium derivatives,† which can also be prepared by the action of sodamide on the corresponding hydrols in liquid ammonia solution:‡

$$Ph_2\dot{C}—O—Na + Na\cdot \longrightarrow Ph_2\overset{-}{C}—\overset{-}{O}\overset{+}{Na}, \quad \underset{\overset{+}{Na}}{}$$

$$Ph_2CH—OH + 2NaNH_2 \longrightarrow Ph_2\overset{-}{C}(\overset{+}{Na})—\overset{-}{O}\overset{+}{Na} + 2NH_3.$$

The free radical nature of the metallic ketyls was confirmed in 1934 by Sugden,§ who showed that their solutions in dioxane were paramagnetic (Chapter II, p. 31). Hence the formation of the ketyls from aromatic ketones is to be represented as follows:

$$Ph_2C{=}\ddot{\underset{\cdot\cdot}{O}} + Na\cdot \longrightarrow Ph_2\dot{C}—\overset{-}{\ddot{\underset{\cdot\cdot}{O}}}{:}Na^+,$$

one electron adds on to the $\rangle C{=}O$ double bond, entering at the more electrophilic atom, the oxygen, and converting it to an anion linked by a single covalence to a tercovalent carbon atom having only seven electrons. Simultaneously there is formed a sodium cation.

Alkali metals other than sodium will give up electrons in this way, and so too will a mixture of powdered magnesium and magnesium iodide, which behaves like an active alkali metal:‖

$$Mg + MgI_2 \rightleftharpoons 2\cdot MgI.$$

Whilst more recent magnetic measurements by Müller have confirmed that the aromatic ketyls exist in reversible equilibrium with diamagnetic pinacolates,¶

$$\begin{matrix} Ar_2C—\overset{-}{O}\overset{+}{Na} \\ | \\ Ar_2C—\overset{-}{O}\overset{+}{Na} \end{matrix} \rightleftharpoons 2Ar_2\dot{C}—\overset{-}{O}\overset{+}{Na},$$

the corresponding compounds in the aliphatic series, which have been prepared from di-tertiary ketones, such as di-*tert*-butyl ketone,

† Schlenk and Bergmann, *Annalen*, 1928, **464**, 22.

‡ Schlubach, *Ber.* 1915, **48**, 12; Wooster, *J.A.C.S.* 1928, **50**, 1388.

§ Sugden, *Trans. Faraday Soc.* 1934, **30**, 18.

‖ Gomberg and Bachmann, *J.A.C.S.* 1927, **49**, 236.

¶ Müller and Janke, *Z. Elektrochem.* 1939, **45**, 380; Müller and Wiesemann, *Annalen*, 1938, **537**, 86.

$(CH_3)_3C—CO—C(CH_3)_3$,† rapidly undergo complete dimerization. Again, the alkali-metal derivatives of xanthones and chromones are diamagnetic.‡

It is obvious that ketones containing primary or secondary alkyl radicals will react with alkali metals by enolization, and separation of hydrogen ion, rather than by electron addition:

$$\underset{\text{O}}{\overset{\|}{—\text{C}}}—\underset{\text{H}}{\overset{|}{\text{C}}}\langle \rightleftharpoons \underset{\text{O}}{\overset{|}{—\text{C}}}—\text{C}\langle \;\; \text{H}^+ \rightleftharpoons \underset{\text{O}^-\overset{+}{\text{Na}}}{\overset{|}{—\text{C}}}=\text{C}\langle$$

mesomeric anion

The carbonyl group is probably not the only unsaturated linkage to which electrons can add on singly. Schlenk and his colleagues§ have shown that both sodium and potassium can be added on to compounds containing the C=N, N=N, and C=C groups, provided that the resulting radical can be stabilized by resonance with *directly attached* aromatic nuclei; e.g.

$$Ph_2C=CPh_2 + \cdot Na \longrightarrow Ph_2\dot{C}—\overset{-}{\ddot{C}}Ph_2\ Na^+,$$

$$Ph_2C=\underset{\cdot\cdot}{N}Ph + \cdot Na \longrightarrow Ph_2\dot{C}—\underset{\cdot\cdot}{\overset{-}{\ddot{N}}}—Ph\ Na^+.$$

Lithium adds on to double bonds still more easily, for its reaction products are usually soluble in organic solvents.

With excess of alkali metal, substances such as tetraphenylethylene give deeply coloured metallic di-alkyls, e.g. $Ph_2\overset{-}{\ddot{C}}—\overset{-}{\ddot{C}}Ph_2\ Na_2^+$, whilst the initial product from *unsym*-diphenylethylene promptly dimerizes, and therefore was considered by Schlenk to be the neutral free radical (B):

$$Ph_2C=CH_2 + \cdot Na \longrightarrow \underset{\text{(B)}}{\underset{Na^+}{Ph_2\underset{\cdot\cdot}{\overset{-}{C}}—CH_2\cdot}} \longrightarrow \underset{Na^+}{Ph_2\underset{\cdot\cdot}{\overset{-}{C}}}—CH_2—CH_2—\underset{Na^+}{\underset{\cdot\cdot}{\overset{-}{C}}Ph_2}.$$

The addition of sodium to aromatic olefines has been compared to the addition of sodium to hexaphenylethane (p. 42) and written as a single-electron addition following non-polar dissociation of a weak C—C link, thus:

$$Ph_3C—CPh_3 \rightleftharpoons 2Ph_3C\cdot \xrightarrow{2Na\cdot} 2Ph_3\overset{-}{C}{:}Na^+,$$

$$Ph_2C=CPh_2 \rightleftharpoons Ph_2\underset{\cdot}{C}—\underset{\cdot}{C}Ph_2 \xrightarrow{2Na\cdot} (Ph_2\underset{\cdot\cdot}{\overset{-}{C}}—\underset{\cdot\cdot}{\overset{-}{C}}Ph_2)Na_2^+,$$

† Favorsky and Nazarov, *Bull. Soc. Chem.* 1934, (5) **1**, 46.
‡ Müller and Janke, loc. cit.; Müller and Wiesemann, loc. cit.
§ Schlenk and Bergmann, *Annalen*, 1928, **463**, 1; 1930, **479**, 42, 58.

but alternatively it may be a two-electron addition:

$$Ph_2C{=}CPh_2 \rightleftharpoons Ph_2\overset{+}{C}{-}\overset{\overline{\cdot\cdot}}{C}Ph_2 \xrightarrow{2e} Ph_2\ddot{C}{-}\ddot{C}Ph_2(Na^+)_2,$$

since many metallic alkyls,† such as lithium alkyls and potassium *iso*-propyl-phenyl, $\overset{+}{K}\ C_6H_5{-}\underset{\cdot\cdot}{\overset{-}{C}}(CH_3)_2$, which are evidently salts,‡ can be added on to aromatic olefines in a very similar way. It is of interest to note that whereas metallic sodium reacts with *unsym*-diphenylethylene to give a dimer, the metallic alkyl gives a simple reaction product:

$$Ph_2C{=}CH_2 + \overset{+}{K}\ Ph{-}\underset{\cdot\cdot}{\overset{-}{C}}Me_2 \longrightarrow \underset{K^+}{Ph_2\underset{\cdot\cdot}{\overset{-}{C}}}{-}CH_2{-}\underset{Ph}{\underset{|}{C}}Me_2.$$

Evidently detailed magnetic investigations are needed to establish the exact mechanisms of these alkali-metal reactions, which are on the borderline between the atomic and the ionic reaction processes.

Though alkali-metal addition products have not been isolated from aliphatic olefines, it is quite possible that even in the aliphatic series the C=C double bond may pick up electrons singly from metallic surfaces, since metals such as sodium are well-known catalysts for chain polymerization. The earliest synthesis of a rubber-like compound was Tilden's discovery of the polymerization of isoprene in the presence of metallic sodium. This may be depicted as follows:

$$CH_2{=}CMe{-}CH{=}CH_2 + \cdot Na \longrightarrow \underset{Na^+}{:\overset{-}{C}H_2}{-}CMe{=}CH{-}CH_2\cdot,$$

$$Na^+:\overset{-}{C}H_2{-}CMe{=}CH{-}CH_2\cdot + CH_2{=}CMe{-}CH{=}CH_2$$

$$\longrightarrow Na^+:\overset{-}{C}H_2{-}CMe{=}CH{-}CH_2{-}CH_2{-}CMe{=}CH{-}CH_2\cdot, \quad \text{etc.},$$

though an ionic mechanism, similar to that concerned in the formation of Melville's surface-active polymer of methyl methacrylate (p. 193) cannot be excluded, for Ziegler and his colleagues§ have shown that in this reaction too the metallic alkyls can act as polymerization catalysts. The use of metallic catalysts was formerly of technical importance for the preparation of synthetic rubbers from styrene, butadiene, and other di-olefines, but these processes are now being superseded by the use of the more controllable peroxides.

† Ziegler and Bähr, *Ber.* 1928, **61**, 253; Ziegler, *Annalen*, 1929, **473**, 7.

‡ Compare Wooster, *Chemical Reviews*, 1932, **11**, 1; Morton, ibid. 1944, **35**, 1.

§ Ziegler and Bähr, *Ber.* 1928, **61**, 253; Ziegler and Kleiner, *Annalen*, 1929, **473**, 57; Ziegler and Jakob, ibid. 1934, **511**, 45.

2. The Wurtz–Fittig reaction. The synthesis of a hydrocarbon by the reaction of a metal, such as sodium, with an alkyl or aryl halide may proceed *either* by the union of two neutral radicals,

$$CH_3I + Na\cdot \longrightarrow CH_3\cdot + NaI, \qquad 2CH_3\cdot \longrightarrow CH_3{-}CH_3,$$

or by the intermediate formation of an organo-alkali compound,

$$CH_3I + 2Na\cdot \longrightarrow CH_3^-{:}Na^+ + NaI,$$

$$CH_3^-Na^+ + C_6H_5Br \longrightarrow CH_3{-}C_6H_5 + Na^+Br^-,$$

and experimental evidence can be adduced in favour of both hypotheses.

Thus Bachmann and Clarke† showed that triphenylene and *o*-diphenylbenzene were both formed as by-products in the synthesis of diphenyl from chlorobenzene and sodium, and suggested that these products were most probably formed from free phenyl radicals by the following reactions:

$$(a)\ 2C_6H_5\cdot \longrightarrow C_6H_6 + C_6H_4\langle$$

$$(b)\ 3C_6H_4\langle \longrightarrow \text{[triphenylene]}$$

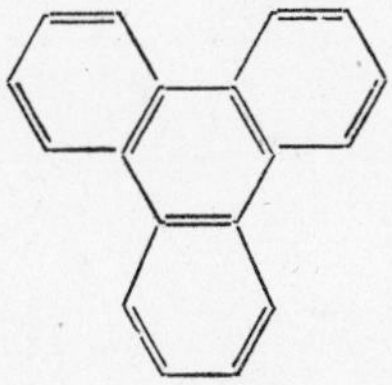

$$(c)\ 2C_6H_5\cdot + C_6H_4\langle \longrightarrow \text{[o-diphenylbenzene, } C_6H_4Ph_2]$$

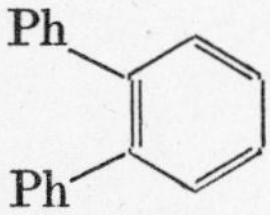

Other investigators have shown that similar complex by-products are formed in reactions involving alkyl halides, and have explained their results by an ionic mechanism.‡ It is possible to obtain sodium phenyl, $(Ph{:})^-Na^+$, in 70–80 per cent. yield by the action of sodium on chlorobenzene, whilst sodium alkyls can be obtained with still greater ease. These metallic alkyls, which can be identified in reaction mixtures by blowing in carbon dioxide, and thus converting them to carboxylic acids, e.g.

$$C_5H_{11}Na + CO_2 \longrightarrow C_5H_{11}COONa,$$

can, by a direct substitution process which has been termed *trans-metallation*, transfer their metallic atoms to other hydrocarbon molecules,§ e.g.

$$C_6H_6 + C_2H_5^-K^+ \rightleftharpoons C_6H_5^-K^+ + C_2H_6.$$

† Bachmann and Clarke, *J.A.C.S.* 1927, **49**, 2089. Compare Blum-Bergmann, ibid. 1938, **60**, 1999.

‡ Morton and Fallwell, ibid. 1937, **59**, 2387; 1938, **60**, 1429; Morton and Richardson, ibid. 1940, **62**, 123; Morton, *Chemical Reviews*, 1944, **35**, 1.

§ Compare Gilman, *Treatise on Organic Chemistry*, vol. i, chap. iv.

Again, metallic alkyls and aryls can substitute intermolecularly,† e.g.

$$C_5H_{11}Na \xrightarrow{CO_2} C_4H_9—CH_2—COONa \xrightarrow{C_5H_{11}Na} C_4H_9—\underset{}{\overset{Na}{\overset{|}{C}}}H—COONa$$

$$\xrightarrow{CO_2} C_4H_9—CH(COONa)_2,$$

$$C_6H_5Na + C_6H_{11}Na \longrightarrow m.C_6H_4Na_2 + C_6H_{12}$$

$$\downarrow CO_2$$

iso-Phthalic acid.‡

and, moreover, the organic anions of metallic alkyls can act as dehydrogenating agents, e.g.

$$R—CH_2^-Na^+ + R'CH_2—CH_2—Cl$$
$$\longrightarrow RCH_2—H + R'—CH{=}CH_2 + NaCl,$$

$$\text{(1,4-dihydronaphthalene)} + C_6H_5Li \longrightarrow C_6H_6 + LiH + \text{(naphthalene)}.\S$$

Hence all the complex by-products of the Wurtz–Fittig reaction can conceivably be formed from the ionic metallic alkyls.

Since it has been established by investigations in the triarylmethyl series|| (p. 43) that the formation of organo-alkali metal compounds is a reversible process,

$$Ph_3C\cdot + \cdot Na \rightleftharpoons (Ph_3C:)^-Na^+,$$

it follows that both hydrocarbon radicals and hydrocarbon anions may be formed together by the action of an alkali metal on an organic halide, and hence the exact mechanism of the final stage of the Wurtz–Fittig reaction must often be left as an open question. Morton, Davidson, and Hakan,¶ however, have pointed out that if sodium metal reacts with an alkyl halide merely to give a free neutral hydrocarbon radical, then its subsequent reactions should be independent of the nature of the halogen element present: i.e.

Stage 1. $R—Hal + Na\cdot \longrightarrow R\cdot + NaHal,$

Stage 2. $2R\cdot \longrightarrow R—R$ . . . *halogens not concerned*,

† Morton and Hechenbleikner, *J.A.C.S.* 1936, **58**, 1697, 2599; Morton and Newey, *J.A.C.S.* 1942, **64**, 2247. ‡ Morton, Little, and Strong, *J.A.C.S.* 1943, **65**, 1339.
§ Gilman and Bradley, ibid. 1938, **60**, 2333. || Bent, ibid. 1930, **52**, 1499.
¶ Morton, Davidson, and Hakan, ibid. 1942, **64**, 2243.

whereas if metallic alkyls are first formed then the second stage of the reaction does involve the halogen element: i.e.

Stage 1. $R—Hal + 2Na\cdot \longrightarrow R^-Na^+ + NaHal$,

Stage 2. $R^-Na^+ + R—Hal \longrightarrow R—R + NaHal$ ... *bimolecular reaction.*

Since both the rate of reaction and the composition of the final product (i.e. the ratio between dimerization and disproportionation products) does depend very much on whether the halogen is chlorine, bromine, or iodine, they consider that the normal course of the Wurtz–Fittig reaction is ionic in type.

Since the equilibrium constant for the reversible reaction between a metal, an organic radical, and the corresponding ions (free metal being present),

$$R\cdot + \cdot M \rightleftharpoons \bar{R}: + \overset{+}{M}; \qquad K = \frac{[R^-][M^+]}{[R\cdot][M\cdot]} = \frac{[M^+]e}{[Metal]} \times \frac{[R^-]}{[R\cdot]e},$$

is obviously dependent upon the electron affinities of both the hydrocarbon radical and the metallic cation concerned, it follows that ion formation will be favoured by metals of low electron discharge potentials, such as potassium, and by hydrocarbon radicals of electrophilic character, such as alkyl groups, whilst radical formation will be more probable with less reactive metals, and with radicals of low electron affinity, such as aryl radicals.

Of the alkali metals, lithium has the highest electron discharge potential, and therefore is much more likely to yield radicals than are either sodium or potassium, and in particular the lithium aryls will tend to reach an equilibrium in which the atomic rather than the ionic structure is favoured:†

$$Li^+Ph^- \rightleftharpoons Li\cdot + \cdot Ph.$$

Even lithium alkyls are reasonably soluble in hydrocarbons, such as benzene, and have abnormally low melting-points and electrical conductivities for salts, showing marked resemblances to the ether-soluble Grignard reagents. Unlike sodium and potassium compounds, the lithium alkyls react easily with oxygen, and by this reaction lithium phenyl gives a 65 per cent. yield of diphenyl, whilst as much as 85 per cent. of quaterphenyl can be obtained from lithium diphenyl. These particularly high yields of diaryls are much more indicative of reactions of neutral radicals than of organic anions. Catalysis of the chain polymerization of olefines by organo-lithium compounds (p. 206) may also be dependent upon the reversibility of the ion–radical equilibrium.

† Müller and Töpel, *Ber.* 1939, **72**, 273.

Metals of still higher discharge potential, such as silver or copper, would be expected to favour the radical state still more. Many striking cases of catalysis of the Wurtz–Fittig reaction by these metals and their salts have been recorded,† whilst the synthetic value of amalgams and other metallic couples is well known. It must be remembered, however, that the Wurtz reaction can no longer occur when the metal is not sufficiently electro-negative to break a covalent carbon–halogen bond.

The special value of copper-bronze powder in the synthesis of diaryls from aryl halides (Ullmann's reaction) is more satisfactorily explained, as above, by the production of neutral radicals on the metallic surface than by the intermediate formation of unstable organo-copper compounds.†

Strong evidence in support of the free radical mechanism for the Ullmann reaction has been brought forward by Rapson and Shuttleworth,‡ who have pointed out that when an aryl halide, Ar—X, is treated with copper-bronze powder in an organic solvent an appreciable percentage of the corresponding hydrogen compound, Ar—H, is formed. This indicates occurrence of a reaction between a free aryl radical and solvent molecules. They showed that when iodobenzene was decomposed by copper powder in ethyl benzoate solution the reaction products included both the diphenyl-2- and diphenyl-4-carboxylic esters but not the 3-carboxylic ester, and pointed out that phenylation of ethyl benzoate in the *ortho* and *para* positions was characteristic of attack by neutral phenyl radicals, as evidenced by the reactions with dibenzoyl peroxide and with aromatic diazo compounds (Chapter VIII):§

$$\mathrm{Ph\cdot + C_6H_5{-}COOEt \longrightarrow Ph{-}C_6H_4{-}COOEt + (2\text{-}Ph)C_6H_4{-}COOEt.}$$

If phenyl cations $(\mathrm{Ph})^+$ had been present, then *meta*-substituting ethyl benzoate should have yielded chiefly the 3-carboxylic ester, whilst phenyl anions, $(\mathrm{Ph}:)^-$, derived from $\mathrm{Ph^-Cu^+}$, should have yielded benzophenone, the normal product of attack on ethyl benzoate by the Grignard reagent:

$$\mathrm{C_6H_5{-}C(OEt){=}O + Ph^-(MgI)^+ \longrightarrow C_6H_5{-}C(OEt)(Ph){-}OMgI \longrightarrow Ph_2C{=}O.}$$

† See Gilman's *Organic Chemistry*, vol. i, pp. 454–7 (1938 edn.)
‡ Rapson and Shuttleworth, *Nature*, 1941, **147**, 675.
§ See, however, Hey, *J.* 1934, p. 1966.

In the synthesis of covalent organo-mercury halides by the reaction of an organic halide with mercury, e.g.

$$CH_3I + Hg \longrightarrow CH_3—Hg—I,$$

the attack on the mercury atom may follow the initial production of a neutral hydrocarbon radical.

3. Abnormal reactions of Grignard reagents. Grignard reagents generally behave as polar compounds, $R^-Mg^{++}Hal^-$, though in ether they may be covalent co-ordination compounds, and they owe their general activity to the fact that they are a convenient source of hydrocarbon anions, as evidenced by their interactions with carbonyl compounds, e.g.

$$CH_3CO—CH_3 + PhMgBr \longrightarrow (CH_3)_2\overset{\overset{\textstyle Ph}{|}}{C}—O^-(MgBr)^+.$$

Whilst the usual reaction between a Grignard reagent and a reactive alkyl halide can be represented as a simple ionic interchange, e.g.

$$CH_3I + Ph^-(MgBr)^+ \longrightarrow CH_3—Ph + I^-(MgBr)^+,$$

the process can, on occasions, exhibit all the complexity of the Wurtz–Fittig reaction. Thus benzyl halides and methyl magnesium iodide yield both ethane and dibenzyl in addition to ethylbenzene,† whilst, similarly, reactive ketones will sometimes yield benzil derivatives.‡ Again, diaryl derivatives are occasionally formed if the magnesium contains traces of silver or copper, alkyl magnesium halides under the same conditions yielding olefines and some free hydrogen.§

Though many workers had tentatively suggested that Grignard reagents, other than triphenylmethyl magnesium halides, might dissociate to free alkyl or aryl radicals, very little definite evidence for this view could be adduced until Kharasch, Mayo, and Goldberg‖ in 1938, showed that when organo-magnesium halides, containing traces of free magnesium, were heated in aromatic solvents in the presence of a minimum amount of ether, interaction with the solvent occurred, just as if free neutral radicals had been formed. For example, phenyl magnesium bromide and toluene gave a 10 per cent. yield of 4-methyldiphenyl, whilst benzyl magnesium bromide in benzene gave a 29 per cent. yield of diphenylmethane.

Kharasch and his colleagues thereupon followed up earlier indications

† Fuson, *J.A.C.S.* 1926, **48**, 2681.
‡ Fuson and Corse, ibid. 1938, **60**, 2063.
§ Linn and Noller, ibid. 1936, **58**, 816.
‖ Kharasch, Mayo, and Goldberg, ibid. 1938, **60**, 2004.

that metallic salts had an effect on the Grignard reaction, and found that the addition of from 2 to 5 mols. per cent. of cobaltous chloride very significantly changed the mechanism of the reaction between Grignard reagents and organic halides from an ionic to a free radical process.† Ferrous and nickel chlorides produced similar, but much less pronounced effects, whilst most other metallic chlorides had no apparent action. A significant example, selected from amongst the many reactions that have been worked out in detail, is the reaction between butyl magnesium bromide and bromobenzene.‡ Whereas Grignard reagents do not react with simple aromatic halides without a catalyst, the addition of cobalt chloride brings about an energetic chemical change, as a result of which 83 per cent. of the butyl magnesium bromide is converted to butane or butylene, whilst 44 per cent. of the bromobenzene gives benzene, and 14 per cent. diphenyl or polyphenyls. In general, alkyl groups are eliminated as mixtures of paraffins and olefines, whilst aromatic groups yield the corresponding aromatic hydrocarbons together with diaryls and poly-aryls. There is distinct evidence, too, that in the presence of cobaltous chloride Grignard reagents react with the ether used as the solvent, giving products similar to those formed by electrolysis of Grignard reagents in ether solution (pp. 144, 172).

These striking results are all simply explicable by the hypothesis of an initial interchange of metallic halides giving an unstable organo-cobalt compound which then breaks down:

$$R^1MgBr + CoCl_2 \longrightarrow R^1CoCl + MgClBr,$$
$$R^1CoCl \longrightarrow R^1\cdot + \cdot CoCl \quad (\textit{fast}),$$
$$\cdot CoCl + R^2Br \longrightarrow R^2\cdot + CoClBr.$$

Two different hydrocarbon radicals, $R^1\cdot$ and $R^2\cdot$, one from the Grignard reagent and the other from the organic halide, are formed in quick succession, and each may react subsequently in its own characteristic, independent, fashion. In these studies too it has been confirmed that though lower aliphatic radicals, R^1, R^2, react with the solvent rather than dimerize; dimerization becomes more prevalent with radicals of higher molecular weight, being 26 per cent. for the *cyclo*-hexyl radical and 63 per cent. with the bornyl radical.

Urry and Kharasch§ have obtained evidence indicating that whereas the β-phenyl-ethyl radical, $C_6H_5—CH_2—CH_2\cdot$, when produced in this

† Kharasch and Fields, *J.A.C.S.* 1941, **63**, 2316 et seq.; Kharasch, *et al.*, ibid. 1943, **65**, 491, 493; 1944, **66**, 365.

‡ Kharasch, Sayles, and Fields, ibid. 1944, **66**, 481.

§ Urry and Kharasch, ibid., p. 1438.

way, reacts, as would be expected, either by disproportionation or dimerization,

$$C_6H_5—CH_2—CH_2\cdot \longrightarrow C_6H_5—CH_2—CH_3 + C_6H_5—CH=CH_2,$$
$$2C_6H_5—CH_2—CH_2\cdot \longrightarrow C_6H_5—CH_2—CH_2—CH_2—CH_2—C_6H_5,$$

its $\beta\beta$-dimethyl analogue (neophyl), which cannot disproportionate, seems to isomerize:

$$C_6H_5—C(CH_3)_2—CH_2\cdot \xrightarrow{\text{(i)}} C_6H_5—CH_2—\dot{C}(CH_3)_2 \quad \text{(i)}$$
$$C_6H_5—C(CH_3)_2—CH_2\cdot \xrightarrow{\text{(ii)}} C_6H_5—\dot{C}(CH_3)—CH_2—CH_3, \quad \text{(ii)}$$

since phenyl magnesium bromide and neophyl chloride react, though only in the presence of cobalt chloride, to give *tert*-butylbenzene, *iso*-butylbenzene, *iso*-butenylbenzene, and $\beta\beta$-dimethylstyrene as well as dimerides and diphenyl:

$$2C_6H_5—CH_2—\dot{C}(CH_3)_2 \longrightarrow C_6H_5—CH_2—C(CH_3)=CH_2 + C_6H_5—CH_2—CH(CH_3)_2$$
$$2C_6H_5—CH_2—\dot{C}(CH_3)_2 \longrightarrow C_6H_5—CH=C(CH_3)_2 + C_6H_5—CH_2—CH(CH_3)_2$$

Isomerization (i), which involves the migration of a phenyl radical, seems to be well substantiated, but migration (ii), involving a methyl radical, has not yet been confirmed. These reactions have given the first undoubted proof that neutral hydrocarbon radicals can isomerize in solution just as they undoubtedly can do, at much higher temperatures, in gas-phase reactions.

A new synthesis of the dimethyl ether of the valuable drug hexoestrol, from readily accessible anaethole hydrobromide, illustrates the synthetic value of this new reaction of Grignard reagents:†

$$PhMgBr + CoCl_2 \longrightarrow PhCoCl + MgClBr,$$
$$PhCoCl \longrightarrow Ph\cdot + \cdot CoCl,$$

† Kharasch and Kleiman, ibid. 1943, **65**, 491.

$$p.\text{MeO—C}_6\text{H}_4\text{—CHBr—C}_2\text{H}_5 + \cdot\text{CoCl} \longrightarrow p.\text{MeO—C}_6\text{H}_4\text{—}\dot{\text{C}}\text{H—C}_2\text{H}_5 + \text{CoClBr},$$

$$2p.\text{MeO—C}_6\text{H}_4\text{—}\dot{\text{C}}\text{H—C}_2\text{H}_5 \longrightarrow p.\text{MeO—C}_6\text{H}_4\text{—CH(C}_2\text{H}_5\text{)—CH(C}_2\text{H}_5\text{)—C}_6\text{H}_4\text{—OMe}.$$

Cobaltous chloride has a similar effect on reactions between Grignard reagents and acyl halides. Thus whereas phenyl magnesium bromide and benzoyl chloride normally give triphenyl carbinol, when 2 per cent. of cobalt chloride is added there are also formed ethyl benzoate, diphenyl, benzophenone, phenylbenzoin, tetraphenylethylene oxide, and stilbene dibenzoate, so that evidently the active radicals phenyl, $C_6H_5\cdot$, and benzoyl, C_6H_5—$CO\cdot$, must have been formed.†

Kharasch, Morrison, and Urry‡ have found that when methyl magnesium *iodide* reacts with 2:4:6-trimethylbenzoyl chloride the product contains 35 per cent. of mesityl methyl ketone and 38 per cent. of the corresponding benzil, which, they consider, must be derived from the neutral acyl radical:

$$\text{Me}_3\text{C}_6\text{H}_2\text{—CO—Cl} + \text{CH}_3\cdot \longrightarrow \text{Me}_3\text{C}_6\text{H}_2\text{—CO}\cdot + \text{CH}_3\text{Cl} \longrightarrow \text{Me}_3\text{C}_6\text{H}_2\text{—CO—CO—C}_6\text{H}_2\text{Me}_3.$$

When methyl magnesium bromide is used in place of methyl magnesium iodide in this reaction the benzil derivative is produced only when cobalt chloride is added to the reaction mixture. They therefore consider that whereas methyl magnesium bromide (and chloride) react only in the ionic form $CH_3\text{—Mg—Br} \rightarrow (CH_3:)^-Mg^{++}(Br)^-$, except in the presence of cobalt, magnesium methyl iodide can react either by heterolytic or by homolytic bond fission,

$$\text{CH}_3\cdot + \cdot\text{MgI} \longleftarrow \text{CH}_3\text{MgI} \longrightarrow (\text{CH}_3:)^-\text{Mg}^{++}\text{I}^-,$$

though the ionic dissociation is usually the faster.

A similar difference between iodides and other halides has of course been noted in the reactions of the diazonium salts (pp. 156–65).

Surface Catalysis by Metals

Metals such as nickel, platinum, palladium, copper, and iron are widely used as surface catalysts for bringing about, at moderate temperatures, many chemical reactions such as hydrogenations, dehydrogenations, oxidations, and dehydrations which, in the absence of any catalyst, only proceed as high-temperature homogeneous gas reactions.

† Kharasch, Nudenberg, and Archer, *J.A.C.S.* 1943, **65**, 495.
‡ Kharasch, Morrison, and Urry, ibid. 1944, **66**, 368.

Since gas reactions in general are processes of atomic rather than of ionic type, it is of interest in this volume to consider briefly how their mechanisms are modified when they occur as surface processes.

It was first pointed out by Faraday that the velocity of a gas reaction might be enormously accelerated by the increase in local concentration due to the adsorption of reactant molecules on a solid surface, but this general theory is inadequate, since both the chemical nature and the surface structure of the solid catalyst have to be taken into consideration in order to explain the specificity and the enormous variability in rate of catalysed processes. Langmuir in 1916† suggested that at catalytically active surfaces *activated adsorption*, or, as it is now termed, *chemi-sorption*, occurred, adsorbed molecules being held in a mono-layer by ordinary valency forces, that is to say by covalences rather than by van der Waals forces or electrostatic attractions, since at very low pressures the initial heat of adsorption of a gas such as hydrogen or oxygen was often a large fraction of its covalent bond energy. The adsorbed gas thereby acquired different chemical properties. Thus he suggested that when carbon monoxide is adsorbed on to a nickel surface it becomes attached to nickel atoms as in nickel carbonyl, and is in fact only detachable as such. Similarly oxygen forms oxide films and hydrogen hydride films in which the molecular structures of the stable diatomic gases no longer exist undisturbed.

Langmuir showed,‡ and later workers have confirmed,§ that hydrogen gas at very low pressures forms a mono-layer of atomic and not molecular hydrogen on a clean tungsten wire, for when such a wire is heated there is driven off free atomic hydrogen capable of combining with cold phosphorus, or of reducing tungsten or molybdenum oxides. From a study of ionization potentials Gauger|| and Wolfenden¶ deduced that catalytically active surfaces of nickel and copper initially adsorbed hydrogen in the form of a mono-atomic rather than a mono-molecular film, and this conclusion has been substantiated by Kistiakowski,†† who found that the same was also true for surfaces of iron and platinum. Mono-atomic films of nitrogen can also be formed.

Since the covalent bond of a diatomic gas such as hydrogen can be broken by the process of 'chemi-sorption', it is not surprising that

† Langmuir, *J.A.C.S.* 1916, **38**, 2221, 2269.

‡ Langmuir, ibid. 1912, **34**, 1310; 1915, **37**, 417.

§ Roberts, *Proc. Roy. Soc.* 1935, A **152**, 445; *Annual Reports of the Chemical Society*, 1938, **35**, 52–69.

|| Gauger, *J.A.C.S.* 1924, **46**, 674.

¶ Wolfenden, *Proc. Roy. Soc.* 1926, A **110**, 464.

†† Kistiakowski, *J. Phys. Chem.* 1926, **30**, 1356.

chemical reactions involving single hydrogen, oxygen, or nitrogen atoms can result. The 'surface hydrides' of metals such as nickel or platinum may have covalent structures, not unlike those of the unstable hydrides NiH_2, CuH_2, FeH_2, CrH_3, described by Weichselfelder and Thiede.† On 'desorption' they may dissociate to free atomic hydrogen and bare nickel or platinum, just as the covalent lead alkyls dissociate at a somewhat higher temperature to free metal and neutral alkyl radicals. Whilst there is some indication that adsorbed atoms can migrate over the surfaces of some metallic catalysts, or even through such metals as palladium,‡ it is generally believed that chemi-sorption of stable gases occurs only at irregularly dispersed 'active centres' on a metal catalyst, and that an active catalyst may be rendered inert, or 'poisoned', by the adsorption on these centres of even minute traces of compounds such as carbon monoxide which do not readily 'desorb' or evaporate from the surface once more.

Chemical reactions involving chemi-sorbed atoms or radicals may be of three distinct types.

Firstly, the adsorbed radical may, on evaporation as a 'free' atom or radical, initiate a homogeneous gas reaction upon collision with a normal gas molecule. As mentioned in Chapters V and VII a large number of chain reactions in gases are believed to start in this way from active centres on the walls of the reaction vessel. Again, chain reactions in solution are often catalysed by solid surfaces.

Secondly, two reactants may be adsorbed simultaneously at adjacent centres of the active catalyst, where they may interact and then re-evaporate in combination: e.g.

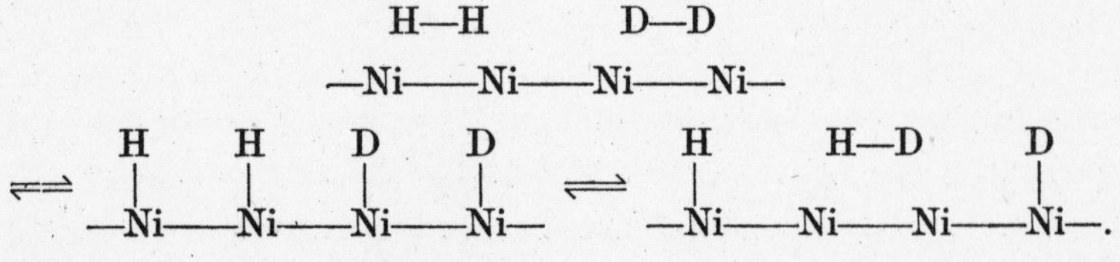

```
                    H—H        D—D
                 —Ni——Ni——Ni——Ni—

      H     H     D     D              H       H—D      D
      |     |     |     |              |                |
 ⇌  —Ni——Ni——Ni——Ni—      ⇌     —Ni——Ni——Ni——Ni—.
```

Thirdly, one chemi-sorbed substance may react on collision with an outer, unadsorbed molecule: e.g.

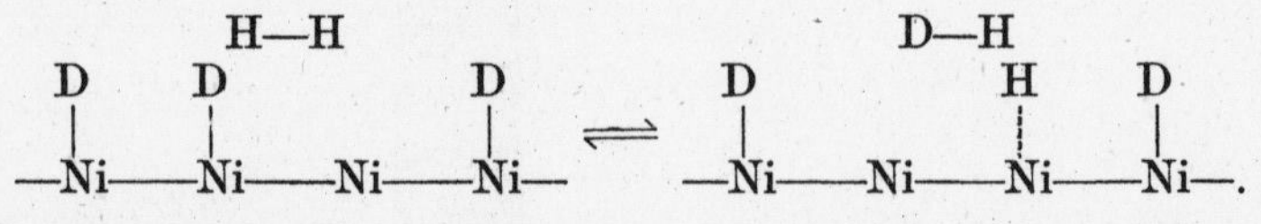

```
          H—H                              D—H
    D    D          D               D          H     D
    |    |          |       ⇌       |          ¦     |
  —Ni——Ni——Ni——Ni—               —Ni——Ni——Ni——Ni—.
```

Differentiation between these last two processes is not easy. The

† Weichselfelder and Thiede, *Annalen*, 1926, **447**, 64.

‡ Melville, *Annual Reports of the Chemical Society*, 1938, **35**, 77–80.

former would be expected to occur under conditions of slight adsorption (e.g. with gases at very low pressures) or between gases of very similar absorptive powers, whilst the last process corresponds to conditions of strong adsorption, and would be expected to hold when one reactant is adsorbed much more strongly than the other, or when the reagents are introduced successively. It affords the most satisfactory picture of surface catalysis of liquid systems (e.g. fat hydrogenation) in which chemical change can only occur at the occasional 'holes' in the mono-layer of adsorbed molecules on the catalyst surface.

Though surface reactions of these two latter types can scarcely be described as reactions of 'free' atoms or radicals, it will be seen that they are essentially two-dimensional gas reactions of the electrically neutral, or 'atomic type', and not ionic exchanges. This view has been well substantiated by investigations of catalytic hydrogenations and dehydrogenations on metal surfaces.

1. Hydrogen-deuterium exchange. Catalytically active nickel† and tungsten‡ surfaces, even at liquid-air temperature, can bring about both the interchange between the *ortho* and *para* states of molecular hydrogen (p. 31) and the atomic exchange between hydrogen and deuterium. Whilst the former reaction *may* be due to localized magnetic fields, the atomic exchange necessarily involves covalent bond fission, and it is significant that it requires approximately the same activation energy when it occurs as a surface reaction at low temperatures, or as a high-temperature gas reaction involving free atoms (p. 86):

$$H\cdot + D—D \rightleftharpoons H—D + \cdot D.$$

By pumping out an active tungsten surface which had been exposed to deuterium and then admitting only light hydrogen, Eley showed that isotope exchange still occurred rapidly.‡ This indicates that the essential reaction is one occurring between a gas molecule and a chemi-sorbed atom (mechanism 3 of p. 216) and not between two simultaneously adsorbed reactants.

Surfaces of platinum or palladium black catalyse the exchange reaction between deuterium gas and liquid water, and reaction occurs at a rate proportional to the square root of the gas pressure, which is again indicative of dissociation of the hydrogen molecule.

Many other substances, such as ammonia and alcohols, undergo deuterium exchange on metallic surfaces, and since this often proceeds

† Gould, Bleakney, and Taylor, *J. Chem. Phys.* 1934, **2**, 362; Bonhoeffer, Bach, and Fajans, *Zeit. phys. Chem.* 1934, A **168**, 313.

‡ Eley and Rideal, *Proc. Roy. Soc.* 1941, A **178**, 429; Eley, ibid., p. 452.

at a rate considerably less than that of *ortho*- to *para*-hydrogen interconversion, it has been suggested that these hydrides too are first chemi-sorbed and then dissociated to atoms and radicals upon the metal surfaces.† This has been substantiated by Morikawa, Benedict, and Taylor,‡ who have shown that methane, CH_4, and tetradeuteromethane, CD_4, will undergo isotope exchange on heated nickel surfaces. Again, just as in its gas reactions, the C—C link of a hydrocarbon such as ethane is broken more easily by catalytic hydrogenation than is a C—H link.

2. Hydrogenation of olefines. A clean nickel surface is an excellent catalyst for the hydrogenation of olefines. In 1934, by using deuterium, A. Farkas, L. Farkas, and Rideal§ showed that the catalytic hydrogenation of ethylene was accompanied by deuterium exchange, and suggested that on the nickel surface two concurrent, but independent, processes could occur,

$$C_2H_4 + D_2 \rightleftharpoons C_2H_4D_2, \qquad C_2H_4 + D_2 \rightleftharpoons C_2H_3D + HD,$$

since only hydrogenation occurred at low temperatures and only isotope exchange at high temperatures. More detailed investigations by Twigg,‖ however, have shown that the catalytic hydrogenation of olefines is a reversible process, which occurs at temperatures much below that at which hydrogen–deuterium exchange can be effected with saturated hydrocarbons such as methane. In olefine hydrogenation the olefine molecule is strongly chemi-sorbed on the metallic surface, and the hydrogen molecule reacts by subsequent collision, or at occasional 'holes' in the mono-layer. The exchange reaction thus has an associative mechanism

$$C_2H_4 + D_2 \rightleftharpoons C_2H_4D\cdot + D\cdot \rightleftharpoons C_2H_3D + H—D$$

and may be represented diagrammatically as follows,

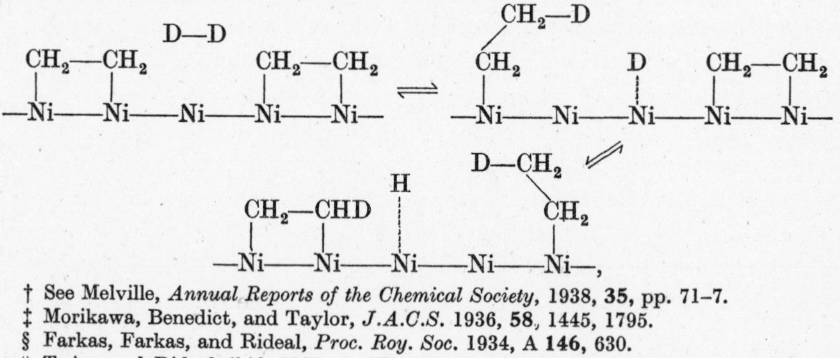

```
                                                         CH2—D
             D—D                                        /
CH2—CH2                 CH2—CH2                      CH2         D       CH2—CH2
 |    |                  |    |         ⇌             |          ¦        |    |
—Ni———Ni———Ni———Ni———Ni—                            —Ni———Ni———Ni———Ni———Ni—

                                                      D—CH2      ⇗
                                      H                    \
                   CH2—CHD            ¦                    CH2
                    |    |            ¦                     |
                  —Ni———Ni———Ni———Ni———Ni—,
```

† See Melville, *Annual Reports of the Chemical Society*, 1938, **35**, pp. 71–7.

‡ Morikawa, Benedict, and Taylor, *J.A.C.S.* 1936, **58**, 1445, 1795.

§ Farkas, Farkas, and Rideal, *Proc. Roy. Soc.* 1934, A **146**, 630.

‖ Twigg and Rideal, ibid. 1939, A **171**, 55; Twigg and Conn, ibid., p. 70; Twigg, ibid. 1941, A **178**, 106.

nickel–ethylene complexes being reversibly hydrogenated to nickel–ethyl complexes, which again by further attack of hydrogen may desorb as ethane. With higher olefines this same process can lead to isomerization, e.g.

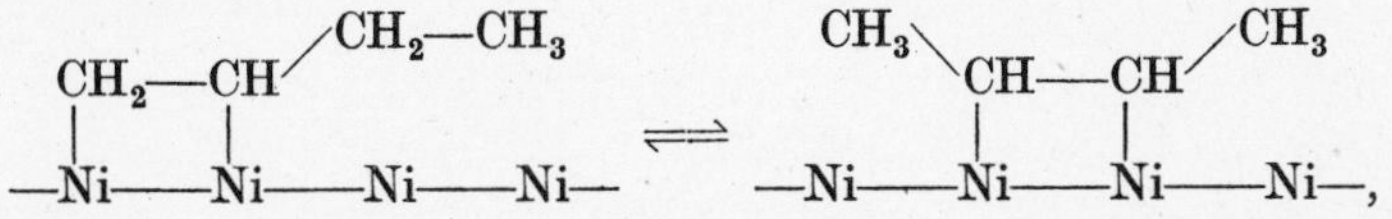

```
              /CH2—CH3            CH3\           /CH3
CH2—CH                                CH——CH
 |       |                  ⇌          |       |
—Ni——Ni——Ni——Ni—           —Ni——Ni——Ni——Ni—,
```

and it has been shown that on nickel 1-butene isomerizes to 2-butene.

Ipatieff and Komarewsky† have pointed out that there are many instances of polymerization of olefines during catalytic hydrogenation. Thus at 300° C. amylene and hydrogen give decane with a reduced iron catalyst, whilst *iso*-butane gives *iso*-octane. This is a further confirmation of the formation of univalent alkyl radicals upon metal surfaces.

Acetylene polymerizes still more extensively when hydrogenated on nickel.‡

This interpretation of the mechanism of olefine hydrogenation also serves to explain why metallic catalysts, such as platinum and palladium, can be used to effect the dehydrogenation of homocyclic compounds, such as tetralin,§ and the cyclization of paraffins to aromatic hydrocarbons.||

It may be noted that the mechanism of hydrocarbon dehydrogenation by means of sulphur¶ or selenium†† is similar. With both these reagents the detached hydrogen, or angular alkyl group, separates in the form of a covalent compound (H_2S, CH_3SeH, etc.) with the dehydrogenating agent.

The dehydrogenation of alcohols on copper surfaces,

$$R\text{—}CH_2\text{—}OH \longrightarrow R\text{—}CHO + H_2,$$

is probably a reaction of the same type.

In all these surface catalyses, great attention has to be paid to the experimental technique of preparing the catalyst. Evidently the active centres on the metallic surface are only those atoms at which there are active free valencies, and consequently great care must be taken to exclude all traces of strongly adsorbed impurities which may cover the free surfaces. There is much experimental evidence to indicate that catalytic activity is to be found at crystal edges, or at interfaces between

† Ipatieff and Komarewski, *J.A.C.S.* 1937, **59**, 720. ‡ Sheridan, *J.* 1945, p. 133.
§ Linstead *et al.*, *J.* 1937, p. 1146; 1940, pp. 1127, 1134, 1139.
|| Rideal, *Chemistry and Industry*, 1943, **62**, 335.
¶ Vesterberg, *Ber.* 1903, **36**, 4200.
†† Diels and Karstens, *Ber.* 1927, **60**, 2323; Cook and Hewett, *J.* 1933, p. 398.

different crystals at which there is a disorderly array of atoms.† Thus finely powdered metals, such as Raney nickel, or thin metallic films supported on inert powders such as kieselguhr, form very active catalysts,‡ whilst again the heating of a metallic surface until sintering occurs invariably leads to a loss of catalytic activity. Willstätter and Waldschmidt-Leitz§ showed that traces of oxygen were needed to activate platinum catalysts, and, in fact the most effective platinum catalyst is that of Adams, prepared by reducing platinum oxide *in situ*.

Whilst metallic surfaces are amongst the most efficient catalysts for hydrogenation, activated charcoal and some mixed oxides of heavy metals, such as copper chromite, can also be used. All these active surfaces have in common one structural feature which is characteristic of the metallic state, namely that they possess loosely bound electrons which can either be released to an adsorbed molecule or used to bind it, by a covalence, to the surface. It is significant that the surfaces of those oxides, such as Al_2O_3 or ThO_2, or inorganic salts in which there are no unpaired electrons but intense local electrostatic fields, are not hydrogenation catalysts, though they can often be used, at somewhat high temperatures, to effect reactions such as the dehydration of alcohols, which, when they occur in homogeneous solution, are ionic processes.

3. Other surface reactions. There is abundant, but often inconsistent, evidence of the catalysis by metals of radical-chain reactions other than hydrogenations or dehydrogenations. Oxidation by gaseous oxygen is invariably a chain reaction, and high-temperature combustion is often a surface process. The vapour-phase oxidations of both carbon monoxide and simple hydrocarbons can be initiated at surfaces of metals such as platinum, silver, copper, and iron, though at higher temperatures these same metals tend to retard the ignition of inflammable gas mixtures.

At low temperatures the autoxidation of olefines can be catalysed by metallic osmium,|| when it evidently follows the normal course, giving a hydroperoxide and then hydroxylic decomposition products. Again, dissolved oxygen can be reduced to hydrogen peroxide at surfaces of silver, copper, or mercury,¶ an action which is a source of trouble in the

† For a review see N. K. Adam, *The Physics and Chemistry of Surfaces*, chap. vii.

‡ For good reviews of experimental methods see Fieser, *Experiments in Organic Chemistry*, New York, 1941; Linstead, *Annual Reports of the Chemical Society*, 1937, **34**, 221–7.

§ *Ber.* 1921, **54**, 113.

|| Willstätter and Sonnenfeld, *Ber.* 1913, **46**, 2952.

¶ Furman and Murray, *J.A.C.S.* 1936, **58**, 429, 1846; Fryling and Tooley, ibid., p. 826.

use of metallic 'reductors' in the volumetric analysis of iron, vanadium, and other metals. In contrast to this, clean surfaces of copper, iron, and other metals have been advocated for inhibiting peroxide formation in stored ether. Metals may therefore be regarded both as chain-promoters and as chain-breakers in autoxidation, a dual action which is obviously explicable in terms of the electrochemical properties of metallic surfaces, for in the reversible system,

$$\text{metal } (= \textit{electron source}) + O_2 \rightleftharpoons (\cdot O{-}O{:})^-,$$

electron donation, equivalent to chain-initiation, is a cathodic process, and electron abstraction, equivalent to chain-breaking, is an anodic process, between which a potential balance will be reached.

The reaction between gaseous hydrogen bromide and olefines can also be catalysed by clean, finely divided, metals, such as reduced iron, nickel, or cobalt, but not by metals which are not attacked by aqueous acids.† In the complete absence of peroxides these metals bring about the 'abnormal' radical-chain addition of hydrogen bromide to allyl bromide, whereby 1:3-dibromopropane is formed,

$$H{-}Br + Br{-}CH_2{-}CH{=}CH_2 \longrightarrow Br{-}CH_2{-}CH_2{-}CH_2{-}Br,$$

though metallic salts, as for instance cadmium, copper, lead, and tin halides catalyse the 'normal' ionic addition, which gives 1:2-dibromopropane.

Single-electron release to molecular hydrogen bromide affords the best explanation of this metal catalysis:

$$e + H{-}Br \longrightarrow H\cdot + Br^-,$$

or $$Fe + HBr \longrightarrow (FeBr)^+ + H\cdot, \quad \textit{on surface film}$$

followed by

$$H\cdot + Br{-}CH_2{-}CH{=}CH_2 \longrightarrow Br{-}CH_2{-}CH_2{-}CH_2\cdot, \quad \text{etc.}$$

Electrode Reactions

Whenever a metal is placed in an electrolyte, electron movement promptly occurs and there is set up a potential difference between the metallic surface and the liquid. This potential reaches a steady and reproducible value

$$V = V_0 + \frac{RT}{nF}\log\frac{[Ox]}{[Red]}$$

for any *reversible electrode* (where [Ox] is the *activity* of the electron acceptor, [Red] that of the electron provider,‡ and V_0 depends on the

† Kharasch, Haefele, and Mayo, *J.A.C.S.* 1940, **62**, 2047.

‡ This is, of course, a constant for a solid metallic surface, but not for an amalgam.

chemical nature of the electrode reaction) at which the chemical reactions of electron uptake and electron release can both take place at the metal–solution interface: e.g.

$$\text{a metallic electrode: } Cu^{++} + 2e \rightleftharpoons Cu^{0},$$
$$\text{an oxidation electrode: } Fe^{+++} + e \rightleftharpoons Fe^{++}.$$

If, however, the electrolysis is not a reaction in which the solid–liquid interface remains unchanged, on account of the discharge of ions of the same metal as the electrode concerned, or on account of removal by diffusion of the electron acceptor (the reduction product), then the electrode becomes polarized when a measurable current passes.

Though even reversible electrodes become polarized if the electrolysis leads to concentration changes in the solution which are too large to be restored immediately by diffusion processes, there are many cases in which the passage of even a minute current produces a large change in the potential difference between the electrolyte and the electrode.

Irreversible electrodes of this type are invariably chemically inert conductors at which stable diatomic gases, such as hydrogen or oxygen, are evolved when electrolysis occurs. The behaviour of a polarizable electrode in the initial stage before there is detectable gas evolution is hard to follow, but a steady gas evolution can usually be obtained from a polarizable electrode if it is given an 'over-potential', V_w, greater than the calculable reversible electrode potential, where

$$V_w = a + b \log I,$$

where I is the current density and a and b are constants, dependent upon the nature of the surface of the electrode. Typical values of a and b for cathodic over-voltage (i.e. hydrogen discharge) are given below, though both constants depend upon the nature of the pre-treatment which has been given to the electrode surface.

TABLE XXI

Overpotentials for Electrolysis of Dilute Acid (V_w in volts, I in amps.)

Electrode material	*a*		*b*‡
	†	‡	
Platinized platinum	0·005	0·000	—
Smooth platinum	0·09	—	0·085
Gold	0·02	0·016	0·123
Silver	0·15	0·097	0·120
Copper	0·23	0·19	0·105
Mercury	0·78	0·57	0·147
Lead	0·64	0·402	0·200

† From Glasstone and Hickling, *Electrolytic Oxidation and Reduction*, London, 1935.
‡ From N. K. Adam, *The Physics and Chemistry of Surfaces*, Oxford, 1938.

Anodic over-voltages, though of the same order of magnitude, are much less reproducible than cathodic over-voltages, since electrode passivity due to the formation of adherent oxide films causes experimental difficulties.

Two rival theories of *over-voltage* have been proposed:

A. That the transfer of electrons to a hydrated ion is slow and requires activation energy; e.g.

$$e + H_3O^+ \longrightarrow H\cdot + H_2O \textit{ is slow.}$$

B. That the union of discharged atoms to the normal molecule is a slow reaction on the metal surface; e.g. that

$$2H\cdot \longrightarrow H\text{—}H \textit{ is a slow reaction.}$$

Both theories indicate that there should be a logarithmic connexion between the value of the over-potential and that of the current density, but this is not surprising. According to theory *A* the electrons must surmount an energy barrier in passing across the electrical double layer which immediately forms at the electrode surface, and, as would be expected, the over-potential for the discharge of deuterium is higher than that for hydrogen. If this theory were true it is not easy to explain why *no* over-potential is required for electron transfer to an oxidation-reduction system composed of two dissolved ions, as, for example, ferrous and ferric salts, or quinol and quinhydrone.

According to theory *B* the potential difference between the electrode and the solution is proportional to the concentration of the absorbed atoms (atomic hydrogen at a cathode) at the electrode surface, whilst their rate of recombination is proportional to the square of their concentration, from which it follows that

$$V_w = \frac{RT}{F}\log_e H\cdot + \text{const.},$$

$$\frac{I}{F} = \frac{dH\cdot}{dt} = k[H\cdot]^2,$$

whence

$$V_w = \frac{RT}{2F}\log_e I + \frac{RT}{2F}\log\frac{1}{Fk} + \text{const.} = a + 0{\cdot}029\log_{10} I.$$

Though this simple theory, due to Tafel, can scarcely be expected to be quantitatively correct, since an adsorbed layer of atoms is not wholly like a gas phase, it does show that the over-potential should increase the slower the rate of atomic recombination, and it is to be noted that Bonhoeffer's figures (p. 84) for the relative powers of different metals in catalysing the recombination of hydrogen atoms gives an order of catalytic power almost the same as the order of metals in respect to their over-potential for hydrogen, the lowest a values being found with metals which catalyse the recombination best.

Further discussion of this problem cannot be given here,† but, though it may eventually be found necessary to make use together of both postulates A and B, it does seem at present as if the slow rate of recombination of discharged atoms on metal surfaces is a factor of great importance in connexion with electrode reactions, and recent work tends to strengthen this conclusion.‡

Since electrolytic oxidation and reduction processes are of technical, as well as of academic importance, the experimental conditions requisite for obtaining high yields have been studied in detail, and it has been shown that the current density, the over-potential at the electrode, and its chemical nature, are all factors of significance.§ The researches of Tafel showed that, in general, electrolytic reduction was much more effective at cathodes of high over-potential, such as lead or mercury, than at cathodes of low over-potential, such as nickel, carbon, or platinum. Thus aldehydes, ketones, purines, and pyridine derivatives can all be reduced at cathodes of lead or mercury, but in most cases no reaction occurs at cathodes of low over-potential. Again the reduction of nitrobenzene at mercury or lead cathodes gives aniline in good yield, whilst at nickel or platinum the intermediate reduction product phenylhydroxylamine or its isomerization product p-aminophenol is formed. As would be anticipated, traces of metallic impurities, which may deposit on an electrode surface and alter its over-potential, can often inhibit or promote specific reductions.

The experimental results are in general accord with the view that electrolytic reduction is largely a reaction of discharged hydrogen atoms, facilitated by electrodes of high over-potential at which the atomic hydrogen is either liberated with a high activation energy (theory A, p. 223) or else remains in high concentration on the electrode surface (theory B). Specific catalytic effects are often found however. Thus spongy copper cathodes are particularly effective for reducing nitrates to ammonia or nitro-compounds to amines, whereas at other electrodes hydroxylamines are formed in high yields.

† See N. K. Adam, *The Physics and Chemistry of Surfaces*, chap. viii, 2nd ed., Oxford, 1938, for a critical review; also Bowden and Agar, *Annual Reports of the Chemical Society*, 1938, **35**, 90–113.

‡ Hickling and Salt, *Trans. Faraday Soc.* 1942, **38**, 474.

§ For a general survey see Glasstone and Hickling, *Electrolytic Oxidation and Reduction*, London, 1935.

It is rather significant that the effective metals for cathodic reduction are not those which are good catalysts for the catalytic reduction of organic compounds by hydrogen gas, but the reason for this is easily seen. Whilst surfaces of nickel, platinum, or palladium may catalyse both the dissociation and recombination of hydrogen, $H—H \rightleftharpoons 2H\cdot$, surfaces of lead or mercury have not this strong catalytic power. Thus under the conditions of catalytic reduction they would not dissociate molecular hydrogen to the chemically active atomic state, whereas in electrolysis they would retain on their surfaces the atomic hydrogen liberated by ionic discharge.

It is likely that still higher concentrations of atomic hydrogen may be produced at the surfaces of metals during chemical reduction in acid or alkaline solution, and in this way the high efficiency of sodium amalgam as a reducing agent can be explained.

Further evidence that uncharged atoms and radicals can be formed in contact with metals of high over-potential is afforded by the many instances of separation of the metal in the form of a covalent hydride or as an alkyl derivative. Thus both lead and mercury alkyls can be obtained by the cathodic reduction of ketones, whilst electrolysis is the only way of preparing the hydride of tin.†

† Paneth *et al.*, *Ber.* 1919, **52**, 2020; 1922, **55**, 769.

XI
SOME OXIDATION MECHANISMS
THEORETICAL INTRODUCTION

THE term 'oxidation' is used by organic chemists to denote processes involving oxygen addition or hydrogen subtraction, e.g.

$$C + O_2 = CO_2, \qquad C_2H_2 + Cl_2 = 2C + 2HCl,$$

whilst inorganic chemists find it more convenient to picture oxidation as electron removal, and its converse, 'reduction', as electron gain, thus

$$Fe^{++} \underset{\text{reduction}}{\overset{\text{oxidation}}{\rightleftharpoons}} Fe^{+++} + e.$$

The two descriptions are equivalent, in that in any oxidation process there is a net gain of electrons by the oxidizing agent, but, since in practically all covalent compounds every atom is always surrounded by completed electron shells, it is often difficult to gauge the oxidation levels† of organic compounds except by reference to their hydrogen or oxygen contents.

It will be obvious that since all free radicals and atoms, other than atomic hydrogen or free metallic atoms such as sodium, contain depleted electron shells, they should be capable of acting as oxidizing agents by abstracting electrons from other substances, e.g.

$$:\ddot{\underset{..}{Cl}}\cdot + e \longrightarrow (:\ddot{\underset{..}{Cl}}:)^-,$$

and the rapidity with which hydrocarbon radicals, such as methyl and phenyl, can dehydrogenate organic molecules is marked evidence of their strong oxidizing powers.

Nevertheless it must be pointed out that, since two shared electrons together form a single covalent bond, *two successive displacement reactions*, such as

$$\cdot CH_3 + C_nH_{2n+2} \longrightarrow CH_4 + \cdot C_nH_{2n+1},$$

$$\cdot C_nH_{2n+1} + \cdot C_nH_{2n+1} \longrightarrow C_nH_{2n} + C_nH_{2n+2}$$

(together equivalent to $2CH_3\cdot + C_nH_{2n+2} = 2CH_4 + C_nH_{2n}$),

† The *oxidation level* of an organic compound can be assessed by counting the number of hydrogen atoms in its fundamental paraffin structure that have been replaced by hydroxyl (OH) groups or their equivalents.

Thus $CH_4 + Cl_2 = CH_3Cl + HCl$ is an oxidation of methane, since CH_3Cl has the oxidation level of methyl alcohol, which it yields on hydrolysis. Similarly the Wurtz reaction, $2CH_3Cl + 2Na = C_2H_6 + 2NaCl$ is a reduction, since the oxidation level of ethane is that of $(CH_4 + CH_3OH)$ and not that of $2CH_3Cl$ ($= 2CH_3OH$).

Removal of a molecule of water, or more generally of both a positive and a negative ion, does not change the oxidation level of a compound.

are needed to change the oxidation level of a covalent compound by one unit (corresponding to the net loss of one unshared electron), and that the combination of two radicals is not an oxidation-reduction process of either. Consequently many oxidation processes can be represented equally well as homolytic or as heterolytic processes. For instance the oxidation $HOCl + 2HI = H_2O + HCl + I_2$ can be represented either as

$$HO{-}Cl \rightleftarrows HO\cdot + \cdot Cl \quad (\textit{Homolysis}),$$

followed by

$$HO\cdot + I^- \longrightarrow (HO\colon)^- + I\cdot,$$

$$\colon\ddot{\underset{\cdot\cdot}{Cl}}\cdot + I^- \longrightarrow (\colon\ddot{\underset{\cdot\cdot}{Cl}}\colon)^- + I\cdot,$$

$$2I\cdot \rightleftharpoons I{-}I,$$

or as

$$HO{-}Cl \rightleftarrows (HO\colon)^- + Cl^+ \quad (\textit{Heterolysis}),$$

followed by

$$Cl^+ + I^- \longrightarrow Cl^- + I^+,$$

$$I^+ + I^- \rightleftharpoons I{-}I.$$

Oxidation reactions play so important a part in practical chemistry that their mechanisms deserve careful study. As will be shown below many oxidations undoubtedly involve free neutral radicals, since (*a*) neutral radicals can be shown to be present in the reaction mixture, or (*b*) kinetic studies have shown that the oxidation is a chain reaction.

Some oxidations, e.g.

$$CH_3CO{-}CH_2{-}CH_3 + HNO_2 \longrightarrow CH_3{-}CO{-}\underset{\underset{NOH}{\|}}{C}{-}CH_3 \longrightarrow CH_3{-}CO{-}CO{-}CH_3,$$

undoubtedly are heterolytic, involving electron pairs **only,** whilst others may involve processes of both types. To instance the complexity of oxidation mechanisms it may be pointed out here that many well-known oxidizing agents, such as chromic acid and potassium permanganate, seem to undergo valency changes in which three or more electrons are simultaneously involved, e.g.

$$CrO_3 \longrightarrow Cr^{+++} + 3e, \qquad MnO_4^- \longrightarrow Mn^{++} + 5e,$$

although the compounds concerned may contain no more than electron pair bonds. However, it may well be that in these cases a rapid succession of reactions occurs.

Oxidation with Lead Tetra-acetate, $Pb(OCOCH_3)_4$

Lead tetra-acetate, which is easily prepared by warming red lead in glacial acetic acid, was first introduced as an oxidizing agent by Dimroth and Schweizer,† who showed that it could be used to convert

† *Ber.* 1923, **56**, 1375.

$>CH_2$ groups to $>CH—OCOCH_3$, and that in a few cases it could be used to add two $OCOCH_3$ groups on to double bonds, e.g.

$$CH_2(COOEt)_2 + Pb(OAc)_4 \longrightarrow CH_3COO—CH(COOEt)_2 + Pb(OAc)_2 + CH_3COOH,$$

$$C_6H_5—CH_3 + Pb(OAc)_4 \longrightarrow C_6H_5—CH_2—OCOCH_3 + Pb(OAc)_2 + CH_3—COOH.$$

In 1930 R. Criegee† investigated the reactions of lead tetra-acetate more fully, and showed that, in glacial acetic acid solution, it seemed to react by splitting into lead diacetate, $Pb(OCOCH_3)_2$, and two acetate groups, $OCOCH_3$, which could

(*a*) both abstract hydrogen atoms, forming acetic acid, e.g.

$$C_6H_4(OH)_2 + Pb(OAc)_4 \longrightarrow C_6H_4O_2 + Pb(OAc)_2 + 2CH_3COOH;$$

(*b*) abstract one hydrogen atom from CH_2, etc., and then add on one acetoxy group to the residue, as in the oxidation of toluene (above); or

(*c*) add on two acetoxy groups to a double bond, e.g.

$$\text{cyclopentene } (CH_2) \longrightarrow \text{cyclopentane-1,2-diyl diacetate: } (CH_2)\; \overset{H}{C}—OCOCH_3,\; \underset{H}{C}—OCOCH_3 \;+\; \text{cyclopentene with } \overset{H}{C}—OCOCH_3,\; CH—OCOCH_3,\; \underset{OCOCH_3}{CH}$$

and pointed out that in systems containing the group $—CH_2—CH{=}CH—$ reactions (*b*) and (*c*) could both occur. Thus *cyclo*-hexene when oxidized with lead tetra-acetate gave 30 per cent. of Δ^2-*cyclo*-hexenol and 16 per cent. of *cyclo*-hexanediol acetate.

These oxidations were all slow reactions, but a year later Criegee showed that lead tetra-acetate in glacial acetic acid was a rapid specific agent for the quantitative oxidation of α-glycols,‡ which can thereby be split to give ketones:

$$\begin{matrix} R_1R_2C—OH \\ | \\ R_3R_4C—OH \end{matrix} + Pb(OCOCH_3)_4 \longrightarrow \begin{matrix} R_1R_2C{=}O \\ + \\ R_3R_4C{=}O \end{matrix} + Pb(OCOCH_3)_2 + 2CH_3COOH.$$

Compounds of the types of

$$\begin{matrix} | \\ —C—OH \\ | \\ —C—NH— \\ | \end{matrix} \quad \text{and} \quad \begin{matrix} | \\ —C—NH— \\ | \\ —C—NH— \\ | \end{matrix}$$

† *Annalen*, 1930, **481**, 263.

‡ Criegee, *Ber.* 1931, **64**, 260.

react in the same way, and of cyclic compounds *cis* diols react very much faster than *trans* diols, the maximum reaction velocity being reached with *cis* diols of the *cyclo*-pentane series.

On account of its simplicity, and specificity, this reaction found an immediate useful application in the elucidation of the structures of natural products,† for, as will be appreciated, reaction sequences such as

$$R_1—CH_2—CH(OH)—R_2 \longrightarrow R_1—CH{=}CH—R_2$$
$$\longrightarrow R_1—CH(OH)—CH(OH)—R_2 \longrightarrow R_1—CHO + OCH—R_2$$

can be used to disrupt cyclic alcoholic, or olefinic, compounds into more easily characterizable fragments. In carbohydrate chemistry too the reaction is of value, for it enables one to split the carbon chain of a sugar without affecting the C—O—C bond of a pyranose or furanose ring. Periodic acid, which acts on glycols in exactly the same way,‡ is however a preferable reagent to use with carbohydrates since it reacts in aqueous solution (see p. 257).

By 1933 Criegee, Kraft, and Rank,§ from a careful study of reaction velocities, came to the conclusion that the essential step in the glycol fission was the removal of the two hydrogen atoms of the hydroxyl groups, but, not favouring the idea of the transient formation of a biradical (I) or a 'moloxide' (II), they suggested that a cyclic lead compound (III) might be an intermediate:

$$\begin{matrix} | \\ —C—OH \\ | \\ —C—OH \\ | \end{matrix} \longrightarrow \underset{(I)}{\begin{matrix} | \\ —C—O\cdot \\ | \\ —C—O\cdot \\ | \end{matrix}} \left[or \quad \underset{(II)}{\begin{matrix} | \\ —C—O \\ |\quad\;\; | \\ —C—O \\ | \end{matrix}} \right] \longrightarrow \begin{matrix} | \\ —C{=}O \\ + \\ —C{=}O \\ | \end{matrix} \qquad (A)$$

$$\begin{matrix} | \\ —C—OH \\ | \\ —C—OH \\ | \end{matrix} + Pb(OAc)_4 \longrightarrow \begin{matrix} | \\ —C—OPb(OAc)_3 \\ | \\ —C—OH \\ | \end{matrix} + CH_3COOH$$

(slow, bimolecular)

$$\rightleftharpoons \underset{(III)}{\begin{matrix} | \\ —C—O \\ | \\ —C—O \\ | \end{matrix}\!\!\!>Pb(OAc)_2} \longrightarrow \begin{matrix} | \\ —C{=}O \\ + \\ —C{=}O \\ | \end{matrix} + Pb(OAc)_2 \qquad (B)$$

(reversible equilibrium, very fast)

† For a survey of the subject see *Annual Reports of the Chemical Society*, **1937**, **34**, 231–42.

‡ Malaprade, *Compt. rend.* **1928**, **186**, 382.

§ *Annalen*, **1933**, **507**, 159.

and in accordance with this view showed that lead tetra-acetate reacted with dry methyl alcohol to give a yellow product, $Pb(OCOCH_3)_3(OCH_3)$, which subsequently oxidized to formaldehyde.

In considering the mechanism of oxidation by lead tetra-acetate it must be remembered that this important work of Criegee preceded by almost a decade that of Fieser and of Kharasch (pp. 139–42), who have shown that the initial decomposition leads to the production of free, neutral, acetate radicals,

$$Pb(OCOCH_3)_4 \longrightarrow Pb(OCOCH_3)_2 + 2\cdot OCOCH_3, \qquad (C)$$

for to-day it is obvious that all the reactions of Criegee are dehydrogenations and additions, which are typical of the acetate radical. Scheme (A) above does explain satisfactorily the kinetics of the oxidation of glycols, for the decomposition of the tetra-acetate (C) is a slow and possibly reversible process, and hence the concentration of free acetate radicals will be given by the equation

$$[\cdot OCOCH_3] = K[Pb(OAc)_4]^{\frac{1}{2}},$$

whilst the rate-determining stage will be the oxidation of the glycol by two acetate radicals, for which the rate of reaction will be

$$k[\text{Glycol}][\cdot OCOCH_3]^2 = kK[\text{Glycol}][Pb(OAc)_4],$$

which agrees with Criegee's experimental bimolecular reaction.

Whilst Criegee invariably worked in glacial acetic acid as a solvent it has been found more recently by Baer† that the presence of water, or alcohol, is not disadvantageous. Moreover, in the presence of water α-ketonic acids can be decarboxylated, e.g.

$$C_6H_5COCOOH + Pb(OAc)_4 + H_2O$$
$$= C_6H_5COOH + Pb(OAc)_2 + 2CH_3COOH + CO_2,$$

whilst α-hydroxy ketones oxidize similarly,

$$\underset{\underset{OH}{|}}{PhCH}\text{—}CO\text{—}Ph \longrightarrow PhCHO + HOCOPh.$$

Baer considers that these oxidations are all preceded by addition of the elements of water, or alcohol, to the α-keto group, to give a *pseudo*-glycol (IV), (V), since (i) the reaction hardly occurs in anhydrous solvents, and (ii) in the presence of alcohol, or of hydrogen cyanide, esters or nitriles are formed:

$$CH_3CO\cdot COOH + EtOH$$
$$\rightleftharpoons \underset{(IV)}{CH_3\text{—}\overset{}{\underset{OEt\ \ OH}{C}}\text{———}\underset{\underset{HO}{|}}{C}\text{=}O} \longrightarrow CH_3\text{—}\underset{\underset{OEt}{|}}{C}\text{=}O + CO_2 + H_2O$$

† *J.A.C.S.* 1939, **61**, 2607; 1940, **62**, 1597; 1942, **64**, 1416.

$$\text{Ph—CO—COOH} + \text{HCN} \rightleftharpoons \text{Ph—}\underset{\text{CN}\ \ \text{OH}}{\overset{}{\text{C}}}\text{———}\underset{\text{HO}}{\overset{}{\text{C}}}\text{=O} \longrightarrow \text{Ph—}\underset{\text{CN}}{\text{CO}} + CO_2 + H_2O$$

(V)

This decarboxylation reaction of α-ketonic acids may have a great biological significance (see pp. 272–3). Baer has shown that acetyl choline can be obtained by oxidizing pyruvic acid in the presence of choline chloride with lead tetra-acetate† in glacial acetic acid,

$$CH_3CO\text{—}COOH + HOC_2H_4NMe_3\bar{Cl} \xrightarrow{Pb(OAc)_4} CH_3CO\text{—}OC_2H_4\overset{+}{N}Me_3\bar{Cl} + CO_2,$$

and it is thus possible that biological acetylation may, in general, be an outcome of a free radical oxidation of this type.

One very significant feature of oxidation by lead tetra-acetate is the fact that the attack on the OH groups of glycols is both specific and rapid, whereas the attacks on CH_2 groups, or on double bonds, are very much slower, and not so specific. In accordance with Kharasch's mechanism for the reaction between diacetyl peroxide and glacial acetic acid (p. 139), the dehydrogenation of CH_2 groups can best be represented as a reaction of active methyl radicals, resulting from the eventual decomposition,

$$CH_3CO\text{—}O\cdot \longrightarrow CH_3\cdot + CO_2,$$

whilst the attack on the more active hydrogen atoms of OH groups must obviously be a reaction of the acetate radical, $CH_3CO\text{—}O\cdot$, itself, since there is no evolution of carbon dioxide in the glycol fission process. The neutral acetate radical is a stabilized resonance structure, (VI),

$$CH_3\text{—}C\begin{cases} =\ddot{O}: \\ \ \cdot \\ -\underset{\cdot\cdot}{\dot{O}}: \end{cases}$$

(VI)

in which the unpaired electron may reside on either of two symmetrical oxygen atoms, and consequently its available combining energy will not be very high. Again, in glacial acetic acid solution the life of the free acetate radical will be increased by solvent regeneration (p. 19), whilst when water, or alcohol, are present, hydroxyl and similar radicals may be the main oxidizers, e.g.

$$CH_3CO\text{—}O\cdot + H\text{—}OR \rightleftharpoons CH_3\text{—}CO\text{—}O\text{—}H + \cdot OR.$$

In consequence of this regenerative exchange the alkyloxy radicals of monohydric alcohols must be considered as entities of long apparent

† *J. Biol. Chem.* 1942, **146**, 391.

life, and hence the rate of fission of a glycol, which will require the juxtaposition of two R—O· radicals, will be governed very largely by the probability of two R—O· groups coming into steric proximity.

Autoxidation

1. General theories.† The term 'autoxidation' is used to describe oxidations which can be brought about by oxygen gas at normal temperatures without the intervention of a visible flame or of an electric spark. Kinetic studies have shown that autoxidation processes are auto-catalytic chain reactions which can be influenced greatly by both positive and negative catalysts; many can be initiated photochemically.

It has very frequently been found that *peroxides* are the initial products of autoxidations, and therefore it was suggested in 1897 by both Engler and Bach that molecular oxygen acted by an addition process to give a peroxide, or a cyclic 'moloxide', which might subsequently break down, or hand on its oxygen to other molecules, thus

$$A + O_2 \rightleftharpoons AO_2, \qquad AO_2 + B \longrightarrow AO + BO.$$

For instance benzaldehyde reacts with oxygen to give perbenzoic acid, which can oxidize more benzaldehyde,‡

$$PhCHO + O_2 \longrightarrow Ph{-}C(=O){-}OOH;$$

$$Ph{-}C(=O){-}OOH + PhCHO \longrightarrow 2Ph{-}C(=O){-}OH$$

whilst *unsym*-diphenylethylene reacts with oxygen to give a polymeric 'moloxide' which subsequently breaks down to a mixture of benzophenone and formaldehyde, very much in the same way as ozonides break down when treated with water:§

$$Ph_2C{=}CH_2 + O_2 \longrightarrow Ph_2C{-}CH_2(-O{-}O-) \longrightarrow Ph_2C{=}O + CH_2O.$$

Wieland, however, pointed out that autoxidations of many organic substances, such as amines, phenols, and thiols, were dehydrogenations in which molecular oxygen was reduced first to hydrogen peroxide and then to water.

† For literature reviews see Moureu and Dufraisse, *Second Solvay Report*, 1926, pp. 524–80; Milas, *Chemical Reviews*, 1932, **10**, 295–364.

‡ Beek, *Rec. trav. chim.* 1928, **47**, 286, 301.

§ Staudinger, *Ber.* 1925, **58**, 1075.

Since all autoxidations appear to be chain reactions it is reasonable to assume that processes of *neutral* bond fission are concerned. It has already been mentioned that molecular oxygen is paramagnetic, and it may therefore be given the formula of a bi-radical, containing two unpaired electrons, $\cdot\ddot{\underset{\cdot\cdot}{O}}—\ddot{\underset{\cdot\cdot}{O}}\cdot$. Hence it is an attractive theory to suppose that the autoxidations are free radical addition processes. However, whilst an active bi-radical may well be produced by photochemical activation, normal molecular oxygen has a resonance-stabilized structure.† It is too inert to combine immediately with the double bond of an olefine or an aldehyde and a catalyst is usually required to start a reaction chain. Typical catalysts include substances, such as dibenzoyl peroxide, which generate free neutral radicals (Chapter VIII), and metallic cations which can undergo a one-electron valency change, and it is therefore reasonable to suppose that autoxidation catalysts act by generating free peroxide radicals in which there is only one unpaired electron, e.g.

$$R\cdot + O_2 \longrightarrow R—O—O\cdot,$$

$$Fe^{++} + O_2 \rightleftharpoons Fe^{+++} + (\cdot O—O:)^- \quad \text{(the anion of } \cdot O—O—H).$$

These radicals will obviously be capable *either* of adding on to unsaturated linkages, *or* of abstracting hydrogen, generating in each case further active radicals by means of which the chemical change can be perpetuated.

This reaction mechanism has been confirmed experimentally by Ziegler and Ewald,‡ who have shown that the free radical triphenylmethyl can initiate the autoxidation of many aldehydes and olefines, such as anisaldehyde, styrene, and indene. The reaction between hexaphenylethane and oxygen is itself a rapid chain reaction,

$$Ph_3C—CPh_3 \rightleftharpoons 2Ph_3C\cdot,$$

$$\left.\begin{array}{r} Ph_3C\cdot + O_2 \longrightarrow Ph_3C—O—O\cdot, \\ Ph_3C—O—O\cdot + Ph_3C—CPh_3 \longrightarrow Ph_3C—O—O—CPh_3 + Ph_3C\cdot, \end{array}\right\}$$

with an overall reaction velocity much greater than the rate of dissociation of hexaphenylethane (compare p. 47). As many as 50,000 mols. of an olefine such as dimethylbenzofulvene can be oxidized by each reaction chain started by a triphenylmethyl radical,

$$Ph_3C—O—O\cdot + R_2C{=}CR'_2$$

$$\longrightarrow \begin{array}{c} R_2C—CR'_2 \\ | \\ Ph_3C—O—O \end{array} \xrightarrow{O_2} \begin{array}{c} R_2C—CR'_2 \\ |\qquad | \\ Ph_3C—O—O—\quad O—O\cdot \end{array} \text{ etc.,}$$

† See Waters, *Physical Aspects of Organic Chemistry*, 1937 ed., pp. 47 and 150–4.
‡ *Annalen*, 1933, **504**, 162; compare Ziegler and Gänicke, ibid, 1942, **551**, 213.

but the addition of a trace of a substance such as pyrogallol, from which hydrogen can readily be abstracted, promptly inhibits the chain reaction of the olefine in the same way as it inhibits the chain oxidation of hexaphenylethane itself. From the pyrogallol there is formed a radical (a semi-quinone) which has a resonance-stabilized structure and which consequently has too low an energy content for further reaction with either oxygen or any autoxidizable substances.

Pyrogallol has a structure which is typical of the 'anti-oxidants' by means of which one can stabilize unsaturated fats, vitamins, and many other easily oxidized natural and commercial products.†

As described in Chapter IX (p. 177), free halogen atoms can initiate the autoxidation of olefines in an exactly similar way. The autoxidation products of many olefines, such as styrene or indene, can simultaneously initiate their chain polymerization (Chap. IX, pp. 192–200), but in other cases oxygen gas is an inhibitor of chain polymerization. Obviously there will be a competition between the autoxidation and polymerization processes in which the radical of lesser reactivity will eventually be formed.

Many autoxidations are chemi-luminescent, part of the energy of chemical combination being emitted as light.

Further characteristic features of autoxidation are best exemplified by the more detailed discussions of the typical reactions which are dealt with below.

2. The autoxidation of sulphites. The autoxidation of aqueous sodium sulphite,

$$2Na_2SO_3 + O_2 = 2Na_2SO_4,$$

is a typical inorganic chain reaction which has been studied in great detail. It proceeds at a rate proportional to the concentration of the sodium sulphite, but independent of the oxygen concentration, and can be accelerated both photochemically and by traces of the cations of many heavy metals. Copper salts are particularly active, even 10^{-13} molar copper sulphate having a noticeable effect.‡

Aniline, carbohydrates, glycerol, and a number of other alcohols inhibit this autoxidation so successfully that they can be used to stabilize standard solutions of sulphites for volumetric analysis, whilst sulphites can induce the autoxidation of many of these inhibitors, such as arsenites, nitrites, and aldehydes.

† For a review of this see K. C. Bailey, *The Retardation of Chemical Reactions*, London, 1937.

‡ Titoff, *Zeit. phys. Chem.* 1903, **45**, 641.

Haber and Willstätter†, and Bäckström‡, have successfully interpreted this autoxidation as a chain process involving the radical-ion, $\cdot SO_3^-$ (or $HSO_3\cdot$), to which one may assign the electron structure (VII) in which the sulphur atom has an odd number of electrons.

$$\bar{O}\!-\!\overset{\overset{\displaystyle O}{\|}}{\underset{\underset{\displaystyle O}{\|}}{S}}\cdot \qquad \text{(VII)}$$

This accords with the facts (*a*) that copper sulphate and sodium sulphite react in absence of oxygen to give cuprous oxide and sodium dithionate,§ and (*b*) that the photochemical decomposition of sodium sulphite yields sodium dithionate and hydrogen:||

$$Cu^{++} + SO_3^{=} \longrightarrow Cu^{+} + \cdot SO_3^-, \qquad \text{(i)}$$

$$SO_3^{=} + h\nu \longrightarrow \cdot SO_3^- + e, \qquad \text{(ii)}$$

$$2\cdot SO_3^- \longrightarrow S_2O_6, \qquad e + H_2O \longrightarrow H\cdot + (:OH)^-.$$

They consider that reactions (i) and (ii) initiate the metal-catalysed and photochemical oxidations respectively, and represent the subsequent reaction chain as

$$\cdot SO_3^- + O_2 \longrightarrow \cdot SO_5^-, \qquad \text{(iv)}$$

$$(\cdot SO_5)^- + HSO_3^- \longrightarrow (HSO_5)^- + \cdot SO_3^-, \qquad \text{(v)}$$

where the $(\cdot SO_5)^-$ radical has the structure (VIII) and $(HSO_5)^-$ (IX) is the univalent anion of Caro's acid, H_2SO_5, which is a sufficiently powerful oxidizer to convert sulphites directly to sulphates

$$(HO\!-\!O\!-\!SO_3)^- + SO_3^{=} \longrightarrow (O\!\leftarrow\!SO_3)^{=} + (H\!-\!O\!-\!SO_3)^-$$

by a reaction which is typical of the per-acids (p. 245).

$$\bar{O}\!-\!\overset{\overset{\displaystyle O}{\|}}{\underset{\underset{\displaystyle O}{\|}}{S}}\!-\!O\!-\!O\cdot \qquad\qquad O\!-\!\overset{\overset{\displaystyle O}{\|}}{\underset{\underset{\displaystyle O}{\|}}{S}}\!-\!O\!-\!O\!-\!H$$

(VIII) (IX)

When alcohols are used as inhibitors they are oxidized to aldehydes. Bäckström has attributed this action to the active peroxide $(\cdot SO_5)^-$, which again may be concerned in all the other induced oxidations.

It will be recalled that the $(\cdot SO_3)^{-}$ radical (VII) is thought to be

† *Ber.* 1931, **64**, 2844. ‡ *Zeit. phys. Chem.* 1934, B **25**, 122.

§ Baubigny, *Compt. rend.* 1912, **154**, 701; *Ann. chim. phys.* 1910 [8], **20**, 12; 1914 [9], **1**, 201.

|| Haber and Wansbrough-Jones, *Zeit. phys. Chem.* 1932, B **18**, 103.

involved in the peroxide-catalysed addition of bisulphites to olefines (p. 187).

Further evidence for the presence of the $(\cdot SO_3)^-$ radical in the autoxidation of sulphites is afforded by the fact that nuclear sulphonation occurs when phenols are autoxidized in ammonium sulphite solution in the presence of a trace of a copper salt.† Simultaneously an amino group may be introduced into an aromatic ring. Thus the compound (X) may be obtained by passing air through an aqueous mixture of quinol, methylamine, and sulphur dioxide, in the presence of a little copper hydroxide.‡

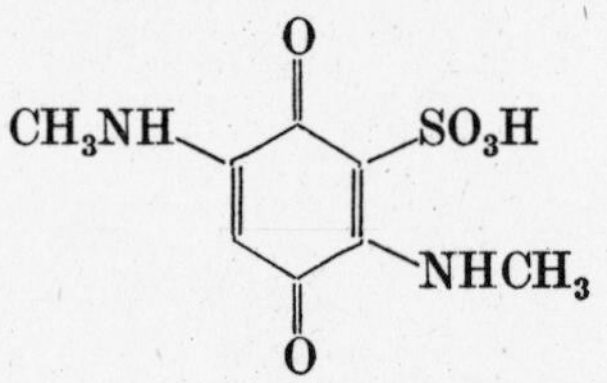

O, CH_3NH, SO_3H, $NHCH_3$, O

(X)

OH, O, H $\cdot + \cdot SO_3H \longrightarrow$ OH, SO_3H, H, O

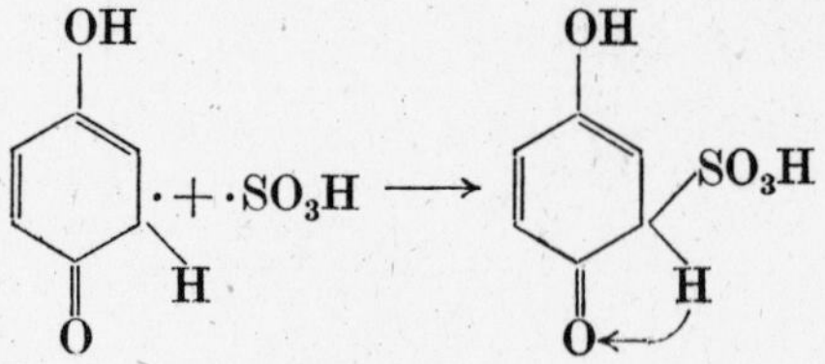

(X a)

Similar reactions to this occur in photographic development, where photo-sensitized silver bromide is reduced by organic agents such as pyrogallol, quinol, or aminophenols in the presence of an excess of sulphite ion. The sulphite is used principally to remove the oxidized form of the developing agent, and by functioning in this way the sulphite also inhibits the autoxidation of the developing agents.

Thus when quinol is used the overall reaction is

$$\text{Quinol} \xrightarrow{2AgBr} \text{Quinone} \xrightarrow{Na_2SO_3} \text{Quinol-monosulphonate,}$$

although the initial process probably involves the formation of a semi-quinone radical§ (compare p. 73). In both these cases it seems probable that the sulphonation is effected by the addition of the bisulphite radical to the semi-quinone, as indicated in (X a).

Addition reactions of similar type may also be involved in the substitutions of quinones by hydrogen sulphide and by mercaptans such as acetyl cysteine and the reduced form of glutathione.‖ Analogous reactions have been reported in the phenazine series¶ in which hydroxy,

† Garreau, *Bull. Soc. Chim.* 1934, (v) **1,** 1563.

‡ Garreau, *Compt. rend.* 1936, **203,** 1073.

§ Compare Weissberger, Thomas, and Lu Valle, *J.A.C.S.* 1943, **65,** 1489. James and Weissberger, ibid. 1939, **61,** 442. See also Chapter IV.

‖ Compare Fieser and Fieser, *Textbook* (1944), p. 738; Snell and Weissberger, *J.A.C.S.* 1939, **61,** 450.

¶ McIlwain, *J.* 1937, p. 1704; Kehrmann, *Ber.* 1913, **46,** 341.

amino, cyano, and sulphonate groups may all be introduced by autoxidation.

3. The autoxidation of aldehydes.† The autoxidation of benzaldehyde has been studied by many workers from the days of Wohler and Liebig, who in 1832 showed that light accelerates the conversion of benzaldehyde to benzoic acid on exposure to air. Other aldehydes, such as acetaldehyde, behave similarly, but are in general more difficult to study experimentally.

The reaction between benzaldehyde and oxygen shows all the typical features of autoxidations. Thus (i) it is photo-sensitive, and one quantum of light may bring about the oxidation of up to 10,000 molecules of aldehyde; (ii) kinetic studies have shown that the reaction has a chain mechanism, both in the light and in the dark; (iii) rapid reaction is usually preceded by an induction period and subsequently the reaction velocity falls off; (iv) traces of many metallic salts, particularly of iron, copper, nickel, manganese, and chromium, can catalyse oxidation in the absence of light, while sulphites, and many organic compounds, such as phenols, amines, and alcohols can act as inhibitors even in concentrations as low as 0·01 per cent.

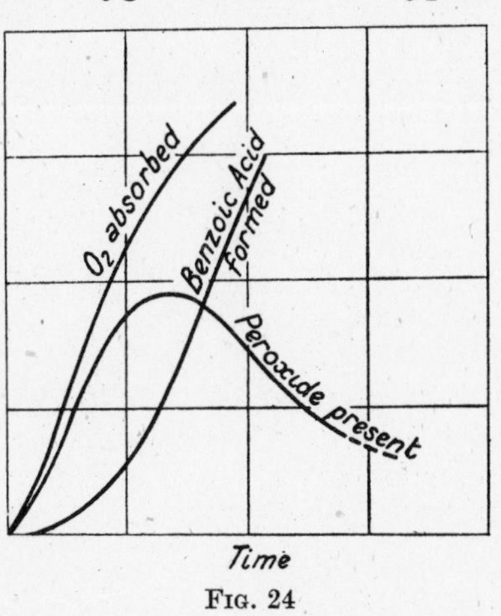

FIG. 24

Many reactions of the autoxidation mixture, such as the oxidation of iodides, ferrocyanides, indigo, and other dyestuffs, have shown that the initial product is a very active peroxide, which subsequently decomposes as benzoic acid forms in quantity, as indicated in Fig. 24.‡ Perbenzoic acid can easily be isolated as an autoxidation product of benzaldehyde. Baeyer and Villiger in 1900§ showed that perbenzoic acid would oxidize benzaldehyde to benzoic acid, and therefore suggested that the reaction process could be expressed as

$$\mathrm{PhCHO} + \mathrm{O_2} \longrightarrow \mathrm{Ph{-}CO{-}OOH},$$

$$\mathrm{Ph{-}CO{-}OOH} + \mathrm{Ph{-}CHO} \longrightarrow \mathrm{2Ph{-}CO{-}OH},$$

† For reviews see Bailey, *The Retardation of Chemical Reactions*; Linstead, *Annual Reports of the Chemical Society*, 1937, **34**, 233–7.

‡ Compare Almquist and Branch, *J.A.C.S.* 1932, **54**, 2293.

§ *Ber.* 1900, **33**, 1569.

but this does not explain all the features of the oxidation, since in presence of acetic anhydride benzaldehyde takes up twice as much oxygen as does free benzaldehyde, and then forms benzoyl-acetyl-peroxide, $Ph—CO—O—O—CO—CH_3$.† Again, an oxidizing mixture of benzaldehyde and air is *much more reactive* than free perbenzoic acid: it will bring about the oxidation of anthracene, which perbenzoic acid will not,‡ and will even cause the breakdown of carbon tetrachloride to hydrogen chloride, phosgene, and other products.§ These facts accord with the view that the initial active product is a free peroxide radical, produced by the addition of oxygen to activated benzaldehyde:||

$$\text{Ph—CHO} + \text{Radical} \longrightarrow \text{Ph—}\dot{\text{C}}\text{=O} + \text{H—Radical}$$

$$\left.\begin{array}{l} \text{Ph—}\dot{\text{C}}\text{=O} + \text{O}_2 \longrightarrow \text{Ph—C}\begin{array}{l}\diagup \text{O—O}\cdot \\ \diagdown\!\!\diagdown \text{O}\end{array} \\ \text{Ph—CH=O} + \text{Ph—C}\begin{array}{l}\diagup \text{O—O}\cdot \\ \diagdown\!\!\diagdown \text{O}\end{array} \longrightarrow \text{Ph—}\dot{\text{C}}\text{=O} + \text{Ph—C}\begin{array}{l}\diagup \text{O—O—H} \\ \diagdown\!\!\diagdown \text{O}\end{array} \end{array}\right\} \textit{chain process.}$$

Bäckström ascribes the initial activation of benzaldehyde by light to the reaction sequence:

$$\text{Ph—C}\begin{array}{l}\diagup \text{H} \\ \diagdown\!\!\diagdown \text{O}\end{array} + h\nu \longrightarrow \text{Ph—}\underset{\cdot}{\overset{\text{H}\,\diagup}{\text{C}}}\text{——}\underset{\cdot}{\text{O}},$$

$$\text{Ph—}\underset{\cdot}{\overset{\text{H}\,\diagup}{\text{C}}}\text{——}\underset{\cdot}{\text{O}} + \text{Ph—CH=O} \longrightarrow \text{Ph—}\underset{\cdot}{\text{C}}\begin{array}{l}\diagup \text{H} \\ \diagdown \text{O—H}\end{array} + \text{Ph—}\dot{\text{C}}\text{=O},$$

in which the C=O group is first converted to a bi-radical. In accordance with this view it has been shown that many aldehydes and ketones can dehydrogenate alcohols on photochemical activation,¶ and again the Cannizzaro reaction is a process of this type (p. 190). The reaction

$$\text{Ph—C}\begin{array}{l}\diagup \text{O—O}\cdot \\ \diagdown\!\!\diagdown \text{O}\end{array} + \text{Ph—}\underset{\cdot}{\text{C}}\begin{array}{l}\diagup \text{H} \\ \diagdown \text{O—H}\end{array} \longrightarrow \text{Ph—C}\begin{array}{l}\diagup \text{O—O—H} \\ \diagdown\!\!\diagdown \text{O}\end{array} + \text{Ph—C}\begin{array}{l}\diagup \text{H} \\ \diagdown\!\!\diagdown \text{O}\end{array}$$

is postulated as a chain-breaking process which destroys the hydrogenation product of the photo-activated benzaldehyde.

† Jorissen, *Zeit. phys. Chem.* 1897, **22**, 34–54.

‡ Bäckström and Beatty, *J. Phys. Chem.* 1931, **35**, 2530; Almquist and Branch, *J.A.C.S.* 1933, **55**, 4052.

§ Jorissen and Beek, *Rec. trav. chim.* 1927, **46**, 43; 1930, **49**, 139.

|| Bäckström, *Zeit phys. Chem.* 1934, B **25**, 99.

¶ Weizmann, Bergmann, and Hirshberg, *J.A.C.S.* 1938, **60**, 1530.

Wieland and Richter† have suggested that reactions such as

$$Fe^{+++} + Ph—CH{=}O \longrightarrow Fe^{++} + H^{+} + Ph—\dot{C}{=}O$$

will account for the activation of benzaldehyde by traces of metallic cations.

Inhibitors of aldehyde autoxidation are all substances which can easily donate hydrogen, or else a single electron, to the free peroxide radical, e.g.

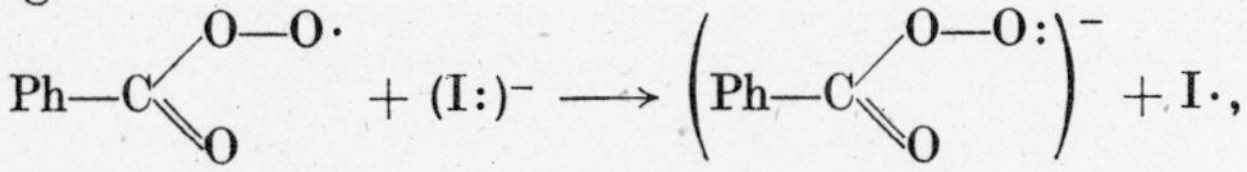

$$Ph—C\begin{matrix}\diagup O—O\cdot \\ \diagdown\!\!\diagdown O\end{matrix} + (I:)^{-} \longrightarrow \left(Ph—C\begin{matrix}\diagup O—O: \\ \diagdown\!\!\diagdown O\end{matrix}\right)^{-} + I\cdot,$$

and this radical interchange may either give a product too inert to react with molecular oxygen, or else start a fresh oxidation chain in which the benzaldehyde is no longer involved, e.g.

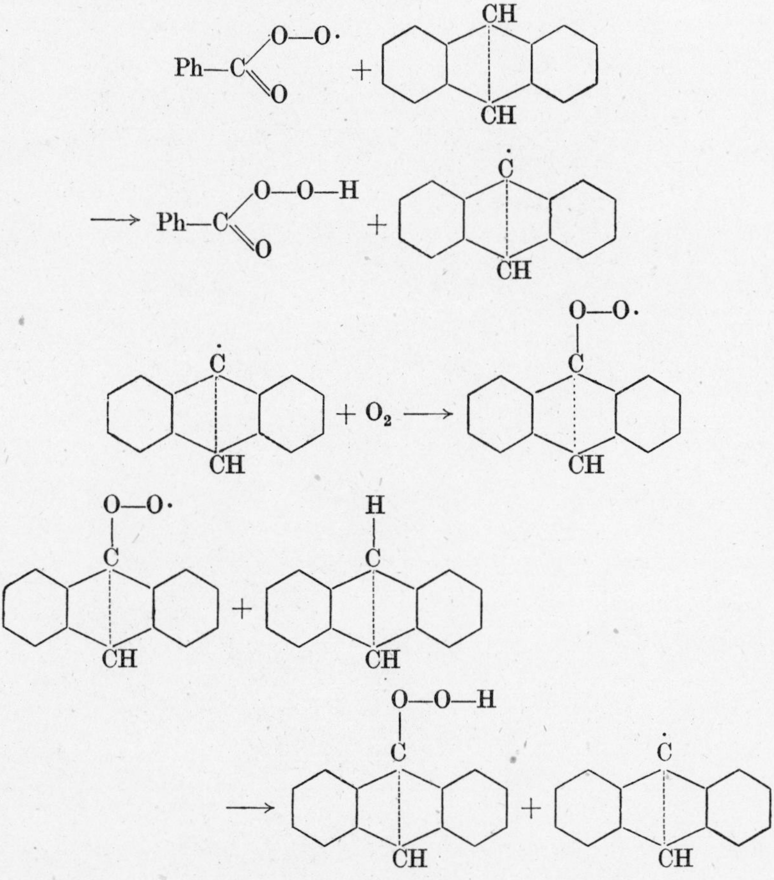

$$Ph—C\begin{matrix}\diagup O—O\cdot \\ \diagdown\!\!\diagdown O\end{matrix} + \begin{matrix}CH \\ \text{(ring system)} \\ CH\end{matrix}$$

$$\longrightarrow Ph—C\begin{matrix}\diagup O—O—H \\ \diagdown\!\!\diagdown O\end{matrix} + \begin{matrix}\dot{C} \\ \text{(ring system)} \\ CH\end{matrix}$$

$$\begin{matrix}\dot{C} \\ \text{(ring system)} \\ CH\end{matrix} + O_2 \longrightarrow \begin{matrix}O—O\cdot \\ | \\ C \\ \text{(ring system)} \\ CH\end{matrix}$$

$$\begin{matrix}O—O\cdot \\ | \\ C \\ \text{(ring system)} \\ CH\end{matrix} + \begin{matrix}H \\ | \\ C \\ \text{(ring system)} \\ CH\end{matrix}$$

$$\longrightarrow \begin{matrix}O—O—H \\ | \\ C \\ \text{(ring system)} \\ CH\end{matrix} + \begin{matrix}\dot{C} \\ \text{(ring system)} \\ CH\end{matrix}$$

† *Annalen*, 1931, **486**, 226.

Whilst all the main kinetic features of the autoxidation of benzaldehyde, such as the action of promoters and inhibitors, and induced oxidations, can be explained satisfactorily by the Bäckström mechanism, it may be noted that the final breakdown of perbenzoic acid to benzoic acid is still represented as a bimolecular reaction with benzaldehyde, as originally suggested by Baeyer and Villiger. The velocity of the direct reaction between perbenzoic acid and benzaldehyde is however too slow to account fully for the rate of production of benzoic acid by the autoxidation of benzaldehyde, and, as Fig. 24 shows, benzoic acid formation is still rapid when the peroxide concentration has passed its peak value. In part perbenzoic acid may decompose directly to benzoic acid and oxygen,† but it is possible that still another chain process is involved in this stage of the autoxidation.

4. The autoxidation of olefines. The autoxidation of olefines usually produces a very complex mixture of substances, but the initial reaction product is undoubtedly a *peroxide* capable of liberating iodine from potassium iodide. Since the degree of unsaturation of an olefine gradually decreases as the uptake of oxygen progresses it was assumed by Engler‡ and by many later workers that the autoxidation involved the formation of a cyclic peroxide which subsequently decomposed.

In 1939, however, Criegee, Pilz, and Flygare§ showed that the liquid peroxide, $C_6H_{10}O_2$, which can be obtained by treating *cyclo*-hexene with oxygen in ultra-violet light, was the hydroperoxide (XI) which still contained the double bond, since (i) it was reduced by sodium sulphite to *cyclo*-hexenol, (ii) it contained one active hydrogen atom, and (iii) it would absorb 1 mol. of bromine per mol.

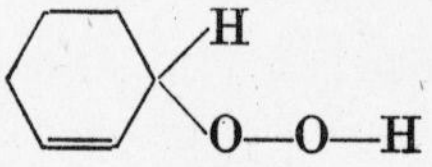

H
O—O—H
(XI)

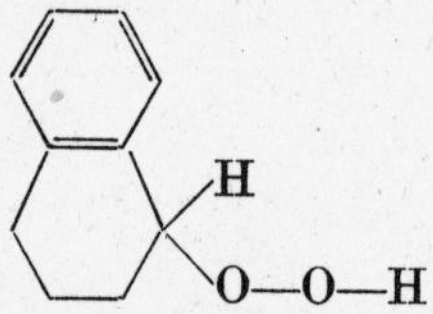

H
O—O—H
(XII)

This has been confirmed by Farmer and his colleagues,|| who have shown that even highly unsaturated substances, such as dihydrofarnesene, $C_{15}H_{26}$, squalene, $C_{30}H_{50}$, and raw rubber, absorb oxygen when exposed to ultra-violet light without any immediate loss of unsaturation. As the initial hydroperoxide subsequently decomposes the degree

† Erlenmeyer, *Helv. Chim. Acta*, 1927, **10**, 620.

‡ Engler, *Ber.* 1897, **30**, 1669; 1898, **31**, 3046; 1900, **33**, 1090.

§ Ibid. 1939, **72**, 1799.

|| Farmer and Sundralingam, *J.* 1942, p. 121; Farmer and Sutton, ibid., p. 139.

of unsaturation decreases. The autoxidation of oleic acid follows a similar course.† Catalysed autoxidations, such as those promoted by osmium metal‡ or by salts of cobalt, manganese, or copper, seem to take a similar course, though frequently the catalyst also accelerates the decomposition reactions of the hydroperoxide.

From extensive work on the autoxidation of analogues of rubber and of the 'drying oils', such as linoleates, Farmer§ has concluded that the primary autoxidation of all olefines which are *not* conjugated systems is, at moderate temperatures,|| an attack on a methylene group adjacent to a double bond, and has pointed out that this is the point at which olefinic substances are attacked by free neutral radicals, as for instance the decomposition products of dibenzoyl peroxide (p. 168). Consequently the first stages in the autoxidation of olefines can be represented as:

(*a*) *Activation of oxygen.*

Probably $R\cdot + O_2 \longrightarrow R{-}O{-}O\cdot$, where $R\cdot$ is a catalyst which can provide a single electron (compare p. 245).

(*b*) *Attack on methylene groups.*

$$-CH_2-CH{=}CH- + \cdot O-O-R \longrightarrow -\underset{\cdot}{C}H-CH{=}CH- + H-O-O-R,$$

$$\left.\begin{array}{l} -\underset{\cdot}{C}H-CH{=}CH- + O_2 \longrightarrow \cdot O-O-\overset{|}{C}H-CH{=}CH-, \\ \cdot O-O-\overset{|}{C}H-CH{=}CH- + -CH_2-CH{=}CH- \\ \quad \longrightarrow H-O-O-\overset{|}{C}H-CH{=}CH- + -\underset{\cdot}{C}H-CH{=}CH-. \end{array}\right\} \textit{chain process}$$

The formation of a hydroperoxide by the chain sequence given above is not a characteristic reaction of an olefine. Many paraffin hydrocarbons can be autoxidized, and under similar conditions these too yield hydroperoxides, though in general saturated compounds are much more resistant to autoxidation than molecules containing double bonds, or attached aromatic rings. Tetralin, which may be regarded as containing a saturated chain attached to an aromatic ring, is a good example of a paraffinic compound which can be oxidized to a well-defined hydroperoxide (XII).¶

† Henderson and Young, *J. Phys. Chem.* 1942, **46**, 670.

‡ Willstätter and Sonnenfeld, *Ber.* 1913, **46**, 2952.

§ Farmer and Sutton, *J.* 1942, p. 139; Farmer, *Trans. Faraday Soc.* 1942, **38**, 348.

|| Compare Atherton and Hilditch, *J.* 1944, p. 105; Gunstone and Hilditch, ibid. 1945, p. 836.

¶ Hartmann and Seiberth, *Helv. Chim. Acta,* 1932, **15**, 1390; Hock and Susemihl, *Ber.* 1933, **66**, 61; A. Robertson and Waters, *Trans. Faraday Soc.* 1946, **42**, 201.

Olefines containing the $—CH_2—CH{=}CH—$ group are autoxidized more easily than are saturated paraffins on account of the enhanced reactivity of the hydrogen atoms in the α-methylene group, which together with the double bond forms a 'three-carbon system'. The reason for this enhanced reactivity becomes obvious when one notes that the initial radical $R—\overset{\alpha}{C}H—CH{=}\overset{\gamma}{C}H—R'$ is a stabilized resonance system in which the 'odd electron' may be located either on carbon atom α or on carbon atom γ of the chain. In consequence of this, autoxidation may lead to the formation of two alternative hydroperoxides† (XIII) and (XIV).

$$R—\underset{\substack{|\\OOH}}{\overset{\alpha}{C}H}—\overset{\beta}{C}H{=}\overset{\gamma}{C}H—R' \qquad R—\overset{\alpha}{C}H{=}\overset{\beta}{C}H—\underset{\substack{|\\OOH}}{\overset{\gamma}{C}H}—R'$$

(XIII) (XIV)

It is significant that the fatty acid components (e.g. linoleic and linolenic acids) of the 'drying oils', which are of such great importance in the paint and varnish industries, contain the system

$$—CH{=}CH—CH_2—CH{=}CH—,$$

in which the autoxidizable methylene group is symmetrically placed between two double bonds, with the result that the initial hydrocarbon radical is a resonance system involving a five-carbon chain. This internal resonance, by stabilizing the initial hydrocarbon radicals, increases their mean free lives, and thereby increases the probability that each activation process will lead to a subsequent reaction of a radical with an oxygen molecule, which of course has to diffuse through the bulk of the inert oil to the activated centres—a very slow process.

The 'drying' of the highly unsaturated oils is not simply a process of oxidation, for polymerization occurs also. This is obviously a peroxide-catalysed chain reaction of the type discussed already in Chapter IX, in which the oil, by its autoxidation, generates its own catalyst. Since all the active radicals by which the two concurrent chain processes of oxidation and polymerization are propagated are mesomeric systems, the number of possible isomeric products is vast, and thus it is obvious why oil paints dry to horny uncrystallizable resins.

Substituent groups have a noticeable effect on the mode of autoxidation of olefines. Groups such as methyl which favour the release of hydrogen from adjacent CH groups promote the reactivity of α-methylenic

† Farmer, Koch, and Sutton, *J.* 1943, p. 541; Farmer, *Trans. Faraday Soc.* 1942, **38**, 356; Farmer and Sutton, *J.* 1946, p. 10.

groups towards oxygen. Thus the olefines formulated below are attacked in the positions marked with an asterisk:†

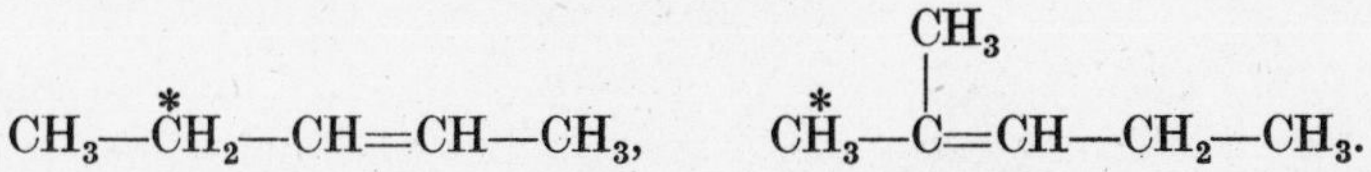

$$CH_3—\overset{*}{C}H_2—CH{=}CH—CH_3, \qquad \overset{*}{C}H_3—\overset{\overset{CH_3}{|}}{C}{=}CH—CH_2—CH_3.$$

Ether groups favour autoxidation, even of saturated hydrocarbon chains, whilst other radicals, e.g. NO_2, can so deactivate the initial radical by internal resonance that chain autoxidation does not occur.

Many conjugated di-olefines seem to be capable of forming simple trans-annular peroxides by a process of 1:4 addition which has obvious analogies with the Diels-Alder reaction,‡ e.g.

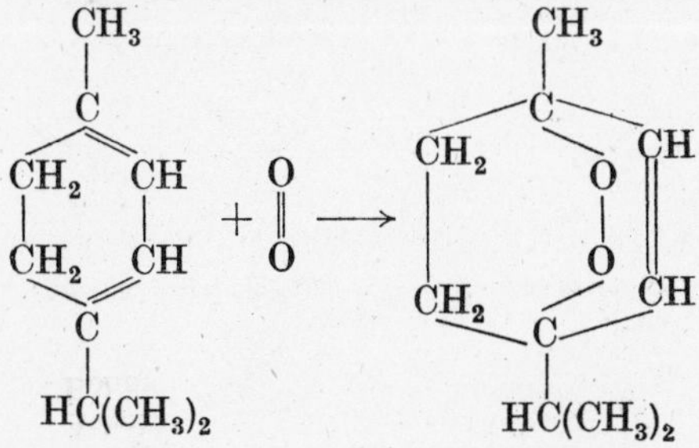

Terpinene + $O{=}O$ ⟶ Ascaridole

The peroxides of ergosterol, anthracene, and rubrene (p. 48) are probably of this type. Like the linear hydroperoxides they are still active catalysts for many free radical reactions.

The subsequent decompositions of the peroxides of the olefines is a complex process in which both heterolytic and free radical reactions may occur according to the experimental circumstances, but in general these changes tend almost entirely towards saturation of the olefinic centres. For instance the autoxidation of *cyclo*-hexene always yields, besides *cyclo*-hexene hydroperoxide (XV), Δ^2-*cyclo*-hexenol (XVI), *cyclo*-hexene oxide (XVII), *trans*-*cyclo*-hexane-diol (XVIII), and a number of polymeric oxidized products. By analogy with the normal reaction between a per-acid and an olefine it might be expected that the following changes would occur:

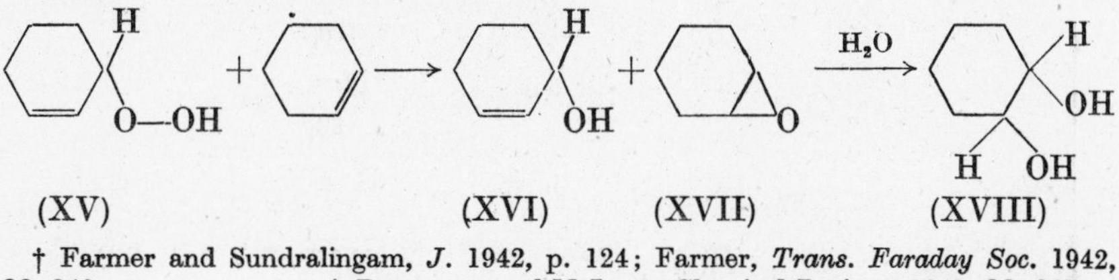

(XV) + ⟶ (XVI) + (XVII) $\xrightarrow{H_2O}$ (XVIII)

† Farmer and Sundralingam, *J.* 1942, p. 124; Farmer, *Trans. Faraday Soc.* 1942, **38**, 340.
‡ Bergmann and McLean, *Chemical Reviews*, 1941, **28**, 367.

In accordance with this representation of the decomposition, ascaridole decomposes, when heated to 150°, in the following way:

$$CH_3-\overset{\large H_2C\,\overset{HC=\!=CH}{}\,CH_2}{C-O-O-C}-CHMe_2 \longrightarrow CH_3-\overset{\large H_2C\,\overset{HC\,(O)\,CH}{}\,CH_2}{C-O-C}-CHMe_2.$$

Adventitious catalysts, however, may alter the whole decomposition process. Thus ferrous salts† can bring about the conversion of hydroperoxides to ketones:

$$\begin{matrix} R \\ R' \end{matrix}\!\!>\!C\!<\!\begin{matrix} H \\ O-O-H \end{matrix} \longrightarrow \begin{matrix} R \\ R' \end{matrix}\!\!>\!C=O + H_2O.$$

In the presence of acids autoxidation is usually accelerated, and often a triol is a main product, probably due to the reaction sequence

$$\underset{\large OOH}{-CH}-CH=CH- \longrightarrow \underset{\large OH}{-CH}-\underset{\quad\large O}{CH-CH}- \xrightarrow{H_2O} \underset{\large OH}{-CH}-\underset{\large OH}{CH}-\underset{\large OH}{CH}-,$$

but the carbon chain is often broken at the olefinic group.

In the presence of alkali the main reactions appear to be oxidations due to free hydrogen peroxide formed by the hydrolysis

$$\begin{matrix} R \\ R' \end{matrix}\!\!>\!CH-O-O-H + H_2O \longrightarrow \begin{matrix} R \\ R' \end{matrix}\!\!>\!CH-OH + H_2O_2.$$

Some of these reactions are discussed more fully below, but it may be pointed out here that neutral radicals formed by the decomposition of hydroperoxides may act as positive catalysts for initiating the uptake of oxygen by a saturated, or unsaturated, hydrocarbon. In this way an autoxidizable compound generates its own catalyst throughout the whole of the main 'steady state' of the oxidation.‡

High-temperature oxidation may have a different mechanism from

† Hartmann and Seiberth, *Helv. Chim. Acta*, 1932, **15**, 1390; A. H. Cook, *J.* 1938, p. 1774.

‡ Medvedev, *Acta Physicochemica U.S.S.R.* 1938, **9**, 395; Medvedev and Podyapolskaya, *J. Phys. Chem. U.S.S.R.* 1939, **12**, 719; A. Robertson and Waters, *Trans. Faraday Soc.* 1946, **42**, 201.

low-temperature autoxidation.† As mentioned on pp. 198 and 250, hydroxyl radicals (·OH) tend to add directly to olefines, and may set up reaction chains in which processes such as

$$RO{-}OH \longrightarrow RO\cdot + \cdot OH,$$

$$\cdot OH + R{-}CH{=}CH{-}R' \longrightarrow R{-}\underset{\displaystyle OH}{\underset{|}{C}H}{-}\dot{C}H{-}R',$$

$$R{-}\underset{\displaystyle OH}{\underset{|}{C}H}{-}\dot{C}H{-}R' + O_2 \longrightarrow R{-}\underset{\displaystyle OH}{\underset{|}{C}H}{-}\underset{\displaystyle O{-}O\cdot}{\underset{|}{C}H}{-}R'$$

also provide radicals which take part in reaction chains. Following upon decomposition of a hydroperoxide there may occur a direct attack on an olefinic centre; further attack on an active methylene group would then follow as a reaction of the radical

$$R{-}\underset{\displaystyle OH}{\underset{|}{C}H}{-}\underset{\displaystyle O{-}O\cdot}{\underset{|}{C}H}{-}R'$$

This direct attack on the double bond would be most evident at temperatures high enough to decompose hydroperoxides rapidly.

Oxidations with Hydrogen Peroxide and the Per-acids

Hydrogen peroxides, and the hydroperoxides and per-acids of the general formula R—O—O—H, such as *tert*-butyl hydroperoxide, $(CH_3)_3C{-}O{-}OH$, Caro's acid, H_2SO_5, perbenzoic acid, and monoperphthalic acid,‡ are all valuable oxidizing agents which are regularly used with both organic and inorganic compounds for adding oxygen to atoms which possess unshared electrons, e.g.

$$(HO)_3As\colon + H_2O_2 \longrightarrow (HO)_3As{=}O + H_2O,$$

$$\begin{matrix} Cl{-}CH_2{-}CH_2 \\ Cl{-}CH_2{-}CH_2 \end{matrix}\!\!\!>\!S + H_2O_2 \longrightarrow \begin{matrix} Cl{-}CH_2{-}CH_2 \\ Cl{-}CH_2{-}CH_2 \end{matrix}\!\!\!>\!S{=}O + H_2O,$$

$$Ph{-}N{=}N{-}Ph + H_2SO_5 \longrightarrow Ph{-}\underset{\displaystyle O^-}{\underset{|}{\overset{+}{N}}}{=}N{-}Ph + H_2SO_4.$$

The organic per-acids can be used specifically to add oxygen to the double bond of an olefine to form an *epi*-oxide:

$$R{-}CO{-}OOH + R'CH{=}CHR'' \longrightarrow R{-}CO{-}OH + R'\underbrace{CH{-}CH}_{O}R''.$$

† Atherton and Hilditch, *J.* 1944, p. 105.
‡ Böhme, *Ber.* 1937, **70**, 379.

Sodium hydrogen peroxide, NaOOH, can also act in this way,† but there is, as yet, little decisive evidence for deciding upon the exact mechanism of any of these processes.

However, the central O—O bond of hydrogen peroxide, and its analogues, is a relatively weak one (bond strength not more than 66 k.cals.)‡ and consequently the compounds of this series can fairly easily be split photochemically, by light of less than 3,000 A, or catalytically, to give H—O· and R—O· radicals. These must necessarily have lower free energies than peroxide radicals of the structure R—O—O· which are formed either by the fission of the strong bonds O—H (110 k.cals.) or O—C (*c.* 87 k.cals.) or else by activation of an oxygen molecule (heat of formation 116 k.cals.), and hence one may well expect to find that hydroxyl and peroxide radicals behave quite differently.

One reaction that seems to be characteristic of the neutral hydroxyl radical is addition to olefinic bonds to give glycols. This can be effected photochemically by exposing mixtures of water-soluble olefines and strong hydrogen peroxide to ultra-violet light in quartz flasks,§ e.g.

$$CH_2{=}CH{-}CH_2OH + 2{\cdot}OH \longrightarrow HO{-}CH_2{-}CH(OH){-}CH_2OH,$$

but can be carried out much more easily by using a catalyst, such as a trace of osmium tetroxide, vanadium pentoxide, or chromium trioxide.|| This catalysed hydroxylation is most conveniently carried out in *tert*-butyl alcohol solution by the use of *tert*-butyl hydroperoxide, $(CH_3)_3C{-}O{-}O{-}H$, which can easily be made by mixing strong aqueous hydrogen peroxide and *tert*-butyl alcohol, removing the aqueous layer, drying the peroxide solution with anhydrous sodium sulphate, and if necessary concentrating the peroxide by distilling off excess of alcohol at a low pressure.

The addition of hydroxyl groups occurs quite vigorously in the cold. Mon-olefines give *cis*-glycols,¶ whilst 1:4 addition takes place with conjugated di-enes.†† Thus maleic acid yields *meso*-tartaric acid and fumaric acid yields racemic acid.

In the case of the reactions brought about by osmium tetroxide Criegee‡‡ has ascribed the production of a *cis*-glycol to the formation of

† Fieser *et al.*, *J.A.C.S.* 1939, **61**, 3216; 1940, **62**, 2866.
‡ Bolland and Gee, *Trans. Faraday Soc.* 1946, **42**, 246.
§ Milas, Kurz, and Anslow, *J.A.C.S.* 1937, **59**, 543.
|| Milas, ibid. 1937, **59**, 2342.
¶ Milas and Sussmann, ibid. 1936, **58**, 1302; 1937, **59**, 2345.
†† Milas and Maloney, ibid. 1940, **62**, 1841.
‡‡ Criegee, *Annalen*, 1936, **522**, 75.

a cyclic ether, and has shown that products of types (XIX) and (XX) can both be obtained by the direct action of osmium tetroxide and olefines in dry ether. Water splits these cyclic ethers to *cis*-glycols, but with excess of hydrogen peroxide, in the absence of water, they are oxidized further to aldehydes or ketones:

$$\begin{array}{c} RCH{-}O \quad\quad O{-}CHR \\ | \quad\quad >Os< \quad\quad | \\ RCH{-}O \quad\quad O{-}CHR \end{array}$$

(XIX)

$$\begin{array}{c} RCH{-}O \quad\quad O \\ | \quad\quad >Os \lessgtr \\ R'CH{-}O \quad\quad O \end{array} + H_2O_2 \longrightarrow \begin{array}{c} RCHO \\ \\ R'CHO \end{array} + OsO_3 + H_2O.$$

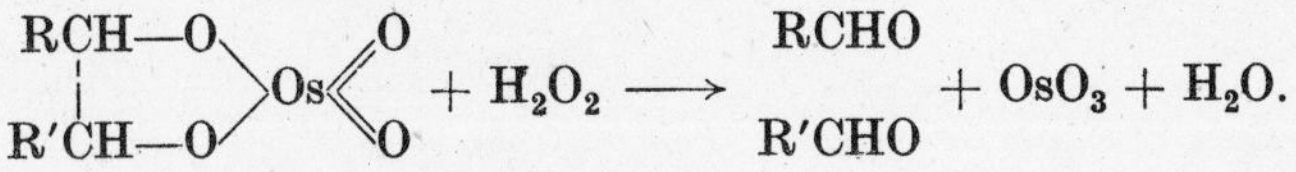

(XX)

Thus in a few cases of the Milas reaction the role of the hydrogen peroxide may be the secondary one of re-oxidizing the reduced catalyst. This, however, is most unlikely with vanadate or chromate catalysts, which themselves do not attack olefines rapidly.

Treibs,† who has studied the vanadate catalysed oxidation, has shown that hydrogen peroxide and vanadium pentoxide, which probably act as pervanadic acid, can oxidize cyclic ketones to di-aldehydes or to aldehydic acids, and suggests that this occurs by hydroxylation of the enolic form of the original ketone.

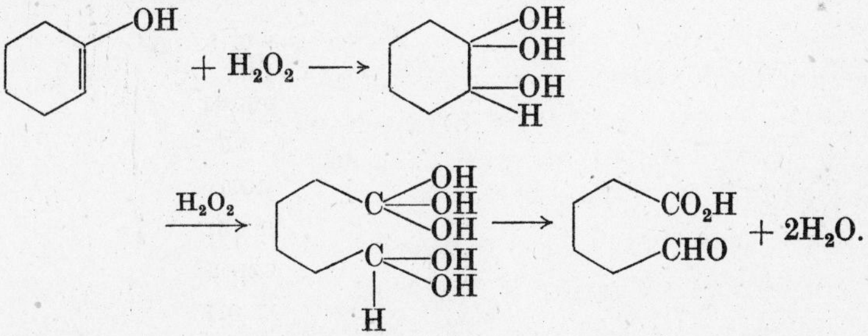

$$C_6H_9{-}OH \text{ (cyclohexenol)} + H_2O_2 \longrightarrow C_6H_{10}(OH)_3 \text{ (ring C bearing OH, OH; adjacent ring C bearing OH, H)}$$

$$\xrightarrow{H_2O_2} \begin{array}{c} C(OH)_3 \\ C(H)(OH)_2 \end{array} \text{ (open chain)} \longrightarrow \begin{array}{c} CO_2H \\ CHO \end{array} + 2H_2O.$$

It will be seen, however, that these bond fissions resemble closely those brought about by lead tetra-acetate (pp. 228–31).

Fenton's reagent. In 1894 Fenton‡ discovered that, in the presence of a small quantity of a ferrous salt, ice-cold hydrogen peroxide would rapidly bring about the oxidation of many α-hydroxy acids. Thus tartaric acid containing a little ferrous sulphate immediately gave di-

† Treibs, *Ber.* 1939, **72**, 7, 1194.
‡ Fenton, *J.* 1894, **65**, 899.

hydroxy-maleic acid (XXI) at 0°, whilst lactic acid yielded pyruvic acid and malic acid gave oxalacetic acid:†

$$\begin{matrix} HO\text{—}CH\text{—}COOH \\ | \\ HO\text{—}CH\text{—}COOH \end{matrix} + H_2O_2 \xrightarrow{Fe^{++}} \begin{matrix} HO\text{—}C\text{—}COOH \\ \| \\ HO\text{—}C\text{—}COOH \\ (XXI) \end{matrix} + 2H_2O.$$

In the sugar series Ruff‡ showed that the reagent could be used to degrade gluconic acid to arabinose:

$$\begin{matrix} COOH \\ | \\ H\text{—}C\text{—}OH \\ | \\ (CH\text{—}OH)_3 \\ | \\ CH_2OH \end{matrix} + H_2O_2 \xrightarrow{Fe^{++}} \begin{matrix} CH{=}O \\ | \\ (CH\text{—}OH)_3 \\ | \\ CH_2OH \end{matrix} + CO_2 + 2H_2O.$$

In the complete absence of iron salts, hydrogen peroxide does not react appreciably with α-hydroxy acids at 0° C., whilst even in the presence of iron it does not, in the cold, oxidize rapidly other carboxylic acids, such as acetic, oxalic, malonic, or maleic acids.† Warm hydrogen peroxide, however, will slowly oxidize even saturated fatty acids,§ and will degrade α-amino acids to aldehydes.

Fenton‖ showed that ethylene glycol gave glyoxal and that mannitol gave mannose, but failed to realize that even the simply monohydric alcohols were rapidly oxidized, first to aldehydes and then to acids.¶

Wieland and Franke†† have shown that for the rapid oxidation of aliphatic hydroxy and amino compounds only the ferrous cation, Fe^{++}, is catalytically active, and that the rate of reaction depends upon the pH of the solution, usually being greatest in the range pH 2–4. Both ferric and ferrous ions, however, will catalyse the oxidation of polyphenols, such as quinol, to quinones. They pointed out that in all these oxidations the essential chemical change is a dehydrogenation, which has many similarities with enzymatic oxidations (Chap. XII).

In 1931 Haber and Willstätter‡‡ pointed out that the chain mechanism which had been proposed for the copper-catalysed oxidation of sulphites

† Fenton and H. O. Jones, *J.* 1900, **77**, 69.
‡ Ruff, *Ber.* 1898, **31**, 1573.
§ Dakin, *J. Biol. Chem.* 1908, **4**, 65, 227; 1909, **5**, 409. Compare Dakin, *Oxidation and Reduction in the Animal Body*, London, 1922.
‖ Fenton, *J.* 1899, **75**, 1. ¶ Compare Goldschmidt and Pauncz, *Annalen*, 1933, **502**, 1.
†† Wieland and Franke, *Annalen*, 1927, **457**, 1; 1929, **475**, 1.
‡‡ Haber and Willstätter, *Ber.* 1931, **64**, 2844.

(p. 235) could be applied to all catalytic dehydrogenations effected by oxidizing agents such as molecular oxygen, hydrogen peroxide, or quinones, provided that one assumed that an initial one-electron transference, which dehydrogenates the substrate (H—R),

$$Fe^{+++} + H\text{—}R \longrightarrow Fe^{++} + H^{+} + \cdot R,$$

produced an active radical ($\cdot$R) capable of attacking the oxidizing agent. To illustrate simply their reaction scheme they interpreted the catalytic decomposition of hydrogen peroxide to oxygen and water, which can be effected by both ferrous and ferric salts, by the enzyme *catalase* and by many active surfaces† (e.g. of Pt, MnO_2, and charcoal), as the chain reaction:

$$Fe^{+++} + H\text{—}O\text{—}O\text{—}H \longrightarrow Fe^{++} + H^{+} + \cdot O\text{—}O\text{—}H, \tag{1}$$

$$\cdot O\text{—}O\text{—}H + H\text{—}O\text{—}O\text{—}H \longrightarrow O_2 + H_2O + \cdot OH, \tag{2 a}$$

$$\textit{or}\ (\cdot O\text{—}O:)^{-} + H\text{—}O\text{—}O\text{—}H \longrightarrow (\cdot O\text{—}O\cdot) + (H\text{—}O:)^{-} + (\cdot O\text{—}H), \tag{2 b}$$

$$\cdot O\text{—}H + H\text{—}O\text{—}O\text{—}H \longrightarrow H\text{—}O\text{—}H + \cdot O\text{—}O\text{—}H, \tag{3}$$

in which both hydroxyl ($\cdot$O—H) and peroxide ($\cdot$O—O—H) radicals were involved.

To accord with the fact that ferr*ous* salts were much more reactive catalysts than ferr*ic* salts, Haber and Weiss,‡ later suggested that the free hydroxyl radical, $\cdot$O—H, was first formed by the process

$$Fe^{++} + H\text{—}O\text{—}O\text{—}H \longrightarrow Fe^{+++} + H\text{—}O\cdot + (:O\text{—}H)^{-} \tag{4}$$

and that liberation of oxygen then followed the Haber–Willstätter scheme above, by reaction (3) and reaction (2) in succession. Reaction (5) was suggested as the chain-breaking process

$$Fe^{++} + \cdot O\text{—}H \longrightarrow Fe^{+++} + (:O\text{—}H)^{-}. \tag{5}$$

By flow experiments with solutions of hydrogen peroxide and ferrous sulphate they showed that the relative rates of consumption of ferrous cations and of hydrogen peroxide molecules on admixture accorded with this scheme over a wide range of pH, and it was evident that process (4) was a very fast reaction.

Ferric salts do catalyse the decomposition of hydrogen peroxide, though slowly, so that reaction (1) of the Haber–Willstätter scheme does occur, and it has been confirmed that even in the presence of an excess

† For reaction mechanisms see Weiss, *Trans. Faraday Soc.* 1935, **31**, 1547.
‡ Haber and Weiss, *Proc. Roy. Soc.* 1934, A **147**, 333.

of hydrogen peroxide the resultant mixture contains both ferrous and ferric cations, the latter being in large excess.†

More recently M. G. Evans and his collaborators have confirmed the presence of free neutral radicals, such as hydroxyl, in 'Fenton's reagent' by showing that, in the presence of a ferrous salt, solutions of peroxides catalyse the chain polymerization of olefines (p. 198). It is also significant that oxygen can be absorbed by the reaction mixture during the course of the polymerization.‡

The occurrence of this polymerization, which is undoubtedly due to the addition of a hydroxyl radical to one end of a double bond, substantiates the view that the hydroxylation of olefines by hydrogen peroxide or per-acids is a free radical reaction. It may possibly be a chain process

$$—CH{=}CH— + \cdot OH \longrightarrow —\underset{\displaystyle OH}{\underset{|}{CH}}—\dot{C}H—$$

$$—\underset{\displaystyle OH}{\underset{|}{CH}}—\dot{C}H— + HO—OH \longrightarrow —\underset{\displaystyle OH}{\underset{|}{CH}}—\underset{\displaystyle OH}{\underset{|}{CH}}— + \cdot OH$$

to which the formation of an *epi*-oxide is an obvious alternative as a second stage:

$$—\underset{\displaystyle O—H}{\underset{|}{CH}}—\dot{C}H— + Ph—CO—O—OH$$

$$\longrightarrow —\underset{\displaystyle O\cdot}{\underset{|}{CH}}—\dot{C}H— + Ph—CO—O—H + \cdot OH.$$

Since organic hydroperoxides, such as tetralin hydroperoxide, can also initiate the chain polymerizations of substances such as styrene, acrylonitrile, and 2-chloro-butadiene,§ these substances too must act by producing either hydroxyl or alkoxyl, R—O·, radicals.

Weiss‖ has developed further the idea that free hydroxyl is produced by the action of a ferrous salt on hydrogen peroxide, and has pointed out that this can lead to two types of catalysed oxidations:

In Type A the oxidizable substance is attacked only by the complete system ($H_2O_2+Fe^{++}$) and oxidation stops when all the iron is in the ferric state, though excess of hydrogen peroxide may still be present.

† Kuhn and Wassermann, *Annalen*, 1933, **503**, 203.
‡ *Trans. Faraday Soc.* 1946, **42**, 155.
§ Robertson and Waters, *Trans. Faraday Soc.* 1946, **42**, 201.
‖ Weiss, *J. Phys. Chem.* 1937, **41**, 1107.

In this case the active oxidizing agent is the neutral $\cdot$O—H radical, and is a short chain process in which the oxidizable material is first converted to a radical capable of attacking molecular hydrogen peroxide.

The oxidation of formic acid is of this type, and may be written as

$$\left.\begin{array}{l}\cdot OH + H—CO—OH \longrightarrow HO—H + \cdot COOH, \\ \cdot COOH + HO—OH \longrightarrow HO—COOH + \cdot OH,\end{array}\right\} \textit{chain}$$

$$HO—CO—OH \longrightarrow H_2O + CO_2.$$

Oxidation of α-hydroxy acids (Fenton's reaction) can be placed in this category, for the reaction sequence can be written as

$$R—CH(OH)—COOH + \cdot OH \longrightarrow R—\dot{C}(OH)—COOH + H_2O,$$

$$R—\dot{C}(OH)—COOH + HO—OH \longrightarrow R—C(OH)_2—COOH + \cdot OH \longrightarrow R—CO—COOH,$$

though more probably the hydroxyl radical initially abstracts hydrogen from the α-hydroxyl group of the acid by the exchange

$$R—CH(O—H)—COOH + \cdot OH \rightleftharpoons R—CH(O\cdot)—COOH + H_2O,$$

giving a radical in which the C—H link may easily be broken by *one-electron* changes favoured by the tendency of the oxygen atom to gain a complete octet of electrons,

$$R—CH(:\ddot{O}\cdot)—COOH + H—O—O—H \longrightarrow R—C(=O)—COOH + H_2O + \cdot OH,$$

as well as by the vicinity of the carboxyl group, which might favour the formation of the radical

$$R—C(O\cdot)=C(O—H)(O—H)$$

from which again a hydrogen atom would easily be released (compare the oxidation of α-glycols and of ketonic acids by lead tetra-acetate, pp. 228–32).

In Type B oxidations the oxidizable substance is readily oxidized by the ferric cation alone, as postulated by Haber and Willstätter, whilst the action of the hydrogen peroxide may be merely that of re-oxidizing the ferrous salt thus formed. Oxidations of this type will proceed even if the radical formed from the oxidizable substance is incapable of attacking molecular hydrogen peroxide.

The oxidation of iodides is of this type, for the reversible reaction

$$Fe^{+++} + I^{-} \rightleftharpoons Fe^{++} + I\cdot$$

occurs in the absence of peroxides, whilst atomic iodine dimerizes to molecular iodine in preference to attacking molecular hydrogen peroxide. In the presence of hydrogen peroxide the ferrous cation is promptly re-oxidized to ferric cation, whilst the reaction

$$I^{-} + \cdot OH \longrightarrow I\cdot + (OH)^{-}$$

also serves to destroy free hydroxyl radicals.

Substances such as quinol, which are oxidized by hydrogen peroxide in the presence of either ferrous or ferric salts, also react in this way, for the corresponding radicals are resonance-stabilized substances of low free energy, which tend to dimerize to quinhydrones, or more complex dyestuffs (e.g. purpurogallin from pyrogallol):

$$Fe^{+++} + H—O—C_6H_4—OH$$
$$\longrightarrow Fe^{++} + H^{+} + \cdot O—C_6H_4—OH \longrightarrow \textit{quinhydrone}.$$

In general it will be noticed that Type A reactions should occur with difficultly oxidized substances, under circumstances in which the hydroxyl radical can accumulate, whereas Type B reactions occur with easily oxidizable substances, which promptly destroy active free radicals. Weiss has suggested that the peroxidase enzymes, as a rule, bring about oxidations of Type B, and in accordance with this Mann and Saunders† have shown that Fenton's reagent is not an exact model for peroxidase enzymes.

Positive Halogen Compounds

Whilst the great majority of both inorganic and organic halides react, either by direct dissociation or by attack of nucleophilic groups, to give halide anions, in which the halogen element retains both bonding electrons of the original covalency, there are many halogen compounds, of which hypochlorous acid, HOCl, is typical, which are oxidizing agents, capable of liberating iodine from solutions of potassium iodide. These

† Mann and Saunders, *Proc. Roy. Soc.* 1935, B **119**, 47.

compounds are commonly represented as containing 'positive halogen atoms', that is to say halogen atoms dissociable as cations, e.g.

$$HO—Cl \rightleftharpoons (HO:)^- + Cl^+,$$

and able to oxidize *two* iodide anions to free iodine:

$$Cl^+ + 2I^- \longrightarrow Cl^- + I_2.$$

In accordance with this view, it has been demonstrated beyond doubt that both the addition and substitution reactions of chlorine, bromine, and hypochlorites in polar solvents such as water or acetic acid are polar processes, representable by mechanisms such as

$$\begin{matrix} CH_2{=}H_2 \\ + \\ Cl—Cl \end{matrix} \longrightarrow \begin{matrix} \overset{+}{C}H_2—\overset{-}{C}H_2 \\ \\ Cl^- \quad Cl^+ \end{matrix} \longrightarrow \begin{matrix} CH_2—CH_2 \\ | \qquad | \\ Cl \qquad Cl \end{matrix}$$

though experimental evidence suggests that these reactions are at least bimolecular, if not of higher order,† and probably involve electron transfers within a circuit of polarized molecules as indicated below, rather than the separation of *free* halogen cations.‡

$$C_6H_5\text{—}H + Cl\text{—}Cl \longrightarrow \overset{\delta-}{C}\text{—}\overset{\delta+}{H} \cdots \overset{\delta+}{Cl}\text{—}\overset{\delta-}{Cl} \longrightarrow C_6H_5\text{—}Cl + H^+ + Cl^-$$

Theoretical calculations§ have shown that whilst the dipolar character of most halogen bonds, e.g. $\overset{+\longrightarrow}{C—Cl}$, favours dissociation into halide anions, it is possible to diminish this polar character of halides by introducing into the same molecule oppositely directed polar groups, e.g.

$$\begin{matrix} C_6H_5 \\ N{\equiv}C \end{matrix}\rangle CH—Br \qquad \begin{matrix} EtO—CO \\ EtO—CO \end{matrix}\rangle CH—Br \qquad I—\underset{I}{\overset{I}{C}}—I,$$

whereupon oxidizing properties characteristic of the 'positive halogens' are conferred on the molecule. The induced polar field is seldom, if ever, powerful enough to reverse the sense of the net electrostatic field around the halogen bond, but it can make the resulting charge distribution so uniform that less activation energy is required to effect homolytic bond fission than heterolytic bond fission (compare p. 14). It is therefore to be expected that some of the reactions of the positive halogen

† G. Williams, *Trans. Faraday Soc.* 1941, **37**, 749.

‡ For a general survey of this, compare Waters, *Physical Aspects of Organic Chemistry*, 1935.

§ Waters, *J.* 1933, p. 1551; 1942, p. 153.

compounds, especially in non-polar solvents, might be reactions of atomic halogens, and electrically neutral radicals, rather than of halogen cations.† As explained on p. 227 these alternative reaction mechanisms cannot be differentiated stoichiometrically, and independent evidence of the production of neutral halogen atoms is required.

One possible test for atomic dissociation of organic halides is reaction, in the free state or in non-ionizing solvents, with metals such as mercury, arsenic, antimony, and tellurium to form covalent organo-metallic compounds. Direct reaction with mercury is noticeable with substances such as α-bromobenzyl cyanide and the N-chloro-imides, and with a few alkyl iodides, such as methyl iodide, which are easily decomposable photochemically (p. 115), but, unlike reaction with more electropositive metals such as magnesium, it is not a general reaction of strongly polar halides such as alkyl chlorides.

Catalysis of the abnormal, or atomic, addition of hydrogen bromide to olefines in the absence of light or of peroxides is more definite evidence of the occurrence of atomic dissociation. Rust and Vaughan‡ have shown that the α-bromo ketones, R—$COCH_2Br$, which are very typical 'positive halogen' compounds, markedly catalyse this reaction, though as would be expected (see p. 184), substances such as methyl iodide and iodine, which are also capable of atomic fission, act as inhibitors.

Whilst most positive halogen compounds are of academic interest only, the N-halogeno-imides are oxidizing agents of considerable technical value. Some, such as chloramine-T and its analogues, can be used as stable alternatives to alkali hypochlorites as bactericides and mild bleaching agents, whilst others such as N-2:4-trichloroacetanilide (XXII) and N-bromo-succinimide (XXIII)

Cl⟨C₆H₃⟩—N—$COCH_3$ with Cl (ring) and Cl (on N)
(XXII)

CH_2—CO
| >N—Br
CH_2—CO
(XXIII)

may be used for effecting halogenation in non-aqueous solvents, and are particularly valuable reagents for the controlled halogenation of aromatic amines and phenols.

Ziegler and his colleagues§ have shown that compounds of this group, and N-bromo-succinimide in particular, are valuable specific agents for

† Waters, *J.* 1937, p. 2010. For confirmation see Robertson and Waters, ibid. 1947, p. 492.

‡ Rust and Vaughan, *J. Org. Chem.* 1942, **7**, 491.

§ Ziegler *et al.*, *Annalen*, 1942, **551**, 80.

substituting olefines in the allyl, or α-methylenic, position without occurrence of simultaneous addition to the double bond:

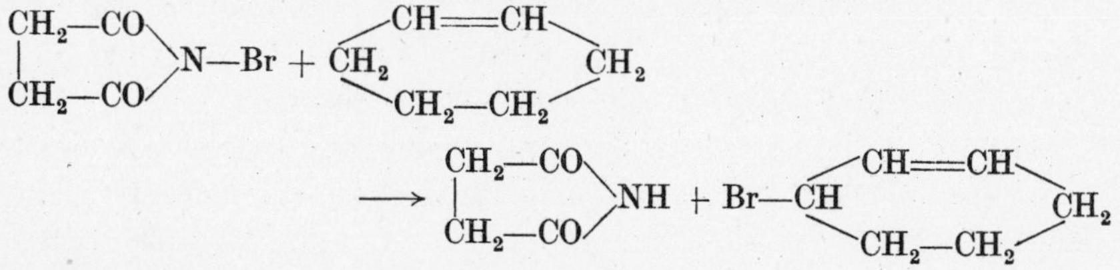

$$\begin{array}{l}CH_2\text{—}CO \\ | \\ CH_2\text{—}CO\end{array}\!\!>\!N\text{—}Br + \begin{array}{c}CH\!=\!CH \\ CH_2 \qquad\quad CH_2 \\ CH_2\text{—}CH_2\end{array}$$

$$\longrightarrow \begin{array}{l}CH_2\text{—}CO \\ | \\ CH_2\text{—}CO\end{array}\!\!>\!NH + Br\text{—}\begin{array}{c}CH\!=\!CH \\ CH \qquad\quad CH_2 \\ CH_2\text{—}CH_2\end{array}$$

This substitution is best carried out by boiling the N-halogen compound with the olefine in carbon tetrachloride solution until the mixture no longer reacts with potassium iodide. If N-bromo-succinimide is used then succinimide crystallizes out on cooling and can be recovered for further preparation of the brominating agent, whilst the bromination product can easily be separated by evaporating the filtrate; its subsequent hydrolysis opens up the route to further controlled oxidative degradation.

This method of oxidative degradation has proved to be particularly useful for attacking the saturated side-chain of naturally occurring sterols and bile acids.† By treating the ester of a saturated fatty acid with a Grignard reagent there can often be formed the system

$$\text{—}CH_2\text{—}CH\!=\!CR_2,$$

which by α-methylenic substitution can be converted to a diene which on ozonolysis loses the end three carbon atoms of the original paraffin chain, e.g.

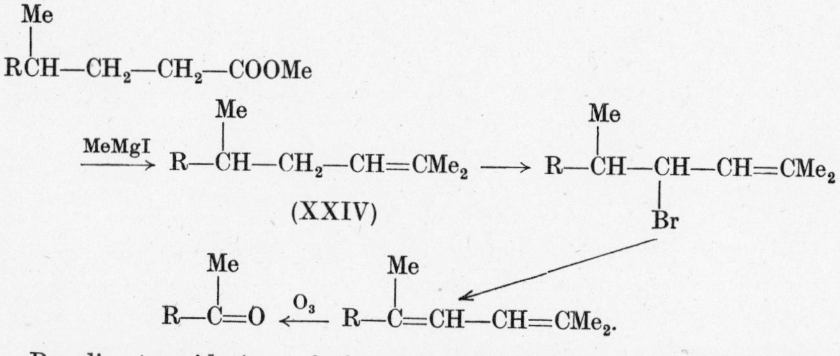

$$R\overset{\overset{\displaystyle Me}{|}}{C}H\text{—}CH_2\text{—}CH_2\text{—}COOMe$$

$$\xrightarrow{MeMgI} \underset{(XXIV)}{R\text{—}\overset{\overset{\displaystyle Me}{|}}{C}H\text{—}CH_2\text{—}CH\!=\!CMe_2} \longrightarrow R\text{—}\overset{\overset{\displaystyle Me}{|}}{C}H\text{—}\underset{\underset{\displaystyle Br}{|}}{C}H\text{—}CH\!=\!CMe_2$$

$$R\text{—}\overset{\overset{\displaystyle Me}{|}}{C}\!=\!O \xleftarrow{O_3} R\text{—}\overset{\overset{\displaystyle Me}{|}}{C}\!=\!CH\text{—}CH\!=\!CMe_2.$$

By direct oxidation of the Grignard reaction product (XXIV), (Wieland's degradation method) the paraffin chain is shortened by only one carbon atom.

† Hey, *Annual Reports of the Chemical Society*, 1944, **41**, 192.

This bromination of olefines, which is exactly paralleled by the high-temperature direct chlorination of olefines (p. 100), by their autoxidation to hydroperoxides (p. 240), or attack by diacyl peroxides or aromatic diazo-compounds (Chapter VIII) (amongst which the reaction with benzene-diazonium chloride can be taken as another case of reaction by a N-chloro-imide), is evidently a reaction of atomic bromine,† produced by the non-ionic fission of the N—Br bond which is a very weak, and virtually non-polar, covalency.

In general N-chloro-imides do not react so smoothly as the N-bromo-imides, and there is experimental evidence to suggest that both atomic and ionic bond fissions can occur in many compounds of this type. Thus Kharasch and Priestley‡ showed that N-bromobenzenesulphonamides reacted with olefines such as styrene and its analogues as follows:

$$RCH{=}CH_2 + Br{-}\underset{\displaystyle CH_3}{\underset{|}{N}}{-}SO_2R' \longrightarrow R{-}\underset{\displaystyle Br}{\underset{|}{CH}}{-}CH_2{-}\underset{\displaystyle CH_3}{\underset{|}{N}}{-}SO_2R';$$

whilst N:N-dibromosulphonamides reacted differently:

$$2R{-}CH{=}CH_2 + Br{-}\underset{\displaystyle Br}{\underset{|}{N}}{-}SO_2R' \longrightarrow \begin{array}{l} R{-}CH{-}CH_2Br \\ \quad\;\, | \\ \;\;HN{-}SO_2R' \end{array} + R{-}CH{=}CHBr.$$

The course of reactions of this type may be very markedly dependent upon the choice of the solvent, and the regular use of carbon tetrachloride by Ziegler may be an essential factor in contributing to the success of his α-methylenic substitution.

When N-halogen compounds are used in water, or other ionizing solvents, hydrolysis may yield molecular halogens, hypochlorous or hypobromous acids, or, in alkali, hypochlorite or hypobromite anions, and these different products react with considerably different velocities, if not by different reaction mechanisms.

Other Oxidizing Agents

The oxidizing agents which have been discussed in the preceding pages are, in the main, dehydrogenators. In this respect, however, they are not unlike many other, commonly used, oxidizing agents such as chromic acid and potassium permanganate which can attack saturated molecules such as alcohols, e.g.

$$R{-}CH_2{-}OH \xrightarrow{-2H} R{-}CH{=}O.$$

† Waters, *Nature*, 1944, **154**, 772.
‡ Kharasch and Priestley, *J.A.C.S.* 1940, **61**, 3425.

Very frequently these well-known oxidizing agents yield products which are chemically identical with those of undoubted free-radical reactions, and this at least is some slight indication of a similarity in reaction mechanism.†

For instance, *Periodic Acid*, H_5IO_6, can be used in aqueous solution to split the C—C bond of α-glycols,‡ just as lead tetra-acetate can be used in acetic acid solution (p. 229). It is particularly useful for elucidating the structure of carbohydrates. Thus with methyl-gluco-pyranoside it reacts as follows:§

$$\begin{array}{l} \text{H—C—OCH}_3 \\ \text{H—C—OH} \\ \text{HO—C—H} \\ \text{H—C—OH} \quad \text{O} \\ \text{H—C} \\ \quad \text{CH}_2\text{OH} \end{array} + 2H_5IO_6 \longrightarrow \begin{array}{l} \text{H—C—OCH}_3 \\ \text{H—C=O} \\ \text{O} \\ \text{H—C=O} \\ \quad \text{C—H} \\ \quad \text{CH}_2\text{OH} \end{array} + \text{H—CO—OH} \xrightarrow{Ba(OBr)_2} \begin{array}{c} \text{COOH} \\ | \\ \text{COOH} \end{array} + \begin{array}{c} \text{COOH} \\ \text{H—C—OH} \\ \text{COOH} \end{array}$$

Again, *Chromic Acid* often attacks the α-methylenic groups in olefines rather than the double bond.‖

At high temperatures *Quinones*, such as phenanthraquinone and chloranil, can be used, in place of selenium (compare p. 219) as specific dehydrogenators for converting cyclic hydro-aromatic hydrocarbons to aromatic products,¶ and so can certain *Disulphides* which are thereby reduced to mercaptans.†† It is most probable that all these processes involve the abstraction of hydrogen *atoms* from organic molecules by non-polar reactions which may be represented as:

$$\begin{array}{l} \text{O} \\ \quad \rangle\text{Cr=O} \\ \text{O} \end{array} + 3\text{H—R} \longrightarrow \begin{array}{l} \text{H—O} \\ \quad\quad \rangle\text{Cr—O—H} \\ \text{H—O} \end{array} + 3\cdot\text{R},$$

$$\text{R—S—S—R} \rightleftharpoons 2\,\text{R—S}\cdot \quad \text{(compare p. 73)},$$

$$\text{R—S}\cdot + \text{H—X} \longrightarrow \text{R—S—H} + \cdot\text{X},$$

since it has been found‡‡ that all these dehydrogenating agents (including

† Farmer, *Trans. Faraday Soc.* 1942, **38**, 340.

‡ Malaprade, *Bull. Soc. Chim.* 1928, [4], **43**, 683; 1934, [5], **1**, 833.

§ Jackson and Hudson, *J.A.C.S.* 1936, **58**, 378; 1937, **59**, 994.

‖ Farmer, loc. cit.; Whitmore and Pedlow, *J.A.C.S.* 1941, **63**, 758. See also Waters, *J.* 1946, p. 1151. ¶ Clar and John, *Ber.* 1930, **63**, 2967; Criegee, ibid. 1936, **69**, 2758; Arnold and Collins, *J.A.C.S.* 1939, **61**, 1407; 1940, **62**, 983.

†† Ritter and Sharpe, *J.A.C.S.* 1937, **59**, 2451.

‡‡ Waters, *Trans. Faraday Soc.* 1946, **42**, 184.

chromic acid, potassium permanganate, and periodic acid) are immediate catalysts for the autoxidation of tetralin, and therefore must, by abstracting hydrogen from this hydrocarbon, be capable of producing the free tetralyl radical (XXV) which then promptly combines with oxygen.

The fact that the process

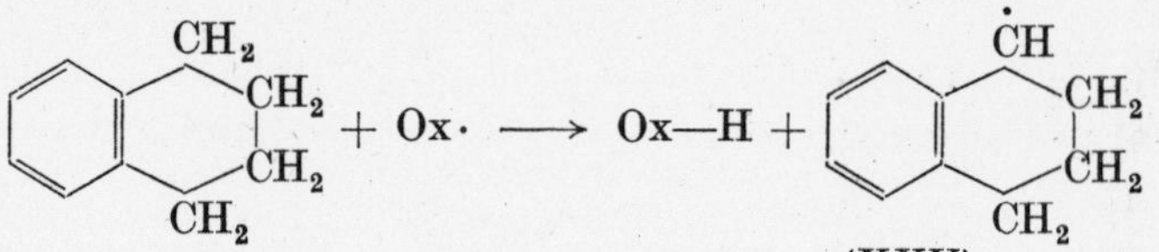

$$C_6H_4(CH_2)_4 + Ox\cdot \longrightarrow Ox{-}H + C_6H_4(\dot{C}H)(CH_2)_3$$

(XXV)

initiates the autoxidation chain

$$\left.\begin{array}{r} {>}CH\cdot + O_2 \longrightarrow {>}CH{-}O{-}O\cdot \\ {>}CH{-}O{-}O\cdot + {>}CH_2 \longrightarrow {>}CH{-}O{-}O{-}H + {>}CH\cdot \end{array}\right\}$$

proves that the oxidizing agent (Ox·) can produce free neutral radicals, although it may not itself be a free radical, just as definitely as the uptake of oxygen by cinnamic acid and other olefines during bromine addition (p. 177) proves that halogen addition to olefines can have a free radical mechanism. However, just as in the case of olefine reactions, it does not follow that all the reactions of such oxidizing agents as chromic acid or potassium permanganate have free radical mechanisms.

Evidence that reduction, like oxidation, may often have a free radical mechanism is given in Chapters III (p. 42) and X (p. 203).

XII
SOME POSSIBLE MECHANISMS FOR BIOCHEMICAL PROCESSES

Nature of Biological Oxidation

Most living creatures derive their energy from regulated oxidation processes, whereby carbohydrates, fats, and proteins are degraded completely to carbon dioxide, ammonia, or urea, by reactions which occur easily in almost neutral aqueous media under moderate temperature conditions.

Although it is obvious that atmospheric oxygen must be the reagent ultimately concerned in biological oxidation, few if any of the main oxidizable cell components (*metabolites*) react with molecular oxygen except in the presence of specific organic catalysts (*enzymes*) which have, as yet, been isolated only from living matter. Biochemical processes can however occur apart from life, for most enzymes can be separated from living cells and obtained as sterile, though still active, concentrates. They are invariably of protein nature, and usually colloidal, and like most proteins are irreversibly changed (and rendered inactive) by heat, strong acid, or strong alkali.

In common with other types of catalytically active surfaces, enzymes are easily 'poisoned' by mere traces of foreign substances (e.g. cyanides), but unlike such inorganic catalysts as platinum black or activated charcoal they are very much more specific in their actions, this specificity undoubtedly being due to their much greater chemical complexity.

The kinetic features of enzyme-catalysed reactions are however so similar to those of many other catalysed processes that it is rational to hope that the ultimate mechanisms of the chemical reactions which they can effect may eventually be explicable in terms of generally valid physico-chemical theories.

In an attempt to apply even still more widely the reaction mechanisms which have been reviewed in preceding chapters, the relevancy in biochemistry of oxidation processes involving free radicals is discussed in the following pages.

The Role of Oxygen in Metabolism

Molecular oxygen is brought to living cells by the circulating bloodstream, in which it is present, in solution or rather loose chemical combination, in the red blood corpuscles, thus

$$\text{Haemoglobin} + O_2 \rightleftharpoons \text{Oxy-haemoglobin},$$

and in the animal body it is largely removed from the blood by a number of chemical actions with cell metabolites. Many of these reactions can be carried out *in vitro* by sterile enzyme systems in which free oxygen gas can take the place of oxy-haemoglobin, and it has therefore been concluded that, in general, the biochemical functions of haemoglobin are physical rather than chemical in nature. Nevertheless certain reagents, such as carbon monoxide, act as body poisons by preventing the formation of oxy-haemoglobin, and thus inhibit the transport of molecular oxygen to living cells.

In the preceding chapter it has been shown that oxidations involving molecular oxygen invariably result in the formation of a peroxide, which may be either hydrogen peroxide, or an organic peroxide of formula R—O—O—R or R—O—O—H, and that this peroxide may subsequently oxidize other organic molecules which are themselves resistant to oxygen gas (compare pp. 232–45). The biochemical role of molecular oxygen seems to be just the same, for it has been shown that some autoxidizable enzyme systems yield free hydrogen peroxide, whilst others can so rapidly utilize, or destroy, hydrogen peroxide that it does not accumulate as an identifiable product.

Thus both from yeast and from milk has been isolated the yellow substance Riboflavin (I), or *Vitamin* B_2, which on catalytic reduction with hydrogen in the presence of platinum, picks up two atoms of hydrogen to yield the colourless product Leuco-riboflavin (II).

Ribityl | N N CH_3 C CO C NH CH_3 N CO (I) $\underset{-\,2H}{\overset{+\,2H}{\rightleftharpoons}}$ Ribityl | N NH CH_3 C CO C NH CH_3 N CO | H (II)

The latter is autoxidizable, and reacts with oxygen as follows:

$$\text{Leuco-riboflavin} + O_2 \longrightarrow \text{Riboflavin} + H_2O_2.$$

A whole series of enzymes, known as the *flavoprotein enzymes*, contain phosphorylated riboflavin linked up in a protein structure, and all these can bring about biochemical oxidations, e.g. of amino acids, or purines, in which oxygen is absorbed directly.

Other autoxidizable enzyme systems are thought to act on molecular oxygen in a similar way. However, hydrogen peroxide does not occur in any appreciable concentration in living cells, since (*a*) it can be utilized very rapidly as an oxidizing agent by a group of widely distributed enzymes known as *peroxidases*, and (*b*) it is rapidly decomposed to oxygen and water, $2H_2O_2 = 2H_2O + O_2$, by an enzyme *catalase* which is present in living cells of all types. In fact the enzyme catalase, the destroyer of hydrogen peroxide, is to be regarded as a protective agent which prevents unduly rapid destruction of many cell components.

Biological oxidation, beyond the stage of direct autoxidation, is effected *either* by hydrogen peroxide in the presence of peroxidases, *or* by autoxidizable substances which, after reduction by a metabolite, are easily re-oxidized by molecular oxygen, e.g.

$$\text{Flavoprotein} + \text{Metabolite} \longrightarrow \text{Leuco-flavoprotein} + \text{Oxidized metabolite},$$

$$\text{Leuco-flavoprotein} + O_2 \longrightarrow \text{Flavoprotein} + H_2O_2;$$

or in brief

$$F + MH_2 \longrightarrow FH_2 + M,$$

$$FH_2 + O_2 \longrightarrow F + H_2O_2.$$

This latter type of oxidation may be a multi-stage process requiring the presence of enzyme catalysts.

Wieland's Dehydrogenation Theory

A quarter of a century ago Wieland† pointed out that the vast majority of oxidations, including both laboratory *in vitro* reactions and enzyme processes, were hydrogen abstractions rather than oxygen, or hydroxyl, additions (compare p. 232), e.g.

$$\text{Ethyl alcohol} \longrightarrow \text{Acetaldehyde} + 2H,$$

$$\text{Succinic acid} \longrightarrow \text{Fumaric acid} + 2H \quad \text{(in muscle tissue)},$$

and that, even in biological systems, oxidation could often be effected quite easily by reagents which did not provide oxygen. Thus Schardinger, Thunberg, and others had shown that *Methylene Blue* (III) could act as an oxidizer in anaerobic enzyme systems. Thus,

$$\underset{CH_3{-}CH(OH)COOH}{\text{Lactic acid}} + \underset{\text{(III)}}{\text{Methylene Blue}} \xrightarrow[\text{(Enzyme catalyst)}]{} \underset{CH_3{-}CO{-}COOH}{\text{Pyruvic acid}} + \underset{\text{(IV)}}{\text{Leuco-methylene Blue.}}$$

† *Ber.* 1921, **54**, 2353; 1922, **55**, 3639; *J.* 1931, p. 1055 (Pedler Lecture).

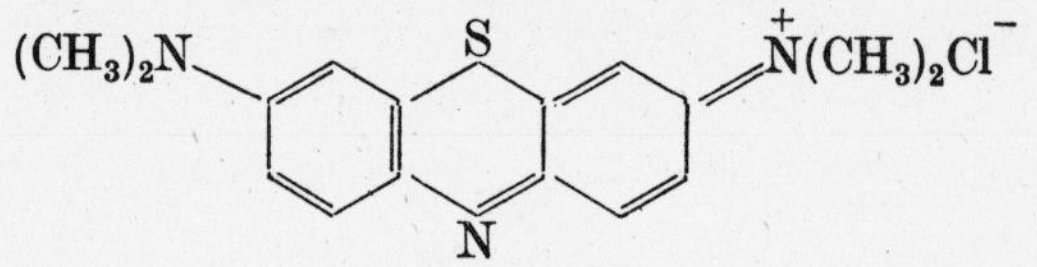

$(CH_3)_2N$ — S — N — $\overset{+}{N}(CH_3)_2Cl^-$

(III)

$(CH_3)_2N$ — S — NH — $N(CH_3)_2,HCl$

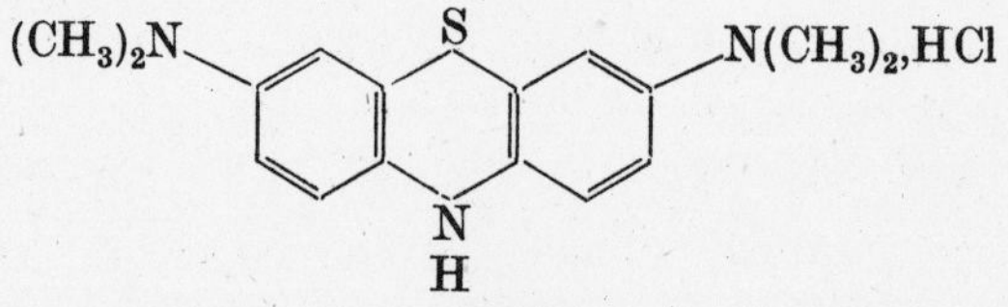

(IV)

The complete decoloration of (III) to (IV) is a valuable index of the completion of an enzyme process, which, as Thunberg showed, can be made the basis of an excellent technique for carrying out quantitative kinetic measurements with enzyme systems.

Many other quinonoid compounds can be used in just the same way, provided that they have sufficiently high oxidation/reduction potentials, and so can several other simpler organic substances such as *m*-dinitrobenzene and alloxan.

In support of this dehydrogenation theory of enzyme oxidation Wieland showed that simple inorganic surface catalysts, such as platinum black or activated charcoal, were able to bring about, at body temperature (37° C.), the removal of hydrogen from neutral aqueous solutions of many compounds of biological interest. He pointed out, too, that even those biochemical oxidations which were not simple dehydrogenations could be formulated as dehydrogenations occurring subsequent to, or immediately followed by, addition of water, e.g.

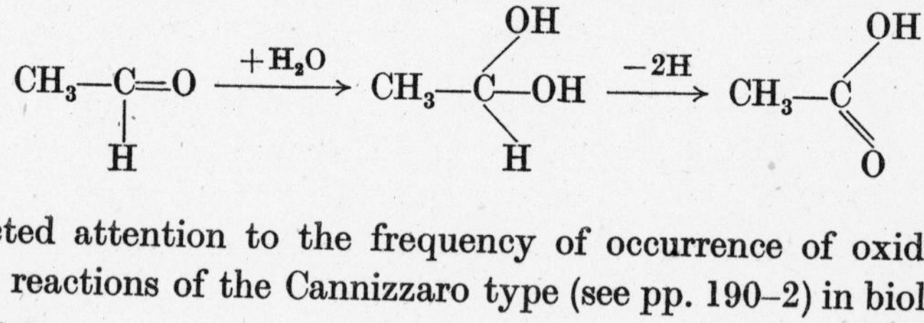

$$CH_3\text{—}\underset{H}{\underset{|}{C}}\text{=O} \xrightarrow{+H_2O} CH_3\text{—}\underset{H}{\overset{OH}{C}}\text{—OH} \xrightarrow{-2H} CH_3\text{—}\underset{O}{\overset{OH}{C}}$$

and directed attention to the frequency of occurrence of oxidation-reduction reactions of the Cannizzaro type (see pp. 190–2) in biological systems, e.g.

Acetaldehyde + β-Hydroxy-butyric acid

⟶ Ethyl alcohol + Acetoacetic acid,

Glyceraldehyde + Pyruvic acid ⟶ Glyceric acid + Lactic acid.

These he formulated as

$$\mathrm{R{-}\underset{\displaystyle H}{\underset{|}{C}}{=}O \rightleftharpoons R{-}\underset{\displaystyle H}{\underset{|}{C}}\!\begin{smallmatrix}\diagup OH\\ \diagdown OH\end{smallmatrix} + O{=}C\!\begin{smallmatrix}\diagup R'\\ \diagdown R''\end{smallmatrix} \longrightarrow R{-}C\!\begin{smallmatrix}\diagup OH\\ \diagdown\!\!\diagdown O\end{smallmatrix} + H{-}O{-}\underset{\displaystyle H}{C}\!\begin{smallmatrix}\diagup R'\\ \diagdown R''\end{smallmatrix}}$$

involving a hydrated form of the aldehyde, for he showed that *dry* aldehydes often resisted attack by fairly strong oxidizers, whereas their hydrated forms reacted much more easily.†

Wieland pointed out that molecular oxygen acted essentially as a dehydrogenator, and suggested that living cells contained, in addition to reducible ketonic compounds, such as pyruvic acid or alloxan, a whole series of organic hydrogen acceptors which might, like methylene blue, be capable of rapid re-oxidation from the reduced form by means of atmospheric oxygen.

To a remarkable degree Wieland's dehydrogenation theory has been substantiated by more recent biochemical research, for from enzyme systems have been isolated a whole range of *co-enzymes*, essential for cell metabolism, which are relatively simple organic substances capable of abstracting hydrogen from metabolites in the presence of enzymes, and, again in presence of enzymes, of being re-oxidized by free oxygen. In fact many enzymes lose their catalytic powers if separated from their associated co-enzymes, though in certain cases synthetic substances such as methylene blue can adequately replace the latter.

The biological specificity of the co-enzymes is very much less marked than that of the enzymes, though each individual evidently operates over a very closely defined oxidation/reduction potential range.

Co-enzymes

Harden and Young‡ in 1906 discovered that yeast juice on dialysis lost its power of fermenting glucose. From the dialysate was separated a thermostable substance of low molecular weight, which was called a 'co-enzyme', since when it was added to the enzyme protein it restored the full catalytic properties. A number of these co-enzymes have now been separated from cell extracts, blood corpuscles, etc., and their chemical properties have been studied in detail. They all prove to be organic compounds which can undergo reversible oxidation-reduction reactions.

Harden and Young's product, now termed *Co-zymase*, or *Co-enzyme-I*

† Wieland and Richter, *Annalen*, 1931, **486**, 226; 1932, **495**, 284.
‡ *Proc. Roy. Soc.* 1906, B **125**, 171.

has been purified by Euler and his colleagues† and proves to be a compound of nicotinamide, adenine, ribose, and pyrophosphoric acid (V):

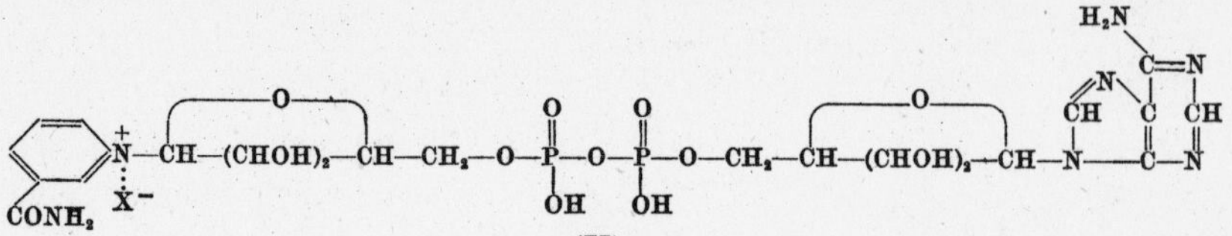

$$\text{(pyridinium ring with } CONH_2\text{)}\overset{+}{N}(\cdots X^-)\text{—}\overbrace{CH\text{—}(CHOH)_2\text{—}CH}^{O}\text{—}CH_2\text{—}O\text{—}\underset{OH}{\overset{O}{\overset{\|}{P}}}\text{—}O\text{—}\underset{OH}{\overset{O}{\overset{\|}{P}}}\text{—}O\text{—}CH_2\text{—}\overbrace{CH\text{—}(CHOH)_2\text{—}CH}^{O}\text{—}N\text{(adenine ring: } H_2N\text{—}C{=}N\text{, CH, C, CH, N)}$$

(V)

Very similar in structure is *Co-enzyme-II*, which was first separated by Warburg and Christian‡ from red blood corpuscles, and differs from co-enzyme-I by containing an additional phosphate residue.

When an aqueous mixture of ethyl alcohol and co-zymase is mixed with the requisite enzyme then the reversible process

$$CH_3CH_2OH + \text{Co-enzyme-I} \rightleftharpoons CH_3CHO + \text{Reduced Co-enzyme-I}$$

proceeds to an equilibrium. Reduction of the co-enzyme can be followed spectrographically, since the reduced compound has a distinctive absorption band in the region of 3,400 A.

A similar reversible reduction can be effected by means of an alkaline solution of sodium hyposulphite ($Na_2S_2O_4$). Karrer and his colleagues§ have shown that a number of salts of nicotinamide, and even quaternary salts of pyridine, can be reduced to products of a similar chemical type, and have concluded that the reduced forms of co-enzymes I and II possess *ortho*-dihydropyridine rings:

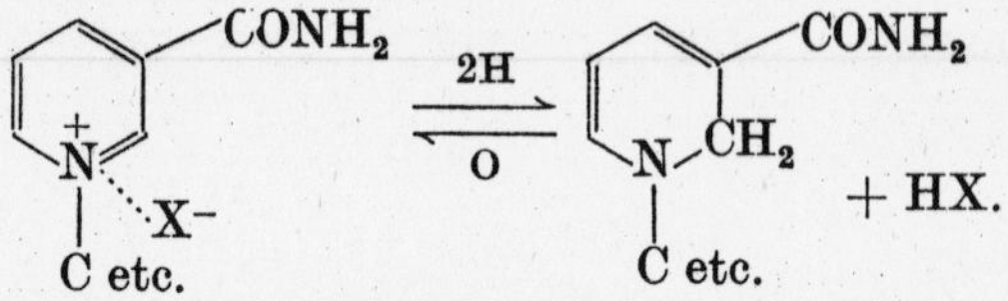

$$\text{(pyridinium ring, } CONH_2\text{, } \overset{+}{N}\cdots X^-\text{, N—C etc.)} \underset{O}{\overset{2H}{\rightleftharpoons}} \text{(dihydropyridine ring, } CONH_2\text{, } N\text{—}CH_2\text{, N—C etc.)} + HX. \quad (A)$$

In biochemical systems co-enzymes I and II both act as hydrogen acceptors, and since the reversible change (A) occurs, for each substance, at a definite oxidation-reduction potential, the co-enzymes help in controlling the oxidation level of cell processes. Many cell processes can be linked together by the successive oxidation or reduction of a single co-enzyme, e.g.

$$\beta\text{-Hydroxy-butyric acid} + \text{Co-enzyme-I} \rightleftharpoons \text{Acetoacetic acid} + \text{Reduced Co-enzyme-I}, \quad (a)$$

$$\text{Reduced Co-enzyme-I} + \text{Acetaldehyde} \rightleftharpoons \text{Co-enzyme-I} + \text{Alcohol}. \quad (b)$$

† *Zeit. physiol. Chem.* 1935, **237**, 1. ‡ *Biochem. Zeit.* 1933, **266**, 377.
§ *Helv. Chim. Acta*, 1936, **19**, 811, 1028; 1937, **20**, 55, 72, 418; 1938, **21**, 223.

Another well-characterized co-enzyme is *Co-carboxylase*, which is the pyrophosphate ester of aneurin, or vitamin-B_1 (VI). This contains a thiazole ring system, and it was at first thought that aneurin could, like co-enzyme-I, be reduced reversibly to a dihydro-compound by the action of sodium hyposulphite. Karrer, Graf, and Schukri,† however, have shown that though this reduction involves the addition of two atoms of hydrogen it is *not* a reversible process, but rather an irreversible change which splits the thiazole ring system from the remainder of the molecule.

Previously R. R. Williams had shown that the milder reducing agent, sodium sulphite, effected a similar fission at pH 5,‡ and this had given the first good clue to the structure of aneurin.

At biological pH's, however, aneurin acts as a thiol (VIII), capable of reversible oxidation to a disulphide, rather than as a thiazole ring compound (VII),§ and so, unlike co-enzyme-I, may be chiefly present in the reduced rather than the oxidized level *in vivo*.

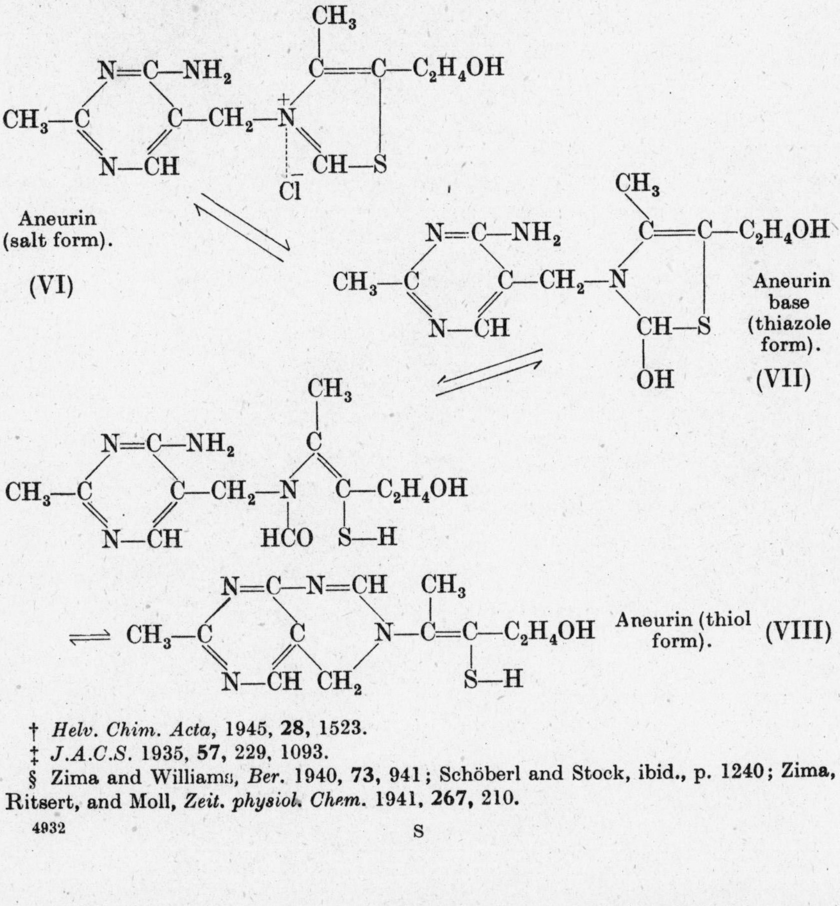

```
                                     CH3
                                     |
          N=C—NH2                    C===C—C2H4OH
         /     \                  +  /    |
  CH3—C         C—CH2—N             |
         \\    //                :  \\    |
          N—CH                   :_  CH—S
                                 Cl

Aneurin (salt form).  (VI)
                         ⇌
                                                      CH3
                                                       \
                         N=C—NH2                        C===C—C2H4OH
                        /     \                        /     |
              CH3—C           C—CH2—N                 |
                        \\    //                      \      |
                         N—CH                          CH—S
                                                       |
                                                       OH

                                          Aneurin base (thiazole form).  (VII)
                         ⇌
                                  CH3
                                  |
          N=C—NH2                 C
         /     \                /  \\
  CH3—C         C—CH2—N          C—C2H4OH
         \\    //       |        |
          N—CH          HCO      S—H

               N=C—N=CH      CH3
              /    \    \     |
  ⇌  CH3—C         C      N—C=C—C2H4OH      Aneurin (thiol form).  (VIII)
              \\   // \   /        |
               N—CH   CH2          S—H
```

† *Helv. Chim. Acta*, 1945, **28**, 1523.

‡ *J.A.C.S.* 1935, **57**, 229, 1093.

§ Zima and Williams, *Ber.* 1940, **73**, 941; Schöberl and Stock, ibid., p. 1240; Zima, Ritsert, and Moll, *Zeit. physiol. Chem.* 1941, **267**, 210.

It will be seen that these co-enzymes play a part in cell reactions similar to that of dyestuffs such as methylene blue in the *in vitro* enzyme reactions discussed on p. 261. It may be noted too that the oxidation-reduction change in riboflavin is similar in character, and actually there is little doubt that flavoproteins in the body have the function of re-oxidizing the reduced forms of the nicotinamide co-enzymes; thus

$$\text{Reduced Co-enzyme-I} + \text{Flavoprotein} \longrightarrow \text{Co-enzyme-I} + \text{Leuco-flavoprotein},$$

$$\text{Leuco-flavoprotein} + O_2 \longrightarrow \text{Flavoprotein} + H_2O_2.$$

Again, the cells of all aerobic organisms contain compounds of the porphyrin type in which there is present a metallic element such as iron, copper, or manganese which can have two valency states. The most important compounds of this group are the *Cytochromes*, which were discovered by MacMunn in 1886. Their physiological significance has been elucidated by Keilin, who showed that the cytochromes normally contain iron in the ferric state of oxidation, but that they can be reduced to the ferrous state by enzyme processes such as

$$\text{Succinic acid} + 2\ \text{Cytochrome}\ (Fe^{+++}) \longrightarrow \text{Fumaric acid} + 2\ \text{Reduced Cytochrome}\ (Fe^{++}) + 2H^+$$

which are again dehydrogenations. In the presence of the enzyme *Cytochrome oxidase*, a reduced cytochrome is easily oxidized by air to the ferric state, but the oxygen is converted to water, and not to hydrogen peroxide. The absorption spectra of the oxidized and reduced forms of the cytochromes are sufficiently distinct for this oxidation-reduction cycle to be followed spectrographically even in living organisms, such as small insects, and in this way it has been established that the cytochromes play a major part in respiratory processes.

The copper-containing porphyrins appear to act in a similar fashion, undergoing a reversible valency change between the cuprous and the cupric states. For all these metallic compounds the dehydrogenation process can be expressed as

$$Fe^{+++}(Cu^{++}) + H{-}R \rightleftharpoons Fe^{++}(Cu^{+}) + H^{+} + \cdot R.$$

Organic disulphides, such as cystine, are still another group of potential hydrogen acceptors in biochemical systems,

$$R{-}S{-}S{-}R + 2H{-}X \rightleftharpoons 2R{-}S{-}H + X{-}X.$$

Amongst these the tripeptide *Glutathione*, first isolated by Hopkins, is of importance.

Free Radical Theories of Enzyme Action

From the foregoing sections it will have been seen that in a number of cases it has been possible to trace the stepwise oxidation of metabolites, and to account for the evident re-formation in metabolic processes of many biochemically abundant substances, such as lactic, succinic, and citric acids, and the co-enzymes. However, even exothermic biochemical oxidations do not take place in the absence of an enzyme catalyst, which seems to be so specific that it evidently must act by activating only one particular organic structure.

Kinetic measurements often give indications that enzyme oxidations are chain processes.† Thus at low concentrations the reaction is usually pseudo-unimolecular, proceeding at a rate proportional to the concentration of the oxidizable metabolite, but reaching, at higher concentrations, a maximum velocity which is independent of the concentration of the metabolite, and which gradually falls off with time as the enzyme becomes irreversibly destroyed. Since chain reactions are essentially of the homolytic type (see pp. 16–17) it is therefore cogent to examine the possibility of occurrence of free radical changes in enzyme systems.

Over thirty years ago it was pointed out by Dakin‡ that hydrogen peroxide, alone of all the various chemical oxidizing agents, could bring about the same types of oxidative degradations in fats, carbohydrates, and amino-acids as do enzyme systems. He contended therefore that the peroxide theory of oxidation, as had been set out by Engler and Bach was equally cogent in living cells as in other branches of chemistry. Dakin's pioneer work is an indication that enzyme oxidations are chain reactions which resemble the free-radical reactions of molecular oxygen and of hydrogen peroxide.

In 1931 Haber and Willstätter§ suggested, from analogy with the processes involved in the autoxidation of sulphites (p. 235), that the 'dehydrogenase' enzymes were reagents which set up long reaction chains by bringing about hydrogen abstraction. They pointed out that many enzymes contained traces of heavy metals such as iron or copper, and postulated that a primary dehydrogenation process representable as

$$R{-}H + Fe^{+++} \longrightarrow R\cdot + Fe^{++} + H^{+}$$

might occur, to give a free radical, R·, which might then set up either

† Moelwyn-Hughes, *Ergebnisse der Enzymforschung*, 1937, **6**, 25.
‡ Dakin, *Oxidations and Reductions in the Animal Body*, 1911.
§ *Ber.* 1931, **64**, 2844.

an autoxidation chain, of the type discussed on pp. 248–52, or else a hydrogen transference of the Cannizzaro type (p. 190).

Thus they represented the aerobic oxidation of alcohol as

$$CH_3{-}CH_2{-}OH + Fe^{+++} \longrightarrow CH_3{-}\dot{C}H{-}OH + Fe^{++} + H^+,$$

$$CH_3{-}\dot{C}H{-}OH + O_2 \longrightarrow CH_3{-}\underset{\displaystyle OH}{\underset{|}{CH}}{-}O{-}O\cdot,$$

$$CH_3{-}\underset{\displaystyle OH}{\underset{|}{CH}}{-}O{-}O\cdot + CH_3{-}CH_2{-}OH \longrightarrow 2CH_3{-}CH{=}O + \cdot OH + H_2O,$$

$$\cdot OH + CH_3{-}CH_2{-}OH \longrightarrow H_2O + CH_3{-}\dot{C}H{-}OH,$$

and the dehydrogenation of succinic acid by a quinonoid dye as

$$\begin{array}{l} CH_2{-}COOH \\ | \\ CH_2{-}COOH \end{array} + Fe^{+++} \longrightarrow \begin{array}{l} \dot{C}H{-}COOH \\ | \\ CH_2{-}COOH \end{array} + Fe^{++} + H^+,$$

$$\begin{array}{l} \dot{C}H{-}COOH \\ | \\ CH_2{-}COOH \end{array} + O{=}C_6H_4{=}O \longrightarrow \begin{array}{l} CH{-}COOH \\ \| \\ CH{-}COOH \end{array} + HO{-}C_6H_4{-}O\cdot$$

$$\begin{array}{l} CH_2{-}COOH \\ | \\ CH_2{-}COOH \end{array} + HO{-}C_6H_4{-}O\cdot \longrightarrow \begin{array}{l} \dot{C}H{-}COOH \\ | \\ CH_2{-}COOH \end{array} + HO{-}C_6H_4{-}OH$$

Their application of this scheme in explaining the action of the enzyme 'catalase' which decomposes hydrogen peroxide, and its further elaboration by Haber and Weiss, has already been discussed in Chapter XI (pp. 249–52), and there is no doubt that in this case the enzyme, which is indeed an iron-containing porphyrin, can in fact be replaced by either a ferrous or a ferric salt.

In a number of other cases too, Fenton's reaction (pp. 247–8), in which a ferrous salt is an effective catalyst, corresponds closely to biochemical actions of 'peroxidase' enzymes,† but in general an enzyme catalyst *cannot* be simply replaced by an oxidizable or reducible heavy metal.

† See, however, Mann and Saunders, *Proc. Roy. Soc.* 1935, B **119**, 47.

However, A. H. Cook† has shown that the metallic phthalocyanines, in which there is present a co-ordination system closely similar to that of the porphyrins, have marked catalytic properties which, in autoxidation at least, closely resemble those of enzymes.

Though it is now evident that free radicals may be generated in metal-free biological systems (pp. 281–2), the normal reaction between a free radical and an aliphatic compound, viz.

$$R\cdot + H{-}X \longrightarrow R{-}H + \cdot X,$$

whereby an *atom* of hydrogen is abstracted from a saturated molecule (compare Chapters VII–IX), can, in almost all cases, be postulated as a possible primary step in any dehydrogenase system.

Hence one can now generalize the Haber–Willstätter scheme, and interpret enzyme oxidations as chain reactions involving only processes which have been proved to be typical of neutral radicals.‡

This view is exemplified by the reaction mechanisms depicted below, in which the initiating radical of the enzyme is depicted by the symbol $\phi\cdot$.

Example 1. LACTIC ACID—PYRUVIC ACID, AND SIMILAR OXIDATIONS INVOLVING

$$>C{<}^{H}_{OH} \longrightarrow >C{=}O.$$

Chain initiation by enzyme action.

(*a*) Abstraction of hydrogen from substrate:

either $CH_3{-}CH(OH){-}COOH + \phi\cdot \longrightarrow CH_3{-}\dot{C}(OH){-}COOH + \phi{-}H$ (i)

or $CH_3{-}CH(O{-}H){-}COOH + \phi\cdot \rightleftarrows CH_3{-}CH(O\cdot){-}COOH + \phi{-}H$ (ii)§

(*b*) Enzyme–co-enzyme union in radical form:

$$\begin{array}{l}H_2NOC{-}C{=}CH{-}CH{=}CH{-}\overset{+}{N}{-}C\text{ etc.}\\ \quad (\text{ring: } C{-}C(H){=}\overset{+}{N}, \; HC{=}C, \; CH{=}CH)\end{array} + \phi\cdot \longrightarrow \begin{array}{l}H_2NOC{-}C{-}\dot{C}(H){-}\overset{+}{N}(\phi){-}C\text{ etc.}\\ \quad (\text{ring: } HC{=}C, \; HC{=}CH)\end{array} \quad \text{(iii)}$$

† Cook, *J.* 1938, pp. 1761, 1768.
‡ Waters, *Trans. Faraday Soc.* 1943, **39**, 142.
§ Compare p. 251.

Of these alternatives reaction (ii) is the most probable: reaction (iii) is only probable if $\phi\cdot$ is a tervalent carbon radical, whereas processes (i) and (ii) are possible with *any* hydrogen acceptor.

Repeating chain sequence.

Either,

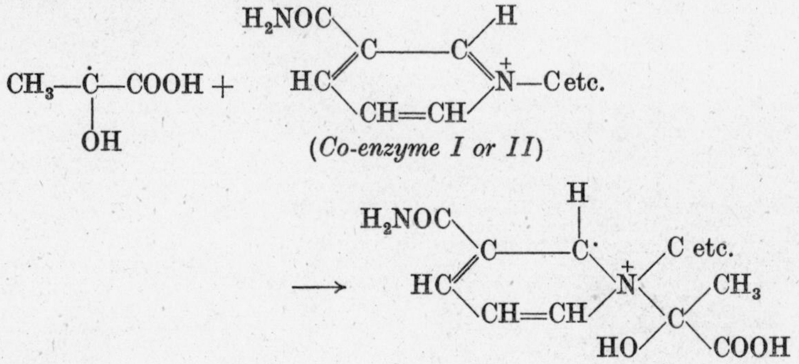

$$CH_3-\dot{C}(OH)-COOH + \begin{array}{c} H_2NOC\diagdown \quad\quad \diagup H \\ C\text{——}C \\ HC \quad\quad\quad \overset{+}{N}-C\ \text{etc.} \\ \diagdown CH{=}CH \diagup \end{array}$$

(*Co-enzyme I or II*)

$$\longrightarrow \begin{array}{c} H_2NOC\diagdown \quad\quad H \\ C\text{——}\dot{C}H \quad\quad \diagup C\ \text{etc.} \\ HC \quad\quad\quad \overset{+}{N} \quad \diagup CH_3 \\ \diagdown CH{=}CH \diagup \quad C \\ HO\diagup \quad \diagdown COOH \end{array} \qquad \text{(iv)}$$

followed by

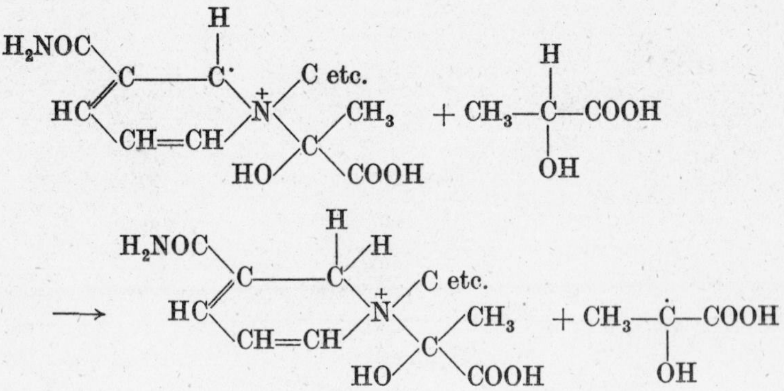

$$\begin{array}{c} H_2NOC\diagdown \quad\quad H \\ C\text{——}\dot{C}H \quad\quad \diagup C\ \text{etc.} \\ HC \quad\quad\quad \overset{+}{N} \quad \diagup CH_3 \\ \diagdown CH{=}CH \diagup \quad C \\ HO\diagup \quad \diagdown COOH \end{array} + CH_3-CH(OH)-COOH$$

$$\longrightarrow \begin{array}{c} H_2NOC\diagdown \quad\quad H \diagup H \\ C\text{——}C \quad\quad \diagup C\ \text{etc.} \\ HC \quad\quad\quad \overset{+}{N} \quad \diagup CH_3 \\ \diagdown CH{=}CH \diagup \quad C \\ HO\diagup \quad \diagdown COOH \end{array} + CH_3-\dot{C}(OH)-COOH \qquad \text{(v)}$$

and then

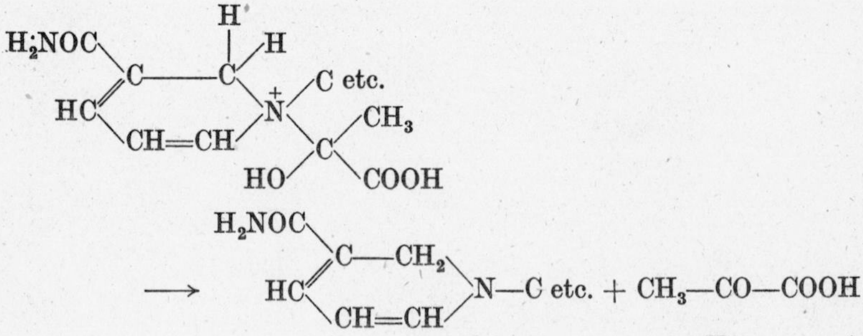

$$\begin{array}{c} H_2NOC\diagdown \quad\quad H \diagup H \\ C\text{——}C \quad\quad \diagup C\ \text{etc.} \\ HC \quad\quad\quad \overset{+}{N} \quad \diagup CH_3 \\ \diagdown CH{=}CH \diagup \quad C \\ HO\diagup \quad \diagdown COOH \end{array}$$

$$\longrightarrow \begin{array}{c} H_2NOC\diagdown \\ C\text{——}CH_2\diagdown \\ HC \quad\quad\quad N-C\ \text{etc.} \\ \diagdown CH{=}CH \diagup \end{array} + CH_3-CO-COOH + H^+ \qquad \text{(vi)}$$

(*Reduced co-enzyme*)

which resembles the splitting of an aldehyde-ammonia in water.

Or, if one presumes that hydrogen abstraction is more facile from C—O—H groups than from C—H groups:†

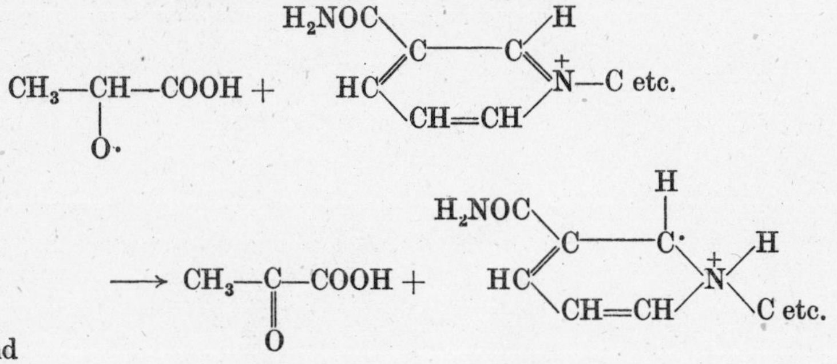

```
                              H2NOC          H
                                   \        /
                                    C——————C
                                   //       \\ +
CH3—CH—COOH +                   HC            N—C etc.
     |                             \         /
     O·                             CH==CH

                                                     H
                                     H2NOC           |
                                          \          |
                                           C—————C·     H
                                          //         \ + /
     ——→ CH3—C—COOH +                  HC             N           (vii)
             ||                           \          /  \
             O                             CH==CH        C etc.
```

and

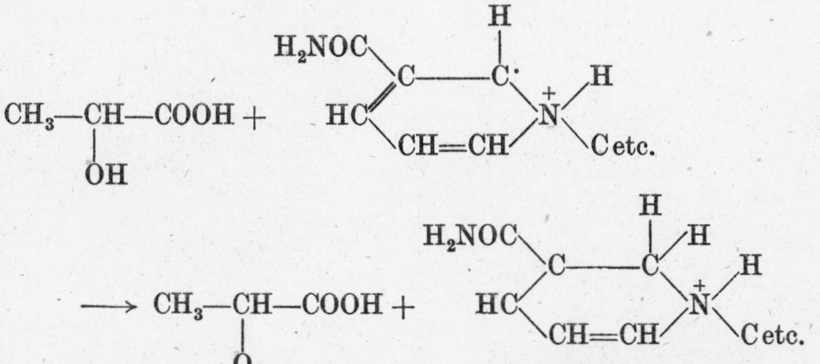

```
                                          H
                             H2NOC        |
                                  \       |
                                   C—————C·     H
                                  //       \ + /
CH3—CH—COOH +                  HC            N
     |                            \         /  \
     OH                            CH==CH       C etc.

                                                   H
                                    H2NOC          | /H
                                         \         |/
                                          C—————C       H
                                         //       \ + /
    ——→ CH3—CH—COOH +                 HC            N             (viii)
             |                           \         /  \
             O·                           CH==CH       C etc.
                                     (Ammonium salt form
                                     of reduced co-enzyme)
```

In the above schemes the only vital assumption is the occurrence of stepwise reduction of the nicotinamide ring system *in its ammonium salt form*. It may be noted that the mechanism resembles that suggested on pp. 249–51 for the Fenton reaction.

Example 2. CARBOXYLASE ACTION, WITH ANEURIN ACTING AS CO-ENZYME

Chain initiation: oxidation of co-enzyme to a thiol radical.

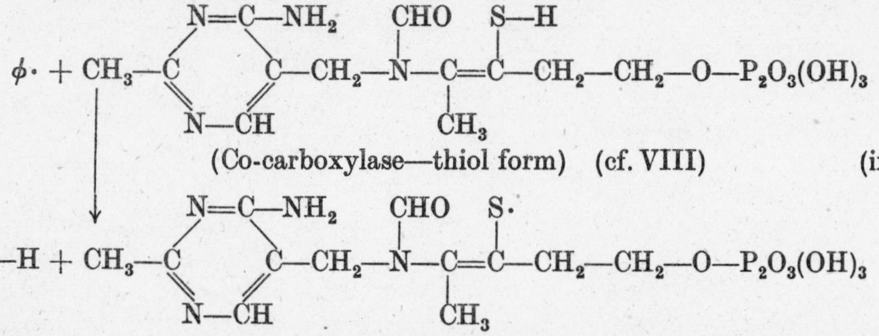

```
              N==C—NH2        CHO    S—H
             /      \          |      |
φ· + CH3—C            C—CH2—N—C==C—CH2—CH2—O—P2O3(OH)3
    |        \\      //               |
    |          N—CH                  CH3
    |       (Co-carboxylase—thiol form)   (cf. VIII)            (ix)
    ↓         N==C—NH2        CHO    S·
             /      \          |      |
φ—H + CH3—C           C—CH2—N—C==C—CH2—CH2—O—P2O3(OH)3
             \\      //               |
               N—CH                  CH3
          (Co-enzyme—thiol radical form)   (IX)
```

† See pp. 251 and 275.

Hydrogen abstraction:

either from free pyruvic acid,

$$R{-}S\cdot + CH_3{-}CO{-}COOH \longrightarrow R{-}S{-}H + CH_3{-}CO{-}CO{-}O\cdot, \qquad \text{(x)}$$

or equivalent electron abstraction from its anion,†

$$R{-}S\cdot + (CH_3{-}CO{-}CO{-}O{:}) \longrightarrow (R{-}S{:})^- + CH_3{-}CO{-}CO{-}O\cdot, \qquad \text{(xi)}$$

giving, in either case the original co-enzyme in its initial reduced form, and the neutral pyruvate radical, which like neutral acetate radicals (p. 138) or benzoate radicals (p. 166) would immediately lose carbon dioxide,

$$CH_3{-}CO{-}CO{-}O\cdot \longrightarrow CH_3{-}CO\cdot + CO_2, \qquad \text{(xii)}$$

and form the free acetyl radical.

This, in water, is capable of either of two reactions, i.e.

$$CH_3{-}CO\cdot + H{-}OH \rightleftharpoons CH_3{-}CH{=}O + \cdot OH, \qquad \text{(xiii)}$$

or

$$CH_3{-}CO\cdot + HO{-}H \rightleftharpoons CH_3{-}CO{-}OH + \cdot H, \qquad \text{(xiv)}$$

both of which are probably reversible.

Reaction (xiv) leads to the formation of acetic acid and atomic hydrogen; the latter would immediately be capable of reducing more co-enzyme to the heterocyclic radical, as in (ix) above, thus continuing the reaction chain.

Reaction (xiii) leads to the formation of the hydroxyl radical, which might be expected to dehydrogenate more pyruvic acid, thus

$$CH_3{-}CO{-}COOH + \cdot OH \longrightarrow CH_3{-}CO{-}CO{-}O\cdot + H{-}OH. \qquad \text{(xv)}$$

In this way the overall degradation of pyruvic acid to acetaldehyde and carbon dioxide might occur with the intervention of but minute amounts of either enzyme or co-enzyme.

In this connexion the discovery by Baer‡ of the acetylating power of pyruvic acid upon free radical oxidation is of great interest. Not only does it suggest that pyruvic acid may, in the body, acetylate both —OH and —NH groups via the reaction sequence (x)–(xii), and thereby act as a detoxicant *in vivo*, but it suggests an explanation of the way in which *phosphorylation* may occur in the course of enzyme reactions.

† pH control, which is important in all enzyme systems, may be a deciding factor in determining the oxidation/reduction potential at which hydrogen transfer from pyruvate to the thiol/sulphide radical system occurs. It is probably significant that the enzyme carboxylase contains an appreciable quantity of magnesium, which may well act as an essential buffer in a complex possibly involving the pyrophosphate group.

‡ *J. Biol. Chem.* 1942, **146**, 391. (See pp. 230–1.)

In Chapter V (p. 84) it was mentioned that surface films of phosphoric acid greatly prolong the apparent life of atomic hydrogen in discharge tubes. This indicates that the H—OP link of phosphoric acid (or of NaH_2PO_4 or Na_2HPO_4) can be broken more easily than the H—O link of a water molecule. Consequently, in the presence of phosphoric acid, one would anticipate that the reaction

$$CH_3—CO\cdot + H—O—PO(OH)_2 \longrightarrow CH_3—CO—O—PO(OH)_2 + H\cdot, \quad \text{(xvi)}$$

giving acetyl-phosphoric anhydride, would be more facile than reaction (xiv) which gives rise to acetic acid. Again in solutions of high pH phosphate anions would be expected to react as follows,

$$CH_3—CO\cdot + \bar{O}—PO(O^-)(O—H) \longrightarrow CH_3—CO—O—PO(O^-)(O^-) + H\cdot, \quad \text{(xvii)}$$

with great ease, since they are relatively bulky groups built up, on the exterior, mainly of oxygen atoms with negative charges, any one of which could unite at once with any active radical.

Lipmann and others† have actually isolated acetyl-phosphoric anhydride from the oxidative decarboxylation of pyruvic acid by enzyme systems. It is a typical acid anhydride, easily hydrolysed by water, and an obvious reagent for the biosynthesis of phosphate amides (e.g. phospho-creatine), esters (e.g. sugar phosphates), or again pyrophosphates, thus

$$CH_3—CO—O—PO(OH)_2 + (HO)_2PO—O—R$$
$$\longrightarrow CH_3—CO—OH + (HO)_2PO—O—PO(OH)(OR) \quad \text{(xviii)}$$

Example 3. SUCCINIC DEHYDROGENASE

The conversion of succinic acid to fumaric acid can easily be represented as a radical disproportionation, following hydrogen abstraction from a C—H group, thus

$$\phi\cdot + HOOC—CH_2—CH_2—COOH$$
$$\longrightarrow \phi—H + HOOC—\dot{C}H—CH_2—COOH, \quad \text{(xix)}$$

$$2HOOC—CH—CH_2—COOH$$
$$\longrightarrow HOOC—CH{=}CH—COOH + HOOC—CH_2—CH_2—COOH. \quad \text{(xx)}$$

† Lipmann, *Annual Review of Biochemistry*, 1943, **12**, 3–5; *J. Biol. Chem.* 1940, **134**, 463; *Nature*, 1939, **143**, 436.

This enzyme reaction does in fact involve the iron porphyrin compound *cytochrome-C* as the co-enzyme factor, and can only be effected in anaerobic systems. In this case the fundamental Haber–Willstätter equation (p. 267) for hydrogen abstraction concurrent with reduction of ferric iron may indeed be valid.

Quite probably the fundamental difference between succinic dehydrogenase enzymes and lactic or pyruvic dehydrogenases may be traceable to the fact that the active enzyme (and co-enzyme) of the succinic system is able to attack the C—H link, whereas in the other cases it is more likely to be O—H links which are attacked.

As shown in Chapter XI free carbon radicals undoubtedly react directly with molecular oxygen to form peroxides, and consequently one would not expect the direct dehydrogenation of succinic acid to fumaric acid to be possible in an aerobic system.

Objections to Free Radical Theories of Enzyme Action

The acceptance of any generalized free radical theory of enzyme oxidation presents several difficulties. Firstly, enzyme actions are extremely specific, and it would therefore be necessary to postulate that each of the radicals involved in any oxidation cycle reacts only with its special substrate, and not with other molecules containing chemically similar groups, including even stereoisomers. Consequently the independent existence of *free* tervalent carbon radicals, such as $CH_3—\dot{C}(OH)—COOH$, is out of the question.

As the preceding chapters have shown, the chemical displacement reactions of the *active* free radicals are not specific: moreover solvent molecules are much more likely to be attacked than solute molecules. Consequently it must be assented that any primary catalyst radical $(\cdot\phi)$ must have too little intrinsic energy to react with a water molecule to produce either free hydrogen or free hydroxyl,

$$\phi\cdot + HO—H \longrightarrow \phi—OH + H\cdot \quad or \quad \phi\cdot + H—OH \longrightarrow \phi—H + \cdot OH,$$

for otherwise all specificity in enzyme action would be obliterated in favour of one general type of oxidation, which would probably be similar to the general oxidative action of aqueous hydrogen peroxide described by Dakin (p. 267).

As the following section will show, the conclusion that the neutral radicals operative in enzyme systems have low free energies and are resonance-stabilized systems does accord with present knowledge of the structures of active 'prosthetic groups' of enzymes. Nevertheless, it must not be forgotten that by enzyme processes it is easily possible to oxidize organic molecules, such as succinic acid, which are not directly attacked by a free hydroxyl radical, in the form of Fenton's reagent.

It may be recalled, however, that in Chapter XI it was suggested that certain reactions of the 'peroxidase' group of enzymes might involve the presence of hydroxyl radicals in very low concentration (i.e. in chain reactions of H_2O_2 of Type A, see p. 250). The more probable biochemical function of molecular hydrogen peroxide is the re-oxidation of a reduced co-enzyme component which need not be sufficiently reactive to interact with water (i.e. in reactions of Type B, see p. 252).

If it be accepted that enzyme oxidations do not, in general, involve free hydroxyl radicals, then it is difficult to explain on physico-chemical grounds why effective radicals which are unable to attack water molecules are yet able to dehydrogenate organic hydroxy compounds, such as carbohydrates or lactic acid. Actually, Wieland originally depicted the dehydrogenation of alcohol as an attack on C—H links rather than on O—H links,

$$CH_3—CH_2—OH + Fe^{++} \longrightarrow CH_3—\dot{C}H—OH + Fe^{+++} + H\cdot,$$

for only in this way could he formulate easily the rest of his hypothetical reaction sequence. F. O. and K. K. Rice† have called attention to the fact that the above assumption accords with the fact that the calculated bond energy of the C—H group is decidedly less than that of the O—H group.‡ However, the order is reversed if *covalent* bond energies only are taken into consideration,§ since as much as 40 per cent. of the bond energy of the hydroxyl group is due to its partial ionic character, a contribution to the total bond energy which may become very small in an aqueous solution.|| Indeed the study of chemical reactions leads one to the conclusion that often O—H groups are more easily attacked by free neutral radicals than are C—H groups. Thus it is only on this assumption that one can explain satisfactorily C—C bond fission of glycols by lead tetra-acetate (p. 228) or periodic acid (p. 257),

$$\begin{array}{l} R—CH—CH—R + 2\cdot OCOCH_3 \longrightarrow 2H—O—COCH_3 + 2RCH{=}O, \\ \quad\;\; | \quad\;\;\; | \\ \quad\; OH \;\; OH \end{array}$$

† Rice, *The Aliphatic Free Radicals*, p. 177 (Johns Hopkins Press, Baltimore, 1935).

‡ Pauling, *The Nature of the Covalent Bond* (Cornell Univ. Press, 1940), gives C—H = 87 k.cals., O—H = 110 k.cals., though later workers give a value of 98 k.cals. for the C—H bond (Kynch and Penney, *Proc. Roy. Soc.* 1941, A **179**, 214).

§ O. K. Rice, *Electronic Structure and Chemical Binding*, p. 190 (McGraw Hill, New York, 1940), gives *covalent* bond energies as C—H = 85 k.cals., O—H = 69 k.cals.

|| Waters, *J.* 1942, p. 153, compare Chapter I, pp. 14–16.

for a primary attack on C—H bonds by acetate radicals would lead to olefine formation as follows:†

$$R{-}CH(OH){-}CH(OH){-}R \longrightarrow R{-}\dot{C}(OH){-}\dot{C}(OH){-}R \longrightarrow R{-}C(OH){=}C(OH){-}R \longrightarrow R{-}C({=}O){-}CH(OH){-}R.$$

Wieland's demonstration that the oxidation of aldehydes usually requires the presence of water (p. 263) is further evidence of the greater reactivity of hydroxyl groups.

However, in dilute aqueous solution there should be no marked differentiability in cases of oxidation of different organic hydroxyl or imino groups, since within liquid water hydrogen bonding will occur to a sufficient extent to diminish to a very small value (1–2 k.cals.) the energy difference between O—H bonds in different molecules, and in particular between C—O—H and H—O—H.

Alternative considerations. To get over the inherent difficulties of reconciling the specificity of enzyme catalysis with thermodynamic requirements, biochemists have made extensive use of hypotheses of (*a*) *energetic coupling of oxidation processes*, and (*b*) *complex formation* between the oxidized substrate and the enzyme catalyst.

They point out that biochemical processes do not occur in homogeneous aqueous solution, since the active enzyme cannot be separated from the bulk of a colloidal protein molecule, and that the oxidizable substrate may first have to be adsorbed on to the surface of the colloid, to fit, in exact 'lock-and-key' fashion on to specific 'prosthetic groups'. The heat of reaction, at each stage in the reaction chain, may then be retained at, or near, the catalytically active centre to a sufficient extent to permit of the occurrence of some endothermic changes in a reaction sequence which is as a whole an exothermic process.

For instance, according to Krebs,‡ the biochemical synthesis of urea, which involves the conversion of ornithine to arginine, necessarily entails a gain of about 14 k.cals. of energy per gram molecule. This endothermic process can only occur in conjunction with an exothermic oxidation, and since arginine synthesis is accelerated by the presence of substances such as glucose, fructose, lactic acid, and pyruvic acid it has

† Fenton's oxidation of tartaric acid to di-hydroxy-maleic acid (p. 248) may be a reaction of this type, though the alternative formulation as

$$HOOC{-}CH(O\cdot){-}CH(OH){-}COOH \longrightarrow HOOC{-}C({=}O){-}CH(OH){-}COOH \longrightarrow HOOC{-}C(OH){=}C(OH){-}COOH$$

is more probable. (Compare the structure and reactions of ascorbic acid.)

‡ Krebs and Henseleit, *Z. physiol. Chem.* 1932, **210**, 33.

been suggested that it is the simultaneous oxidation of these substances which provides the energy for the urea synthesis.

Again phosphorylation and dephosphorylation reactions may play a significant part in regulating the energy transferences in the stepwise oxidation of sugars.† As suggested on p. 273, phosphorylation may accompany decarboxylation, and as much as 11 k.cals. of energy may be liberated per mol. by the subsequent hydrolysis of the mixed acyl-phosphoric anhydride.

Instances of the retention of the heat of reaction of atomic processes on localized catalytic surfaces have already received brief mention in connexion with the chemistry of atomic hydrogen (Chap. V, pp. 81–5) and as a feature of catalysis on metallic surfaces (Chap. X, pp. 214–17), and thus energetic coupling of reaction processes is a feature of chain reactions by no means unique to biochemistry. A hypothesis of this type may well be capable of explaining why strong covalent bonds, such as C—H in succinic acid, can be broken by enzyme oxidation.

The hypothesis of *complex formation* between the oxidizable substrate and the enzyme catalyst is but a natural development of the view that selective adsorption on a protein surface precedes most biochemical changes. It is obvious that molecular rearrangement may follow enzyme+metabolite combination, and give, in the resulting complex, a structure which may break down much more easily than the original simple metabolite molecule.

This idea has been developed most successfully by Langenbeck, who has been able to instance many 'model enzyme systems' in which biochemical reactions may be simulated using much simpler molecules.

By following up an observation of Traube,‡ Langenbeck showed that when a mixture of isatin and an α-amino acid, such as alanine, was refluxed in 50 per cent. acetic acid, carbon dioxide and an aldehyde were liberated whilst the isatin was reduced to isatide.§ In the presence of air, or of a typical hydrogen-acceptor such as methylene blue, however, the isatide was re-oxidized to isatin, so that the whole aerobic system resembled that of an amino-acid oxidase process, i.e.

$$\underset{\displaystyle NH_2}{R\text{—}\overset{}{CH}\text{—}COOH} + O \xrightarrow{\text{Isatin in acetic acid}} R\text{—}CH{=}O + CO_2 + NH_3.$$

Previously Wieland and Bergel‖ had shown that oxidations of this

† Kalckar, *Chemical Reviews*, 1941, **28**, 71–178.
‡ Traube, *Ber.* 1911, **44**, 3145.
§ Langenbeck, ibid. 1927, **60**, 930.
‖ Wieland and Bergel, *Annalen*, 1924, **439**, 196.

type could be effected in the presence of activated charcoal, but here, for the first time, a typical enzyme process was carried out in homogeneous solution by the use of simple molecules only. Further research revealed that this apparent catalytic property of isatin is shared by a large number of its derivatives, and analogues, including water-soluble carboxylic acid and sulphonic acid derivatives, many of which are quite effective in dilute aqueous acid, or pyridine.†

Langenbeck has shown, however, that this degradation of α-amino acids proceeds in a number of well-defined stages. Firstly, the amino group condenses with the active carbonyl group of isatin to yield a Schiff's base, which then undergoes a molecular rearrangement to an unstable product from which carbon dioxide is eliminated, and finally hydrolysis occurs to give an aldehyde and 3-amino-oxindole:

$$C_6H_4{<}\begin{matrix}CO\\|\\CO\end{matrix}{>}NH + H_2N{-}CH(COOH){-}R \longrightarrow C_6H_4{<}\begin{matrix}C{=}N{-}CH(COOH){-}R\\|\\CO\end{matrix}{>}NH$$

$$\downarrow$$

$$C_6H_4{<}\begin{matrix}CH{-}N{=}C(COOH){-}R\\|\\CO\end{matrix}{>}NH$$

$$\longrightarrow C_6H_4{<}\begin{matrix}CH{-}N{=}CH{-}R\\|\\CO\end{matrix}{>}NH + CO_2$$

$$\xrightarrow{H_2O} C_6H_4{<}\begin{matrix}CH{-}NH_2\\|\\CO\end{matrix}{>}NH + R{-}CH{=}O.$$

In the absence of oxygen 3-amino-oxindole and isatin react together to give isatide:

$$C_6H_4{<}\begin{matrix}CH{-}NH_2\\|\\CO\end{matrix}{>}NH + HN{<}\begin{matrix}OC\\|\\OC\end{matrix}{>}C_6H_4$$

$$\xrightarrow{H_2O} C_6H_4{<}\begin{matrix}C(OH){-}C(OH)\\|\qquad\quad|\\CO\qquad OC\end{matrix}{>}C_6H_4 \;(\text{each ring closed through } NH) + NH_3:$$

† Langenbeck, *Ber.* 1928, **61**, 942; 1937, **70**, 672.

but 3-amino-oxindole itself is autoxidizable, and reduces oxygen to hydrogen peroxide:†

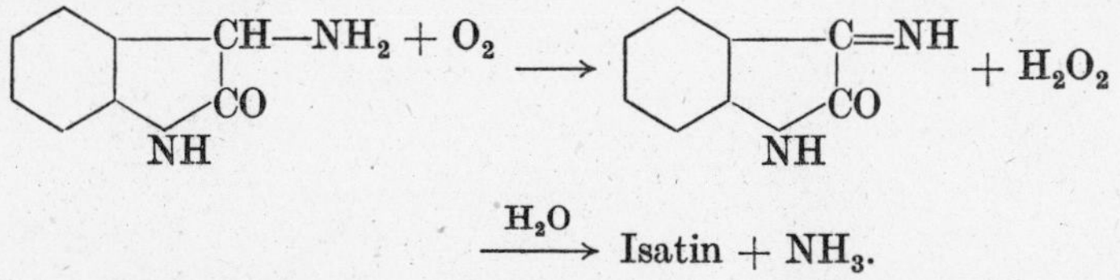

$$\text{(3-amino-oxindole: } C_6H_4\text{—CH—NH}_2\text{, CO, NH)} + O_2 \longrightarrow \text{(} C_6H_4\text{—C=NH, CO, NH)} + H_2O_2$$

$$\xrightarrow{H_2O} \text{Isatin} + NH_3.$$

The condensation of amines and ketones to give Schiff's bases is also a model reaction of interest in connexion with decarboxylation processes, for, as Langenbeck has shown,‡ α-ketonic acids, such as pyruvic acid and phenylglyoxylic acid, yield Schiff's bases which readily lose carbon dioxide. 3-Amino-oxindole, and still more 3-amino-naphthoxindole, are thus characteristic 'model enzymes' for decarboxylase action; thus:

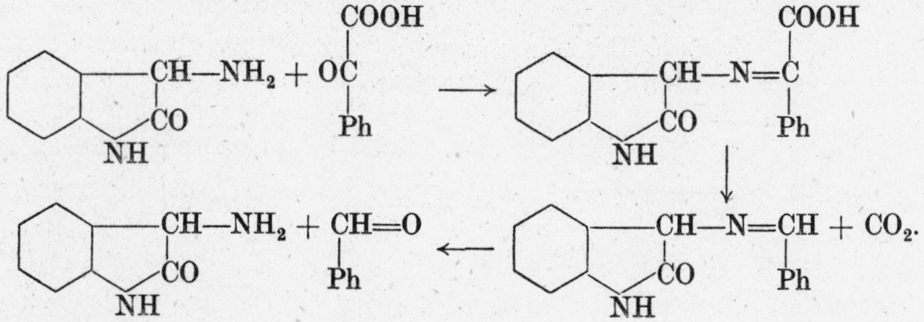

$$\text{(oxindole)—CH—NH}_2 + \text{OC(COOH)(Ph)} \longrightarrow \text{(oxindole)—CH—N=C(COOH)(Ph)}$$

$$\downarrow$$

$$\text{(oxindole)—CH—NH}_2 + \text{CH=O(Ph)} \longleftarrow \text{(oxindole)—CH—N=CH(Ph)} + CO_2.$$

Weil-Malherbe§ has pointed out that co-carboxylase (VI) (p. 265), besides containing an oxidizable and reducible thiazole ring system, possesses a primary amino group, and has proposed therefore that its reactions follow those of Langenbeck's model compounds. He has represented the alternative degradations of pyruvic acid to acetic acid (in animal tissue) or to acetaldehyde (in yeast) as follows:

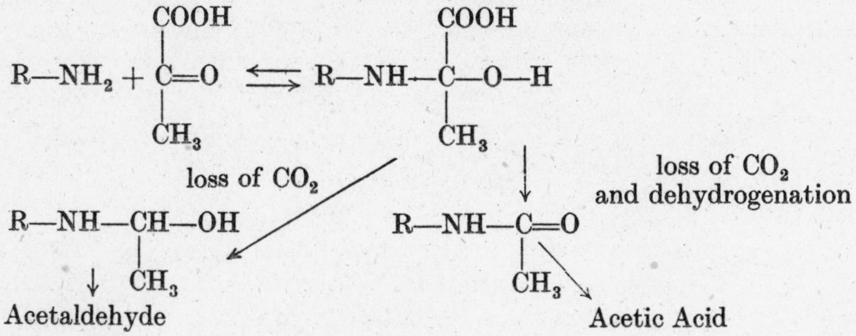

$$\text{R—NH}_2 + \begin{array}{c}\text{COOH}\\|\\\text{C=O}\\|\\CH_3\end{array} \rightleftarrows \text{R—NH—}\begin{array}{c}\text{COOH}\\|\\\text{C—O—H}\\|\\CH_3\end{array}$$

loss of CO_2 →

$$\text{R—NH—}\begin{array}{c}\text{CH—OH}\\|\\CH_3\end{array} \downarrow \text{Acetaldehyde}$$

loss of CO_2 and dehydrogenation ↓

$$\text{R—NH—}\begin{array}{c}\text{C=O}\\|\\CH_3\end{array} \searrow \text{Acetic Acid}$$

† Langenbeck and Ruge, ibid. 1937, **70**, 367.

‡ Langenbeck *et al.*, *Annalen*, 1931, **485**, 53; 1932, **499**, 201; 1934, **512**, 276; *Ergeb. der Enzymforschung*, 1933, **2**, 314.

§ Weil-Malherbe, *Nature*, 1940, **145**, 106.

It is significant, moreover, that the decarboxylation of α-amino-acids requires a specific co-enzyme *Co-decarboxylase*, which has now been isolated in the crystalline state.† This turns out to be *Pyridoxal phosphate*, a substance with an aldehydic group, and corresponds quite closely with Langenbeck's model enzymes.

Examples of the surface catalysis, by proteins and derivatives of cellulose, of hydrolyses and asymmetric synthesis have also been instanced by both Langenbeck and Bredig.‡

It might be concluded therefore that, since it is so easy, on paper, to formulate almost any known change by a plausible reaction process, the generalized free radical theory of enzyme oxidation is of little value. Though theoretical speculation has, in this field, outrun the experimental evidence, it must be admitted, however, that the free radical theory does provide the only rational basis for explaining the two outstanding general features of enzyme oxidation, viz. (i) that they are chain reactions, and (ii) that they are usually dehydrogenations rather than oxygen, or hydroxyl, additions.

Reaction Promoters in Enzymes

Many oxidase enzymes, when separated from inert material, are well-defined crystallizable substances which, by fractional hydrolysis can often be split into non-dialysable 'protein carriers' and characterizable substances of low molecular weight termed 'prosthetic groups'. The specificity of enzyme action is undoubtedly to be associated with the protein component, whilst the catalytic action seems to be more closely connected with the prosthetic group, though the latter is not a catalyst apart from a specific protein. The same prosthetic group has often been isolated from a whole series of biochemically related enzymes.

In general structure and chemical properties, the prosthetic groups of enzymes do not appear to be very different from the co-enzymes which have been mentioned on pp. 263–6. Some are nucleotides containing heterocyclic ring systems, and others are porphyrins containing metallic atoms, but all will undergo well-defined oxidation-reduction reactions. Since equally characterizable oxidation-reduction reactions are often exhibited by enzymes from which it has not yet been possible to separate active prosthetic groups, it may be concluded that the essential reaction promoters in enzymes are located in discrete centres, at definable chemical radicals, and that catalytic activity is not dispersed diffusely over the enzyme protein as a whole.

† Gunsalus *et al.*, *J. Biol. Chem.* 1945, **161**, 743; Karrer and Visconti, *Helv. Chim. Acta*, 1947, **30**, 52, 525.

‡ *Biochem. Zeit.* 1932, **250**, 414.

An inspection of the chemical properties of the reaction-promoting groups in enzymes† reveals in very many cases that they can generate neutral radicals by semi-quinonoid reduction, or by a one-electron change, and thus be capable of initiating free radical chain reactions of the types postulated on pp. 269–74. This is exemplified below:

1. Flavo-proteins, pyocyanine, and allied pigments. Warburg and Christian,‡ and many other workers,§ have isolated from enzymes capable of catalysing the aerobic oxidation of α-amino acids, purines, and aldehydes a yellow prosthetic group which has proved to be phosphorylated riboflavin (compare p. 260).

Now Kuhn and Ströbele|| have shown by magnetic measurements that the reduction of riboflavin to the autoxidizable substance leuco-riboflavine proceeds in two stages, via a free neutral radical of structure (X), which contains a 'divalent nitrogen atom'. A very similar radical (XI) is formed in the first stages of the reduction of the bacterial pigment pyocyanine,¶ which seems to have a biochemical role very similar to that of the flavines.††

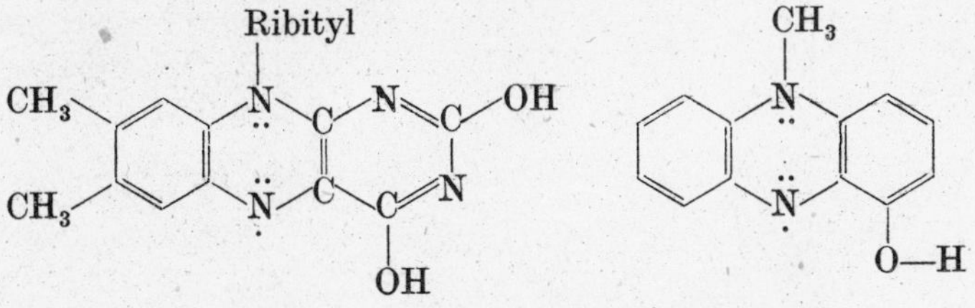

(X) (XI)

Obviously these radicals, which are closely analogous to the radical formed by the thermal dissociation of tetraphenylhydrazine (Chapter IV), can either abstract a hydrogen atom from a metabolite,

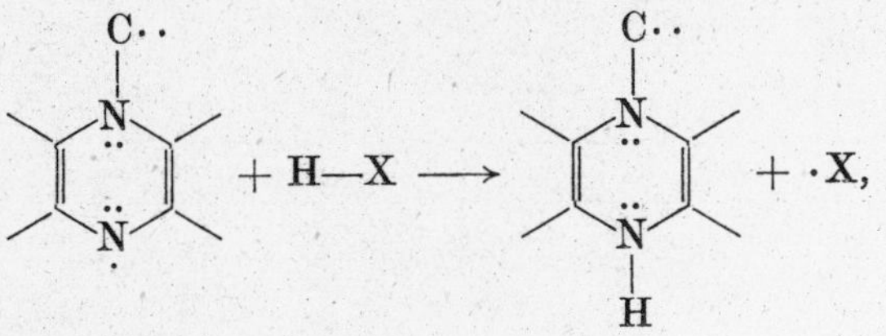

$+ H—X \longrightarrow$ $+ \cdot X,$

† Waters, *Trans. Faraday Soc.* 1943, **39**, 146.

‡ Warburg and Christian, *Biochem. Zeit.* 1932, **254**, 438; 1938, **295**, 261; 1938, **298**, 150.

§ Compare Green, *Mechanisms of Biological Oxidation*, chap. iv (Cambridge Univ. Press, 1941).

|| Kuhn and Ströbele, *Ber.* 1937, **70**, 753. Compare Lingane and Davis, *J. Biol. Chem.* 1941, **137**, 567.

¶ Kuhn and Schön, *Ber.* 1935, **68**, 1537.

†† Friedheim, *Biochem. J.* 1934, **28**, 173; Weil-Malherbe, ibid. 1937, **31**, 2080.

or lose one further electron, e.g. to oxygen, to give the cation of the flavine or phenazine in its oxidized form:

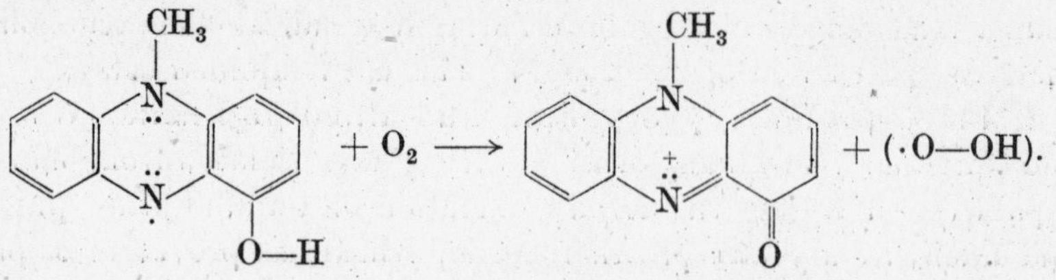

CH_3 — N ... N, O—H $+ O_2 \longrightarrow$ CH_3 — N ... $\overset{+}{N}$, O $+ (\cdot O—OH)$.

Reactions of the former type can initiate dehydrogenase action, whilst reactions of the latter type will explain the autoxidizability of the leucoflavines (p. 260) and of the dihydrophenazines.†

2. Iron and copper porphyrins. Prosthetic groups containing ferric iron are present in the enzymes catalase and peroxidase, which catalyse reactions of hydrogen peroxide. Cytochrome oxidase, which can promote the re-oxidation of reduced (i.e. ferrous) cytochromes by molecular oxygen, is again a ferric compound, whilst the enzymes which can bring about the direct aerobic oxidation of phenols contain copper as an essential component. All these porphyrin derivatives, unlike haemoglobin, but like cytochrome (p. 266), act by chemical processes which involve the reversible oxidation and reduction of the metallic atom, as postulated by Haber and Willstätter (p. 267). It is significant that traces of compounds such as carbon monoxide, hydrogen cyanide, fluorides, and azides, which can form strong non-ionizing bonds with the metallic atom, can inhibit the catalytic activity. In the resulting stable complexes unpaired electron structures are no longer present.‡

With compounds of this type, the specificity of enzyme action may be associable with the oxidation-reduction potential of the coordinated metal.. It is possible that other 'trace elements' such as manganese and cobalt may act in a similar way.

3. Thiols and disulphides. Whereas in stable proteins the element sulphur occurs either in the form of disulphide groups, R—S—S—R, as in cystine, or in stable thio-ether links, as in methionine or in the thiazole ring form of aneurin (p. 265), a number of active enzymes give positive nitroprusside reactions, and therefore must contain free thiol groups, R—S—H. The enzymes of this type can be reversibly deactivated by several mild oxidizing agents which attack the thiol links,

† McIlwain, *J.* 1937, p. 1704.

‡ Pauling *The Nature of the Chemical Bond*, pp. 115–17

and reactivated by reducing agents capable of converting disulphides to thiols;

$$2\text{R—S—H} \underset{\text{Reduction = Activation}}{\overset{\text{Oxidation = Inactivation}}{\rightleftarrows}} \text{R—S—S—R.}$$

Thus succinic dehydrogenase, which belongs to this group, can be deactivated by addition of excess of alloxan, or glutathione in its oxidized form, but reactivated by subsequent treatment with reduced glutathione.†

In view of the considerable amount of evidence which proves that free thiol radicals, R—S·, can be formed either by the dissociation of disulphides, or by the one-electron oxidation of thiols by ferric and cupric salts, it is not unlikely that these enzymes catalyse chain reactions by way of the oxidation and reduction of thiol groups to free thiol radicals in the same way as thiophenol can act as a chain carrier in autoxidation,‡ and amyl disulphide as an autoxidation catalyst (p. 257).

A sulphur-containing protein could become an active catalyst if a minute proportion only of its disulphide links could momentarily dissociate to the radical form and thereupon dehydrogenate a vicinal (i.e. an adsorbed) metabolite and start a reaction chain in biological systems, just as alkyl disulphides can initiate the dehydrogenation of tetralin:

$$\underset{inactive}{\text{R—S—S—R}} \rightleftarrows \underset{active}{2\text{R—S}\cdot}; \qquad \underset{chain\ initiation}{\text{R—S}\cdot + \text{H—X} \longrightarrow \text{R—S—H} + \cdot\text{X}.}$$

It may be significant to note that the bond energy of the S—H link,§ though less than that of the O—H link, is not very different from that of the C—H link and but little affected by electrostatic factors. Consequently a free R—S· radical might be able to effect the dehydrogenation of a C—H bond in a molecule such as succinic acid in which the resultant radical is to some extent stabilized by resonance.

Inhibition of Enzyme Action

It is a characteristic feature of enzyme catalysis that traces of compounds, such as potassium cyanide, carbon monoxide, sodium fluoride. or sodium iodoacetate have specific inhibiting properties on certain enzymes.

As preceding chapters will have shown, the retardation of chemical change, in gases, in the liquid phase, and on surfaces, is a typical feature

† Hopkins and Morgan, *Biochem. J.* 1938, **32**, 611, 1829.

‡ Ziegler and Gänicke, *Annalen*, 1942, **551**, 213.

§ Pauling gives S—H = 87 k.cals. and C—H = 87 k.cals.

of chain processes of the free radical type, and it is very significant that the identical compounds which are inhibitors of radical chain reactions are also inhibitors of enzyme processes.

Thus organic iodides are marked inhibitors of radical substitution or addition processes,† whilst iodoacetates can inhibit many enzyme processes. Substances with loosely bound hydrogen, such as malonic acid, are again inhibitors of autoxidations‡ and also of enzyme-catalysed dehydrogenase processes. These substances undoubtedly react with free organic radicals to give relatively inert products with which the chain processes cannot be continued, e.g.

$$\phi\cdot + \text{I—CH}_2\text{COOH} \longrightarrow \text{I}\cdot + \phi\text{—CH}_2\text{COOH},$$

$$\phi\cdot + \text{CH}_2(\text{COOH})_2 \longrightarrow \phi\text{—H} + \cdot\text{CH}(\text{COOH})_2.$$

Other complex organic radicals as well as many enzymes can be stabilized by reaction with sulphites, cyanides, etc. These substances combine with the organic radical to give a more complex resonance-stabilized product in which the available energy is too low for chain reaction to continue. In the same way the coordination of metallic atoms with radicals such as CO, NO_2, CN, prevents their oxidation or reduction by facile electron transfer.

† p. 184. ‡ p. 234.

INDEX OF NAMES

Abrams, J. R., 156.
Adam, N. K., 220, 222, 224.
Adams, F. H., 56.
Adams, R., 220.
Adkins, H., 192.
Agallides, E., 33.
Agar, J. N., 224.
Alexander, E. R., 191.
Allen, A. O., 104.
Allen, F. L., 31.
Allsopp, C. B., 10.
Almquist, H. J., 237, 238.
Anderson, D., 155.
Anderson, K. D., 125.
Anderson, L. C., 38.
Andreas, F., 46, 47.
Angeli, A., 153.
Angus, W. R., 26, 28, 29.
Anslow, W. P., 246.
Appleyard, M. E. S., 120.
Arbusov, A. E., 42.
Arbusov, B. A., 42.
Archer, S., 213.
Arnold, R. T., 257.
Ashworth, F., 187, 188.
Atherton, D., 241, 244.
Avery, W. A., 113.

Bach, A., 232, 267.
Bach, F., 217.
Bachmann, W. E., 42, 44, 47, 53, 153, 203, 204, 207.
Bäckström, H. L. J., 119, 132, 235, 238, 240.
Bacon, F., 37.
Bader, J., 69.
Baer, E., 230, 231, 272.
Baeyer, A. von, 3, 237, 240.
Bähr, K., 206.
Bailey, K. C., 234, 237.
Ballauf, F., 71.
Bamberger, E., 148, 153.
Bamford, C. H., 118, 120, 121, 123, 124, 125, 137.
Banfield, F. H., 70.
Barak, M., 120.
Bartlett, P. D., 166, 195.
Bates, J. R., 88, 89, 92, 93, 99, 114, 116.
Baubigny, H., 235.
Bauer, L. H., 59.
Bauer, W. H., 176, 177.
Baumann, W. C., 88.
Bawn, C. E. H., 11, 104.
Beach, J. Y., 59.
Beatty, H. A., 238.
Beckman, A. O., 114.
Beckmann, E., 203.
Bedwell, M. E., 155.
Beek, P. A. A. van der, 232, 238.
Benedict, W. S., 91, 218.
Bent, H.E., 40, 43, 50, 58, 208.
Bergel, F., 277.
Bergmann, E., 43, 119, 123, 204, 205, 238, 243.
Berthoud, A., 179, 180.
Berzelius, J. J., 1, 71.
Bigelow, H. E., 42.
Billroth, H. G., 70.
Birtwell, S., 163.
Bizette, H., 62.
Blacet, F. E., 117, 118.
Blanksma, J. J., 191.
Bleakney, W., 33, 217.
Blicke, F. F., 37.
Blomquist, A. T., 195.
Blum-Bergmann, O., 207.
Bockemüller, W., 176.
Bodenstein, M., 62.
Boehm, E., 87, 88, 90.
Boekelheide, V., 159.
Boeseken, J., 138, 169.
Böhme, H., 245.
Bohr, Niels, 5, 80.
Bolland, J. L., 246.
Bone, W. A., 5.
Bonhoeffer, K. F., 5, 81–4, 86–8, 90, 93, 112, 191, 217, 223.
Borgstrom, P., 169.
Borsum, W., 50.
Bost, R. W., 169.
Bowden, F. P., 224.
Bowden, S. T., 36–39, 46, 50.
Bowen, E. J., 49, 102, 106, 120, 132.
Boyd, T. A., 136.
Bradley, C. W., 208.
Bradshaw, B. C., 114.
Braithwaite, D., 144, 145, 172, 173.
Branch, G. E. K., 46, 237, 238.
Bray, W. C., 89.
Bredig, G., 280.
Bredig, M. A., 72.
Breyer, B., 78.
Brookman, E. F., 195.
Brown, H. C., 139, 175, 185–7, 189, 190.
Brown, R. F., 176, 177, 178, 180.
Bruce, W. F., 43.
Buchanan, G. S., 78.
Büchner, E., 158.
Buizov, 169.
Bunge, W., 68.
Bunsen, R. W., 1.
Burkhardt, G. N., 187, 188.
Burton, M., 7, 86, 94, 112, 118, 122, 124, 129, 180.
Burton, H., 67.
Byerly, W., 59, 79.

Cain, C. K., 65.
Cain, J. C., 162.
Calingaert, G., 79, 170.
Calvert, H. R., 110.
Cambi, L., 70.
Cannizzaro, S., 2.
Cario, G., 110.
Carrico, J. L., 99.
Carruthers, J. E., 132.
Chang, F. C., 141.
Chao, T. H., 175, 185, 187.
Christian, W., 264, 281.
Ciamician, G., 109.
Clapp, R. C., 140, 141, 143.
Clar, E., 48, 257.
Clarke, H. T., 207.
Claus, A., 3, 4.
Clemo, G. R., 73.
Cline, J. E., 50, 58, 114.
Coehn, A., 98.
Cohen, S. G., 195.
Collins, C. J., 257.
Conant, J. B., 42, 43, 47, 49, 52, 53, 56.
Cone, L. H., 4, 37, 49.
Conn, G. K. T., 218.
Cook, A. H., 154, 244, 269.
Cook, G. A., 89.
Cook, J. W., 219.
Cordes, H., 98.
Corse, J., 211.
Couper, A. S., 3.
Coward, H. F., 5.
Cox, F. W., 192.
Cramer, P. L., 137.
Cremer, E., 114.
Criegee, R., 228–30, 240, 246, 257.
Crumpler, C. J., 125.
Crum Brown, A., 142.
Cunneen, J. I., 189.
Cunningham, J. P., 129.
Curie, P., 29, 30.
Curry, J., 114.
Cuthbertson, A., 196.
Cuthbertson, G. R., 58.

Dainton, F. S., 125.
Dakin, H. D., 248, 267, 274.
Dalal, V. P., 62.
Danby, C. J., 130.
Daniels, F., 115, 174, 176, 177, 178, 180.

Dannley, R. L., 169.
Daudt, W. H., 140, 141, 143.
Davidson, J. B., 208.
Davis, O. L., 281.
Davis, T. W., 7, 124.
Davy, Sir H., 1.
Dawsey, L. H., 89, 113.
de la Praudière, E. L. A. E., 120.
Diamond, H., 34.
Dickinson, R. G., 99.
Diels, O., 219.
Dimroth, O., 76, 141, 227.
Dorfman, M., 43, 58.
Drikos, G., 56.
Duewell, H., 78.
Dufraisse, C., 48, 232.
Dull, M. F., 170.
Durham (Miss), D. A., 195, 196.

Eberly, K., 180, 190.
Ebers, E. S., 43.
Eley, D. D., 33, 217.
Elks, J., 155.
Eméleus, H. J., 92, 123.
Emschwiller, G., 116.
Engelmann, F., 139, 182.
Engler, C., 232, 240, 267.
Erlenmeyer, H., 166, 240.
Estermann, I., 25.
Euler, H., 264.
Euler, K., 69.
Evans, A. G., 194.
Evans, M. G., 198, 250.
Evans, M. W., 47, 56.
Evans, T. W., 181.
Evans, W. V., 144–5, 172, 173.
Evering, B. L., 128, 146.
Ewald, L., 38, 40, 44, 46, 47, 54, 233.
Eyring, H., 10.

Fajans, K. 217.
Fallwell, F., 207.
Fandrich, B., 163.
Faraday, Michael, 215.
Farkas, A., 31, 86, 87, 218.
Farkas, L., 32, 87, 90, 119, 123, 218.
Farmer, E. H., 161, 168, 240–3, 257.
Faull, R. F., 133.
Favorsky, A. E., 205.
Fay, J. W. J., 13.
Fenton, H. J. H., 247, 248, 276.
Fichter, F., 142, 143.
Field, E., 144, 145.
Fields, E. K., 212.
Fieser, L. F., 140, 141, 143, 178, 220, 230, 236, 245.
Fisher, H. L., 169.
Fletcher, C. J. M., 133, 134.
Flory, P. J., 195, 199.
Flygare, H., 240.
Forbes, G. S., 113, 114.
Forrester, G. C., 38.
Forsyth, J. S. A., 128, 134.
Foy (Mrs.), M., 191.
France, H., 149.
Franck, J., 18, 110, 120.
Franke, W., 248.
Frankenburger, W., 88, 90.
Frankland, P., 1, 2.
Frazer, J. H., 62.
Fredenhagen, H., 191.
Fressel, H., 66.
Friedheim, E. A. H., 281.
Friedman, B. S., 189.
Friess, H., 97, 98.
Frisch, R., 25.
Frister, F., 76.
Frobenius, L., 148.
Furman, N. H., 220.
Fuson, R. C., 211.
Fryling, C. F., 220.

Gänicke, K., 47, 73, 233, 283.
Garcia-Banus, A., 49.
Gardner, J. H., 37.
Garratt, A. P., 126.
Garreau, Y., 236.
Gattermann, L., 162, 163–5.
Gauger, A. W., 215.
Gay Lussac, 1.
Gedye, G. R., 114.
Gee, G., 196, 246.
Geib, K. H., 84, 86, 87, 88, 93, 114.
Gelissen, H., 138, 166, 167, 168, 169.
Gerhardt, K., 2.
Gerlach, W., 22, 24.
Giauque, W. F., 62.
Gibson, K. E., 116.
Gilman, H., 41, 162, 207, 208, 210.
Ginsberg, E., 38.
Gladstone, M. T., 139.
Glass, J. V. S., 133.
Glasstone, S., 142, 143, 222, 224.
Glazebrook, H. H., 119, 120, 139, 146.
Glückauf, E., 13.
Goldberg, W., 211.
Goldschmidt, S., 67–9, 72, 248.
Gomberg, M., 3, 10, 35, 37, 38, 42, 44, 45, 49, 50, 60, 147, 153, 204.
Goodeve, Sir C. F., 62, 111, 113, 114.
Gorin, E., 122.
Gould, A. J., 33, 217.
Gouy, L. G., 26.
Graf, W., 265.
Granick, S., 74, 75.
Green, D. E., 281.
Green, T. E., 63.
Griess, P., 157.
Grieve, W. S. M., 149, 150.
Griffiths, J. G. A., 95.
Groll, H. P. A., 100.
Grosse, A. V., 183.
Gumlich, W., 73.
Gunsalus, I. C., 280.
Gunstone, F. D., 241.

Haber, F., 112, 190, 198, 235, 248, 249, 252, 267–9, 274, 282.
Haefele, W. R., 221.
Haggerty, C. J., 145.
Hakan, B. L., 208.
Hammett, L. P., 15.
Hammick, D. Ll., 125.
Hanby, W. E., 156, 158.
Hannum, C., 183.
Hantzsch, A., 148, 153, 156, 163.
Harden, A., 263.
Haresnape, J. N., 105.
Harris, I., 172.
Hart, E., 176.
Harteck, P., 84, 86–90, 93–6, 112, 114.
Hartley, G. S., 109.
Hartmann, M., 241, 244.
Haworth, J. W., 151, 152.
Hearne, G., 100.
Hechenbleikner, I., 208.
Heene, R., 76.
Heilbron, Sir I. M., 149, 152, 154, 162.
Hein, F., 12, 144, 170.
Heitler, W., 20.
Heller, W., 105.
Henderson, J. L., 241.
Henseleit, K., 276.
Hermans, P. H., 166, 167, 168.
Herte, P., 46, 51.
Herzenstein, A., 50.
Herzfeld, K. F., 130, 133.
Herzfeld, K., 128.
Hewett, C. L., 219.
Hey, D. H., 137, 142, 149–52, 154–6, 162, 166, 182, 195, 210, 255.
Hickinbottom, J. W., 171.
Hickling, A., 142, 143, 222, 224.
Hilditch, T. P., 241, 244.
Hill, D. G., 92.
Hill, E. S., 76.
Hill, W. K., 26, 28, 29.
Himel, C. M., 51, 56.
Hinshelwood, C. N., 63, 86, 88, 130, 133–6.
Hirschfelder, J. O., 10.

Hirschlaff, E., 125.
Hirshberg, Y., 119, 123, 238.
Hobbs, J. E., 133.
Hoch, H., 123.
Hock, H., 241.
Hodgson, H., 153, 163.
Hofeditz, W., 5, 7, 127, 128.
Hofer, H., 142.
Holmberg, B., 189.
Holmes, H. H., 115.
Hopkins, Sir F. G., 266, 283.
Horn, E., 103.
Horton, A. T., 120.
Houston, B., 64.
Huber, H., 154.
Hückel, W., 194.
Hudson, C. S., 257.
Husemann, E., 195.

Ilkovič, D., 12.
Indest, H., 167.
Ingold, C. K., 67.
Ipatieff, V. N., 189, 219.
Iredale, T., 116.
Irwin, F., 170.

Jackson, E. L., 257.
Jahn, F. P., 124.
Jakob, L., 206.
James, T. H., 236.
Janke, W., 204, 205.
Jarrett, K. B., 172.
John, F., 257.
Johnson, B., 64.
Johnson, J. R., 195.
Johnson, Miss P., 162.
Johnston, H. L., 62.
Johnston, W. R., 8, 128.
Jolles, Z., 154.
Jolley, L. J., 123.
Jones, H. L., 41.
Jones, H. O., 248.
Jones, L. T., 99, 116.
Jones, S. O., 186.
Jones, W. H., 126, 130.
Jones, W. J., 39, 50.
Jorissen, W. P., 238.
Jost, W., 98.

Kalckar, H., 277.
Kamenskaya, S., 195.
Kane, S. S., 139, 190.
Kaplan, J. F., 51, 56.
Karagunis, G., 56.
Karrer, P., 264, 280.
Karstens, A., 219.
Katz, H., 67.
Kawamura, T., 43.
Keevil, N. B., 40, 43, 56.
Kehrmann, F., 236.
Keilin, D., 266.
Kekulé, A., 2, 3.
Kell, R. W., 195.
Kenyon, J., 70.
Kernbaum, M., 113.
Kharasch, M. S., 138, 139, 174, 175, 180–3, 185–91, 211–14, 221, 230, 231, 256.
Kirkbride, F. W., 116, 124.
Kirst, W., 145.
Kistiakowsky, G., 93, 94, 95, 152.
Kitchener, J. A., 111.
Kleiger, S. C., 183.
Kleiman, M., 190, 213.
Kleiner, H., 206.
Klemenc, A., 92.
Kliegl, A., 154.
Klimowa, V. A., 161.
Klingelhoefer, W. C., 97, 98.
Klinger, E., 62.
Klinkenberg, L. J., 62.
Klinkhardt, H., 88.
Kloetzel, M. C., 53.
Knoevenagel, C., 46, 47.
Koch, H. P., 242.
Koelsch, C. F., 159, 160, 171.
Kögl, F., 70.
Kolbe, H., 142.
Kolker, I., 187.
Kolthoff, I. M., 12.
Komarewsky, V., 219.
Kopsch, U., 93, 94, 96.
Korczynski, A. von, 163.
Kornfeld, G., 62.
Koton, M. M., 169, 170.
Kozeschkow, K. A., 161.
Kraft, L., 229.
Kraus, C. A., 36, 43.
Krause, E., 78.
Krauss, W., 62.
Krebs, E., 195.
Krebs, H. A., 276.
Kühling, O., 154.
Kuhn, R., 250.
Kurt, O. E., 24.
Kurz, P. F., 246.
Kvalnes, D. E., 159.
Kynch, G. J., 275.

Landé, A., 22, 24.
Langenbeck, W., 277–80.
Langevin, P., 28, 29, 30.
Langmuir, I., 85, 215.
Lapworth, A., 187.
Laurent, A., 2.
Lautsch, W., 7, 104, 146.
Lavin, G. I., 89.
Lavoisier, A. L., 1.
Lawton, S. E., 154.
Lea, D. E., 10.
Leary, R. E., 58.
Lecher, H., 73.
Lee, F. H., 144.
Leermakers, J. A., 8, 117, 118, 133, 146.
Le Fèvre, R. J. W., 155.
Lehmann, H. L., 112.
Leighton, P. A., 7, 109, 117, 118, 125.
Levi, T. G., 169.
Levy, N., 64.
Lewis, B., 89, 95, 131.
Lewis, G. N., 4.
Liebig, J. von, 237.
Lingane, J. J., 12, 281.
Linn, C. B., 183, 211.
Linnett, J. W., 126.
Linstead, R. P., 219, 220, 237.
Lipmann, F., 273.
Lips, E., 62.
Little, E. R., 208.
London, F., 20.
Long, N. O., 62.
Lu, C. S., 13.
Lucy, F. A., 109.
Lüttringhaus, A., 46.
Lu Valle, J. E., 236.

McBay, H. C., 138.
McCoy, H. N., 71.
McClure, F. T., 170.
McIlwain, H., 73, 236, 282.
McLean, M. J., 243.
MacMunn, 266.
Magee, J. L., 174.
Maier, J., 46.
Mair, L., 44.
Malaprade, L., 229, 257.
Maloney, L. S., 246.
Mann, P. J. G., 252, 268.
Mannkopf, R., 110.
Mansfield, J. Y., 180.
Marcus, E., 42.
Margolis, E. T., 174.
Mark, H., 195.
Marsden, E., 153, 163.
Marshall, A. L., 88, 90.
Marshall, I., 172.
Marvel, C. S., 27, 38, 40, 51, 53, 55, 56, 59.
May, E. M., 187.
Mayo, F. R., 174, 180–4, 187–9, 211, 221.
Medvedev, S., 195, 244.
Meerwein, H., 158.
Melville, H. W., 114, 193, 194, 306, 216, 218.
Metzger, H., 166.
Meyer, A., 167.
Meyer, K., 70.
Meyer, V., 2.
Michael, S. E., 161, 168.
Michaelis, L., 12, 74–7.
Midgley, T., 136.
Milas, N. A., 232, 246, 247.
Milsted, J., 11.
Mitchell, J. W., 63.
Mithoff, R. C., 46.
Moelwyn-Hughes, E. A., 162, 267.

Moest, M. 142.
Moll, T., 265.
Molt, E. L., 191.
Morey, G., 123.
Morgan, E. J., 189, 293.
Morikawa, K., 218.
Moore, W. C., 71.
Morris, H., 59, 79.
Morris, J. C., 87, 90.
Morrison, R., 213.
Mortensen, R. A., 7, 125.
Morton, A. A., 206–8.
Moureu, C., 48, 232.
Mrozinski, W., 163.
Müller, E., 48, 55, 60, 61, 67, 68, 76, 77, 204, 205, 209.
Müller, K. L., 176.
Mueller, M. B., 38, 51, 56.
Müller-Rodloff, I., 48, 55, 60, 68.
Murray, W. M., 220.

Nazarov, I. N., 205.
Nernst, W., 87.
Nesmejanow, A. N., 161, 162.
Neujmin, H., 93.
Newey, H. A., 208.
Nicoll, F., 162.
Noller, C. R., 211.
Norrish, R. G. W., 9, 18, 63, 89, 95, 99, 115, 116, 118, 120, 121, 124, 125, 131, 132, 137, 195.
Noyes, W. A., 176.
Nozaki, K., 166.
Nudenberg, W., 213.

Ochs, K., 36, 41.
Offenbächer, M., 69.
Orth, P., 44, 45, 47.
Osborn, G., 44.
Ostromislensky, I. I., 169.
Overhoff, J., 166.
Oxford, A. E., 140.

Paneth, F. A., 5, 7–9, 85, 104, 127, 128, 146, 150, 225.
Parlee, N. A. D., 92.
Pascal, P., 28.
Patat, F., 92, 123, 136.
Paul, B., 116.
Paul, T., 203.
Pauncz, S., 148.
Pauling, L., 57, 58, 62, 275, 282, 283.
Pearson, R., 172, 173.
Pearson, T. G., 7, 9, 85, 117, 119, 120, 124, 139, 146.
Pease, R. N., 87, 90, 99.
Pechmann, H. von, 148.
Pedlow, G. W., 257.
Penney, W. G., 275.
Pernert, J. C., 153.
Pfeuffer, L., 176.
Phipps, T. E., 24.
Piankov, V. A., 63.
Pierce, W. C., 123.
Pietsch, E., 84, 85.
Pilz, H., 240.
Ploetz, T., 167.
Podyapolskaya, A., 244.
Polanyi, M., 11, 97, 100–5, 114, 194.
Polly, O. L., 134.
Pontin, 1, 71.
Popov, B., 93.
Popper, E., 147.
Posner, T., 188.
Pray, H. A. H., 156.
Price, C. C., 178, 195, 196, 197.
Priestley, H. M., 256.
Pschorr, R., 165.
Purcell, R. H., 7, 117, 119, 124.
Purkis, C. H., 125.

Rabinowitch, E., 18, 112, 120.
Raff, R. 195.
Rank, B., 229.
Rapson, W. S., 210.
Razuvaiev, G. A., 166, 169, 170.
Read, A. T., 189.
Reid (Miss), A. T., 186, 189.
Reid, E. E., 188.
Renn, K., 68.
Ricci, J. E., 7.
Rice, F. O., 7–9, 89, 113, 120, 130, 132–4, 146, 202, 275.
Rice, K. K., 7, 9, 128, 275.
Rice, O. K., 275.
Richardson, G. M., 207.
Richter, D., 239, 263.
Rideal, E. K., 114, 196, 217–19.
Rieger, W. H., 51.
Riley, H. L., 33.
Ritsert, T., 265.
Ritter, J. J., 257.
Roberts, J. K., 215.
Robertson, A., 241, 244, 250, 254.
Robinson, P. L., 7, 85.
Rodebush, W. H., 97, 98.
Rollefson, G. K., 86, 94, 112, 133, 134, 180.
Rosen, R., 36, 43.
Rosenblum, C., 129.
Roth, K., 70.
Rowe, R. D., 118.
Roy, M. F., 27, 40, 55.
Ruff, O., 248.
Ruge, U., 279.
Rupp, E., 73.
Rust, F. F., 99, 100, 174, 181, 189, 254.
Rutherford, Lord, 80.

Sachsse, H., 90, 136
Saigh, G. S., 124.
Salley, D. J., 88.
Salt, F. W., 224.
Sandin, R. B., 170.
Sandler, L., 32.
Sandmeyer, T., 162–5.
Saracini, M., 62.
Saunders, B. C., 252, 268.
Saunders, K. H., 155, 165.
Savage, J., 155.
Sayles, D. C., 212.
Scaife, C. W., 64.
Schall, C., 145.
Schapiro, S., 166.
Schardinger, 261.
Schenck, R. T. E., 188.
Scherp, H. W., 49.
Schildknecht, C. E., 120, 132.
Schlenk, W., 11, 36, 42, 43, 44, 50, 53, 60, 203, 204, 205.
Schlubach, H. H., 71, 204.
Schmidlin, J., 42, 49.
Schmidt, W., 72.
Schnurmann, R., 25.
Schöberl, A., 265.
Schoenauer, W., 166.
Schoepfle, C. S., 41.
Schön, K., 281.
Schönberg, A., 73.
Schorlemmer, C., 2.
Schubert, M. P., 12, 74, 75, 77.
Schukri, J., 265.
Schultze, G., 92.
Schulz, G. V., 195.
Schumacher, H. J., 49, 99, 176, 185.
Schwab, G. M., 33, 97, 98.
Schwechten, H. W., 66, 67, 157.
Schweizer, H., 98.
Schweizer, R., 227.
Seefried, H., 147.
Seib, A., 46, 47.
Seiberth, M., 241, 244.
Selwood, P. W.. 34, 59, 79.
Semenoff, N., 86.
Sharpe, E. D., 257.
Shaw, G. T., 125.
Sheppard, N., 155.
Sheridan, J., 219.
Shuttleworth, R. G., 210.
Sibbald, D. D. R., 163.
Sickman, D. V., 130.
Sidgwick, N. V., 36.
Silber, P., 109.
Simamura, O.. 183.

Simmons, N. L., 114.
Simons, J. H., 170.
Smith, A. E. W., 64.
Smith, H. P., 176.
Smith, J. C., 182.
Smith, J. O., 129, 130.
Smith, R. E., 134.
Snell, J. M., 236.
Sonnenfeld, E., 220, 241.
Spence, R., 116, 120.
Spinks, A., 154.
Staudinger, H., 232.
Stauff, J., 185.
Staveley, L. A. K., 133, 134, 135.
Steacie, E. W. R., 91, 92, 93, 125, 130.
Steadman, F., 49.
Steigerwald, C., 72.
Stein, N. O., 113, 114.
Stern, O., 22, 24, 25.
Stenzl, H., 143.
Stephan (Miss), D., 116.
Stephenson, O., 155.
Stevels, J. M., 105.
Stewart, T. D., 99.
Stock, J. T., 78.
Stock, M., 265.
Stoddart, E. M., 7, 85.
Stoner, E. C., 24, 26.
Ströbele, R., 281.
Strong, W. O., 208.
Style, D. W. G., 103, 120.
Sugden, S., 13, 26, 30, 31, 70, 204.
Sullivan, F. W., 38.
Sundralingam, A., 240, 243.
Susemihl, W., 241.
Sussmann, S., 246.
Sutton, D. A., 240, 241, 242.
Swain, G., 154.
Sykes, H. J., 195.

Tafel, J., 145, 223, 224.
Takebayashi, M., 191.
Tate, B. E., 195.
Taylor, H. A., 122–4, 129.
Taylor, H. S., 10, 33, 34, 88, 91–3, 114, 121, 126, 129, 130, 217, 218.
Teller, E., 130.
Thiede, B., 216.
Thomas, D. S., 236.
Thomas, J. C., 39.
Thompson, H. W., 125–6.
Thunberg, T., 261, 262.
Tietz, E., 61.
Tietz, E. L., 132.
Tilden, Sir W., 206.
Tilman, G., 166.
Titoff, A., 234.
Titov, A. I., 63.
Todd, A. R., 154.
Töpel, T., 209.
Tooley, F. V., 220.
Traube, W., 277.
Trautz, M., 62.
Treibs, W., 247.
Trenner, N. R., 91.
Tsai, B., 62.
Turkevitch, J., 34.
Twigg, G. H., 218.

Ubbelohde, A. R., 132.
Ullmann, F., 50.
Urey, H. C., 89, 113.
Urry, W. H., 138, 139, 212, 214.
Urushibara, Y., 183, 191.

Vance, J. E., 88.
Van Emster, K., 158.
Van't Hoff, J. H., 3.
Vaughan, W. E., 99, 100, 174, 181, 189, 254.
Velluz, L., 48.
Vesterberg, A., 219.
Vielau, W., 163.
Villiger, A., 237, 240.
Vine, H., 155.
Visconti, H., 280.
Vogt, A., 72.
Volman, D., 88, 117.
Von Elbe, G., 89, 95, 131.
Von Hartel, H., 103.
Von Wartenberg, H., 92.

Wachholtz, F., 179.
Walden, P., 36.
Waldschmidt-Leitz, E., 220.
Walker, Sir James, 142.
Walker, J., 163.
Walker, O. J., 137.
Wallace, J., 63.
Walling, C., 182, 184.
Wallis, E. S., 56.
Walz, G. F., 99.
Wansbrough-Jones, O. H., 112, 235.
Warburg, O., 264, 281.
Warhurst, E., 105.
Waring, C. E., 156.
Wassermann, A., 250.
Waters, W. A., 15, 18, 137, 150, 151, 154–8, 160–2, 165, 166, 174, 181, 182, 186, 194, 195, 199, 233, 241, 244, 250, 253–7, 269, 275, 281.
Watkins, T. F., 37, 38.
Weber, H., 45, 47.
Wechsler, E. 148.
Weichselfelder, T., 216.
Weickel, T., 203.
Weidenbaum, B., 99.
Weil-Malherbe, H., 279, 281.
Weiss, J., 10, 191, 198, 249, 250, 252, 268.
Weissberger, A., 236.
Weitz, E., 66, 67, 76, 77.
Weizmann, C., 119, 123, 238.
Welge, H. J., 114.
Werner, A., 4.
West, W., 115, 116, 119.
Wetmore, O. C., 123.
Wheland, G. W., 57, 58, 150.
White, P. C., 174.
Whitmore, F. C , 257.
Whitney, A. G., 171.
Whitney, R. B., 51.
Wieland, H., 4, 45, 46, 64, 66, 67, 69, 70, 147, 148, 166, 167, 232, 239, 248, 255, 261–3, 275–7.
Wiesemann, W., 67, 77, 204, 205.
Wigner, E., 32.
Wild, G. L. E., 137.
Wild, W., 120.
Williams, G., 176, 183, 184, 194, 253.
Williams, R. R., 265.
Williamson, A. T., 88.
Willstätter, R., 190, 220, 235, 241, 248, 249, 252, 267, 269, 274, 282.
Wiselogle, F. Y., 47, 65.
Wöhler, F., 237.
Wolfenden, J. H., 215.
Wolff, K., 99.
Wood, R. W., 5, 81, 82, 89, 90, 91.
Wood, W. C., 112.
Wooster, C. B., 56, 204, 206.
Wunsch, A., 128.
Wurtz, A., 2.

Young, H. A., 241.
Young, W. J., 263.

Zaaijer, W. H., 191.
Ziegler, K., 38, 40, 41, 44–7, 51, 53–6, 59, 65, 73, 206, 233, 254, 256, 283.
Zima, O., 265.

INDEX

α-Rays, reactions due to, 10.
Acetaldehyde, photolysis of, **116–18.**
Acetate radicals, 19, **138–43,** 151, 230–1.
Acetic acid, photolysis of, 122, 123.
Acetone: photolysis of, 9, **119–21**; reaction with diazonium chlorides, 157, 162.
Acetyl choline, 231.
Acetyl phosphoric anhydride, 273.
Acetyl radical, $\cdot COCH_3$. 119–20, 272.
Acridine, radical from, 12.
Acrylonitrile, **196–8,** 200, 250.
Activated absorption, *see* Chemi-sorption.
Activated atoms and radicals, 81, 85.
Activated molecules, **106–9,** 111.
Activation energy, 8, 9, 56, 57, 59, 105.
Acylazotriphenylmethanes, decomposition of, 148.
Addition to olefines, **177–80**; stereochemistry of, 179–80; peroxide catalysed, **180–4.**
Alcohols, photolysis of, 123; oxidation of, 268.
Aldehydes, photochemical decomposition of, 9, **116–21**; autoxidation of, **237–40.**
Alkyl halides, photochemical decomposition of, 115, 254.
Alkyl radicals, **5–8**; 63, 99, 115–20, **127**ff. (chap. vii), **173**, 175, 180, 216; discovery of, **5–7**; characterization of, 7–8; gas phase reactions of, **127–31**; reactions in solution, 137 ff.
Allo-cinnamic acid, isomerization of, **178–80.**
Allyl bromide, addition to, 181, 221.
Allyl substitution, 100, 255.
Amines, photolysis of, 123, 124.
Aminium salts, 67, 72.
Amino acids: photolysis of, 123; oxidation of, **277–9.**
Amino (NH_2) radical, 114.
3-Amino-oxindole, 278, 279.
Ammonia, photochemical decomposition of, 114.
Ammonium amalgam, 1, 71.
Ammonium radicals, 71, 72.
Anaerobic oxidation, 261.
Aneurin, 264, 265, 271, 282.
Anode reactions, 12.
Anthracene, oxidation of, 238–9.
'Anti-knock' effects, 136.
Anti-oxidants, 180, 184, 187, 197, 234, 236, 237.
Antimony mirror, 6, 8, 11, 104, 119, 122, 127.
Arc spectra, 81.
Aryl radicals, **146 ff.** (ch. viii).
Arylation, **166–8.**
Arylazotriarylmethanes, decomposition of, 147–8.
1-Aryl-3: 3-dimethyltriazens, 155.
Ascaridole, 182, 243, 244.
Asymmetric synthesis, 280.
Atomic bromine, 13, 87, 90, 112, 113, 174, 175, **177–9,** 182, 183, 256.
Atomic chlorine, 5, 13, 16, 18, 19, 87, **97–100,** 102, 161, 175, 176, 180, **185–7**; preparation, 97; reactions with hydrogen, 97–8; with carbon monoxide, 98; with paraffins, 98–9; with olefines, 99–100.
Atomic hydrogen, 5, **8–10** 16, 24, 33, **80–93,** 95, 110, 113, 114, 122, 123, **128–30,** 167, 191, 193, **215–17, 223–6,** 237, 269, 274, 275, 281; production of, 81–2, 84; use in welding, 85; reactions of, **82–93**; with halogens 87–8; with oxygen, 88–9; with carbon monoxide, 89–90; with carbon dioxide, 89–90; with nitric oxide, 90; with inorganic hydrides, 90–1; with hydrocarbons, **91–3.**
Atomic iodine, 3, 18, 89, **111–13,** 116, 284.
Atomic magnetism, **21–5.**
Atomic oxygen, 5, 24, 25, 63, **93–7,** 115, 131, 216; preparation, 93; reactions of, 93; with hydrogen, 95; with hydrides, 96–7.
Atomic silver, 23.
Atomic sodium, 2, 11, 24, **100–5,** 201, 203, 207; reactions with halogens, **100–3**; with halides, **103–5.**
Auto-catalysis, 232.
Autoxidation, 48, 132, **232–45,** 258, 260, 261, 267, **281–4**; of sulphites, **234–6**; of aldehydes, **237–40**; of olefines, **240–5.**
Azobenzene, *cis-trans* isomerization of, 109.
Azomethane, 8, 124, 130, 146.

Bart-Schmidt reaction, 164.
Beer's law, 65, 68, 73.
Benzaldehyde, autoxidation of, 232, **237–40.**
Benzene diazo-acetate, **148–52,** 160, 166.
Benzene hexachloride, 176.
Benzenediazonium chloride, decomposition of, **156–62**; reactions with radicals, 161–2.
Benzoate radical, 166, 168, 195, 272.
Benzoquinone, reaction with triphenylmethyl, 49.
Benzoyl radical, 238–9.
Benzoylazotriphenylmethane, decomposition of, 148.
Benzyl ethers, radicals from, 171.
Benzyl radical, 7, 58, 104, 146, 160, 171, 172, 175.
Biaryls, synthesis of, **148–55, 166–7.**
Binschedler's green, 74.
Biochemical oxidation, 14, 259ff. (ch. xii).
Biological acetylation, 272.
Bi-radicals, 11, 60, 61, 76, 229, 233.

Bismuth aryls, synthesis of, 162.
Bisulphite radical ($\cdot SO_3$; $\cdot SO_3H$), 188.
Bisulphites, addition to olefines, 187–8.
Bohr magneton, (μ_B), 22, 24, 25, 30, 32, 33.
Bond energy, 9.
Bornyl radical, 212.
Boron trifluoride (as catalyst), 194, 199.
Branched chain reactions, 136.
N-Bromo-benzenesulphonamides, 256.
α-Bromobenzyl cyanide, 253, 254.
α-Bromo-ketones, 254.
N-Bromo-succinimide, 254–6.
Budde effect, 113.
Buna-S, 200; Buna-N, 200.
Butadiene, 206.
tert-Butyl hydroperoxide, 246.
Butyl radical, 7.

Cacodyl, 1.
'Cage' effect = primary recombination, 18, 120, 121.
Cannizzaro reaction, **190–2**, 238, 262, 268.
Canonical states, 70, 75.
Carbohydrates, oxidation of, 257.
Carboxyl radical (COOH), 251.
Carboxylase, 271.
Carboxylate radicals, 196, 197.
Carboxylation: with oxalyl chloride, 189–90; with diphosgene, 189–90.
Carboxylic acids: photolysis of, 122–3; chlorination and sulphonation of, 186–7.
Caro's acid, 235, 245.
Catalase, 249, 261.
Catalysis by radicals, 13, 14, **174 ff.** (ch. ix).
Cathode reactions, 11, 12, 145.
Chain length, measurement of, 135, 136.
Chain reactions, 10, 13, **16–19**, 44, 46–8, 63, **86–8**, 95, **98–100**, 116, **132–6**, 192, 206, 209, **233–6.**
Charcoal, surface catalysis by, 33.
Chemi-luminescence, 234.
Chemi-sorption, 33, 202, **215–21.**
Chlorine cation, 253.
Chlorine dioxide, 31.
N-Chloro-amides, 157, 254, 256.
9-Chloro-10-hydroxy-phenanthrene, radical from, 72.
Chloroprene, 193, 198, 250.
Chromic acid, 227; oxidation by, **256–8.**
Cinnamic acid, photo-bromination of, **177–80.**
Claisen rearrangement, 171.
Cobalt chloride, catalysis by, 212–14.
Co-carboxylase, 264, 265, 271, 279.
COCl radicals, 98, 189–90.
Co-decarboxylase, 280.
Co-enzyme I, 263, 264, 265, 270.
Co-enzyme II, 264, 270.
Co-enzymes, **263–6**, **269–71**, 275.
Co-polymerization, 200.
Copper, reactions of (Ullmann), 120.
Copper as catalyst, 171, 172, 215, 219, 220.
Copper chromite, as catalyst, 220.
Copper salt catalysis, 158, 160, **162–5**, **234–6**, 241, 266, 282.
Covalent bond energies, 275.
Cozymase, 263, 264.
'Crossed' polarity, 199–200.
Cuprene, 93, 131.
Cyanogen radical, 1, 81, 96.
Cyclization of paraffins, 219.
Cyclo-hexene, reactions of, 161, 168, 186, 228, 240, 243, 255.
Cyclo-hexyl radical, 212.
Cytochrome oxidase, 266, 282.
Cytochromes, 266, 274, 282.

Decarboxylation, 279.
Dehydrogenases, **267–74**, 283, 284.
Dehydrogenation, 219, 220, 233, **256–8**; Wieland's theory of, 261–3.
Deuterium, exchange with hydrogen, 33, 86–7, 217–18; interchange with methane and ethane, 91–2.
Diacetyl peroxide, 120, **138–41**, 148, 231.
Diacyl peroxides, radical decomposition of, 138–41.
Dialkyl-diaryl-hydrazines, dissociation of, 66.
Diamagnetism, 26, 28, 29, 60, 61, 74, 77, 79, 204, 205.
Di-*p*-anisyl nitric oxide, 70.
Diaryls, synthesis of, 165, 166, 210, 212.
Diaroyl peroxides, decomposition of, 165–6.
Diazo-acetates, **148–52**, 158 ff., 195, 196.
Diazo-cyanides, 155–6, 172.
Diazo-hydroxides, **152–5**, 162, 165, 195, 196.
Diazomethane, 49, 124.
Diazonium chlorides, 125, 156–62.
Diazotype printing, 125.
Dibenzoyl peroxide, 13, 138, 139, **165–9**, 175, 182, **185–7**, 190, 191, 194, 195, 197, 233, 241.
Dielectric constant, 15, 16.
Diels reaction, 141, 243.
Diphenyl, resonance stability of, 59; Biradicals derived from, 61.
Diphenyl-disulphide, 72, 73.
Diphenyl-ethylene, dimerization of, 205, 206; autoxidation of, 232 ff.
Diphenyl iodonium iodide, 170–1.
Diphenyl nitric oxide, 69–70.
Diphenyl-nitrogen, 63–5.
Diphenylnitrosamine, dissociation of, 65.
αα-Diphenyl-β-picryl-hydrazyl, 34.
αα-Diphenyl-β-trinitrophenyl-hydrazyl radical, 68–9.
Diphenyls, syntheses of, 147, **148–52**, **153–5**, 166–7, 172, 207, 212.
Dipole moments, 15, 16, 253.
Dipyridyls, 76–7.
Discharge tube reactions, 5, 9, 10.
Disproportionation, **50–2**, 55, 66, 121, **129–31**, 137, 172, 173, 188, **207–9**, 212, 213, 273.
Dissociation constant, of hexaphenylethane, etc., **54–6.**
Disulphides, radicals from, 72, 73; as oxidizers, 257; in enzymes, 266, 282, 283.

Divalent nitrogen, 281.
Drying oils, autoxidation of, 241, 242.
Duroquinone radical, 74.

Electrical discharges in gases, 80–1, 85, 86, 93, 97.
Electrical dissociation of molecules, 9–10, **80–5.**
Electrical polarization, 15.
Electrode reactions, 11, 12, **221–5**; *see* Cathode reactions, *also* Anode reactions.
Electrolysis, 172–3, 201, 202, **221–5**; of acids, 142–3; of Grignard reagents, 144–5.
Electron momentum, 20.
Electron spin, 21.
d Electrons, 63, 171.
s, p, σ, and π Electrons, 21.
Electrostatic energy (of bonds), 15, 16.
Emulsion polymerization, 197–8.
'Energetic coupling', 276–7.
Enzymes, **259–63**, **266–84.**
Epi-oxides, **243–5**, 250.
Ethane, reactions with atomic hydrogen and deuterium, 91, 92.
Ethers: thermal decomposition of, **133–6**; reactions with radicals, 144, 145, 157.
Ethyl radicals, 2, 7, 85, 99, 100, 119, 129, 130, **136–8**, 144.
Ethylene: atomic reactions of, 92, 99–100; 253; surface reactions of, 218–19.
Exchange energy, 20, 21.

Fenton's reagent, **247–52**, 268, 271.
Ferric salt catalysis, 249, 250, 252, **266–8.**
Ferromagnetism, 30.
Ferrous salt catalysis, 233, 239, 244, **249–52**, 268, 271.
Flame spectra, 96.
Flavoproteins, 260, 261, 266, 281.
Fluorescence, 106, 109, 110.
Formic acid: photolysis of, 122; oxidation of, 251.
Formyl radical, 118.
Fraunhofer effect, 103.
Friedel-Crafts reaction, 194, 195.

Gattermann reaction, **162–5**, 172.
Germanium, radicals from, 78.
Germanium hydride, 85.
Glutathione, 266.
Glycols, fission of, **228–30**, 275, 276.
Gomberg reaction, 153–4.
Graphite, structure of, 33.
Grignard reagents, 41–2, 144, 145, 172, 173, 202, 209, **211–14**, 255; electrolysis of, 144–5, 172–3; abnormal reactions of, **211–14.**
Guard mirror technique, 7, 8, 122.

Haematin, 33.
Haemoglobin, 48, **259–61**, 282.
Halogen addition to triphenylmethyl, 43–4; to olefines, **176–80.**
Halogen substitution, 174–6.
Halogens, photo-dissociation of, 112–13.
Head-to-tail polymerization, 193, 194, 198–9.
Heterolysis, 14–16, 227, 253.
Hexaphenylethane, 3, 35, 36, **42–7**, 50, **52–60**, 65, 174, 205, 233.
Hexaphenylethane analogues: ionic dissociation of, 35–6; radical dissociation of, **42–7**; degree of dissociation, 53–6; activation energy of dissociation, 56–9; heat of dissociation, 54–6.
Hexaphenyl-tetrazane, dissociation of, 68.
Hexoestrol (dimethyl ether), synthesis of, 213.
'Highly attenuated flames', 100–3.
Homolysis, **14–16**, 192, 205, 227, 253, 267.
Hydrazinium salts, 66, 67.
Hydrazyl radicals, 67–9.
Hydrogen bromide, addition to olefines, **180–4**, 221.
Hydrogen iodide, addition to olefines, 184.
Hydrogen peroxide, photo-dissociation of, 113; reactions of, 197, 198, **244–52**, 260, 266, 274.
Hydrogen spectrum, 5, 80, 82.
Hydrogen sulphide, photo-dissociation of, 113–14; addition to olefines, 189.
Hydroperoxide radical (HOO·), 88.
Hydroperoxides, **240–5.**
α-Hydroxy acids, oxidation of, 251.
Hydroxyl radical, 10, 19, 81, 88, 95, 96, 113, 122, 131, 132, 143, 245, 246, **249–52**, 272, 274, 275. [256.
Hypochlorous acid, oxidation by, 252, 253.
Hyponitrites, decomposition of, 172.

Induced oxidation, 234, 235, 238, 239.
Induced polar fields, 253.
Induction period, 193, 237.
Inhibition of reactions, 17, 18, **134–6**, 185, 197, 234, 235, 237, 239, 283, 284.
Iodides, oxidation of, 252, 253.
Iodoacetic acid, 283, 284.
Iodonium salts, decomposition of, 170–1.
Irreversible electrodes, 222–4.
Isatin and Isatide, 277–9.
Isoprene, 49, 198, 206.

Ketones, photochemical decomposition of, 9, 137 ff.
α-Ketonic acids, oxidation of, 230–1.
Kolbe reaction, 142–3.

Lactic acid, oxidation of, 261, **269–71.**
Landé factor $= g$, 22, 24.
Langmuir's atomic hydrogen torch, 85.
Lauth's violet, 74.
Lead alkyls, 78, 136, 225; synthesis of, 161.
Lead hydride, 85.
Lead mirror, **6–8**, 85, 119, 122, 127.
Lead tetra-acetate, reactions of, 141–2, **227–32**, 275.
Lead tetra-ethyl, 7, 99, 100, 137, 138, 174.
Lead tetra-methyl, 5, 6, 125, 127, 128, 130.

Leuco flavoprotein, 261, 266.
Leuco methylene blue, 261.
Leuco riboflavin, 260, 281.
Lithium, reactions of, 206, 208, 209.
Lithium alkyls and aryls, 206, 208, 209.
'Lucite', 192.

Magnetic moments, **20–5.**
Magnetic quantum number (= m), 22.
Magnetic susceptibility, 4, **25–31**, **54–6**, 60, 74, measurement of, **26–8.**
Markownikow's rule, 181, 188.
Meerwein-Pondorff reduction, 192.
Mercury diaryls, thermal decomposition of, 169.
Mercury dimethyl, photolysis of, 125, 126, 129; thermal decomposition of, 130.
Mercury hydride, 84.
Mercury sensitization, 85, 88, 91, 110.
Mesomerism, *see* Resonance.
Metabolism, 259, 263.
Metabolites, 259, 260, 261, 263, 264, 270, 271, 277.
Metallic alkyls, 144, 205, 206.
Metallic ketyls, 11, 145, 192, **203–6.**
Methyl cation, (CH_3^+), 10.
Methyl methacrylate, 193, 196, 206.
Methyl radical, 2, 5–9, 11, 16, 18, 33, 85, 103, 104, **119–24**, 126, **127 ff.** (ch. vii), 201, 202, 207, 213; average life of, 127–8; reactions with hydrocarbons, 129–31; reactions in solution, 137, **139–45.**
Methylene blue, 261–2, 266, 277.
Methylene radical, 49, 104, 124, 131.
α-Methylenic substitution, 100, 161, 168, 199, **241–3**, **255–7.**
Michael reaction, 194.
Mirror technique, **6–11.**
'Model enzymes', **277–80.**
Molecular rearrangement of radicals, 213.
Molecular (magnetic) susceptibility (χ_m), 25–31.
Moloxides, 229, 232.

N—N link: activation energy, 65; heat of dissociation, 69.
Nature of biological oxidation, **259–61**, ch. xii.
Nature of covalent bond fission, **14–16.**
Neoprene, 193.
Net electron spin (= S), 30.
Neutrons, 13.
Nicotinamide, 78, 264, 266, 269.
Nickel, surface catalysis on, 33, **215–21**, 225.
Nitric oxide, 3, 25, 31, 32, **44–7**, 62, 63, 65, **68–70**, 72, 90, 96, 114, 125, 126, **134–6.**
Nitrobenzene, methylation of, 140–1.
o-Nitrobenzaldehyde, photochemical rearrangement of, 109.
Nitrogen dianisyl, 59.
Nitrogen peroxide (NO_2), 31, 32, 44, 45, 63, 64, 69, 70, 95, 114, 115, 131.
Nitrogen tetroxide (N_2O_4), 63, 64.
Nitrogen trioxide (NO_3) radical, 95.
Nitroso-acetanilide, *see* Benzene diazoacetate.
Nitrosoacyl-arylamines, *see* Diazo-acetates.
Nitrosamines, photolysis of, 125.
Nitrosyl cation and anion, 62; coordination compounds, 63.
Non-polar addition, 159–60.
Non-polar substitution, 150, 153, 154.
Nuclear spin, 20, 25, 31.

Odd electrons, 4, 5, 16, 57, 62, 63, **69–71**, 130, 134, 197, 198, 201, 204, 205, 233, 235, 242.
Olefines: chain polymerization of, 92, 130–1, **192–200**, 250; addition of hydrogen bromide to, **180–4**; of bisulphites to, 187–8; of thiols to, 188–9; hydrogenation of, **218–20**; oxidation of, 229, **240–5**; polymerization of, 250.
One electron change, 251.
·OOH radical, 249.
Oppenauer oxidation, 192.
Organo-metallic compounds: photolysis of, 125–6; electrolysis of, 144–5, 172–3; synthesis of, 161–2; radical decomposition of, **169–79.**
Organo-metallic radicals, 78–9.
Ortho- and *para*-hydrogen, 25, **31–3**, 86, 87, 116, 119, 129, 136, 217–18.
Ortho effect, in hexaphenylethane dissociation, 59, 60.
Osmium (metal) as catalyst, 220, 241.
Osmium tetroxide, 246–7.
Overpotential, **222–5.**
Oxalyl chloride, carboxylating agent, 189–90.
Oxidation, **226 ff.** (ch. xi); biochemical, **259 ff.** (ch. xii); vapour phase, 131, 132, 136; surface, 220–1.
Oxidation level, 226, 227.
Oxidation–reduction potential, 164, 220, 262, 282.
Oxygen, free radicals containing, 72–3.
Oxygen (molecular): magnetic moment of, 25; reactions of, **45–9**, **176–8**, **259–61**; *see also* Autoxidation.
Oxy-rubrene, 48.
Ozone, 93–5.
Ozonides, 232.
Ozonolysis, 255.

Palladium, as surface catalyst, 216, 217, 219, 220, 225.
Paraffins; chlorination of, **174–6**, 185–7; substitution by thiols, 180.
Paramagnetic compounds (Table III), 31.
Paramagnetism, 4, 21, **26–32**, 48, **60–3**, **68–70**, 74, 79, 204.
Pentaphenylethane, 47.
Pentaphenyl chromium salts, 170.
Pentaphenylethyl radical, 59.
Per-acids, oxidation with, **245–7.**
Perbenzoic acid, 182, 232, **237–40**, 245.

Periodic acid, 229, 257, 275.
Peroxidases, 261, 268, 275.
Peroxide-catalysed, reactions, ch. ix, 180 ff.; 198.
Peroxide formation, *see* Autoxidation.
Peroxide radicals, **46–8**, 132, **138–43**, 182, 184, 185, 191, 233, 246.
Perphthalic acid, 245.
Perspex, 14, 192.
Phenazines, radicals from, 12, 74, 281.
Phenyl radical, 7, 104, 119, 137, 138, **146–73**, (ch. viii), 180, 195, 207, 209, 210, **212–14.**
Phenylazotriphenylmethane, decomposition of, 147.
β-Phenylethyl radical, 212, 213.
Phenyl-pyridines, 152, 154, 166.
Phosgene, synthesis of, 98.
Phosphorescence, 106.
Phosphorylation, 272, 273, 277.
Photochemical, decomposition, 9, 18, **49–52**; 93, 97, **106 ff.** (ch. vi), 137.
Photochemical reactions, **174–81**, 189, 190.
Photographic developers, 236.
Photosensitization, 88, 91, **109–11**, 115.
Phthalocyanine (copper), surface catalysis by, 33.
Platinum, surface catalysis on, 33, 217, 219, 225, 259, 262.
'Plexiglas', 192.
Poisoning: of enzymes, 259, 282, 284; of haemoglobin 260 ff.; *see also* Inhibitors.
Polarization, 202, 222–4.
Polarography, 12, 73, 78, 192.
Polymerization, 14, 92, 93, 118, 119, 126, 130, 131, 137, 168, 169, **192–200**, 206, 209, 219, 234, 242, 250.
Polystyrene, 14, 193, 195, 196, 198, 200, 206, 250.
Polythene, 131.
Polyvinyl chloride, 200.
Porphyrins 266, 280, 282; *see also* Cytochrome, Haemoglobin.
'Positive' halogens, **252–6.**
Potassium permanganate, oxidation by, 227, 256, 258.
Potential-energy curves, 107–8.
Potential mediators, 236.
Potentiometric titration, 77–8.
Pre-dissociation, 108, 111.
Propyl radical, 7, 119.
'Prosthetic groups', 274, **280–3.**
'Primary recombination', 18, 120, 121.
Pschorr reaction, 165.
Pyridoxal phosphate, 280.
Pyocyanine, 74, 281.
Pyrogallol, as chain breaker, 46–8.
Pyruvate radicals, 272.

Quantum theory, **20–2**, 80, 82.
Quinhydrones, 12, **73–78**, 252.
Quinol, oxidation of, 252.
Quinoline, radical from, 12.
Quinones, reactions of, 73, 140, 141, 159, 236, 248, 257, 268.
Quinonoid radicals, 11, 12, 60, 61.

'*R* states', 48.
Radical-catalysed reactions, 13, 14; *see* chapters ix, xi, xii.
Radical-ions, 4.
Radioactive bromine, 13.
Radiotherapy, 10.
Radium-D, 7, 125.
Reaction constant (*PZ*), 56, 57, 59, 105, 157.
Redistribution reactions, 79, 170.
Reduction potential, 12.
Resonance, 5, 20, 21, **36–8**, **57–61**, 64, **70–6**, 140, 146, 160, 171, 172, 190, 196, 205, 231, 233, 234, 274, 283, 284.
Riboflavin, 260, 266, 281.
Rubber: oxidation of, 240; synthetic, 197, 200, 206.
Rubrene, 48–9, 243.

Sandmeyer reaction, 160, **162–5**, 172.
Selenium dehydrogenation, 219, 257.
Semi-quinones, **73–8**, 203, 234, 236, 281.
Silent electrical discharges, 81, 82, 86, 93.
Silver hydride, 85.
Single electron transfer, 163–5, 171.
Single electrons, *see* Odd electrons.
$\cdot SO_2Cl$ radical, 185–7.
$\cdot SO_5$ radical, 235.
Sodium ethyl, electrolysis of, 12.
Sodium metal, reactions of, 203–10; *see also* Atomic sodium.
Sodium phenyl, 43, 207.
Solvent regeneration of radicals, 18, 19, 139, 231, 232.
Space quantization, 22.
Spark spectra, 81.
Spectrographic analysis, 80, 81, 88, 93, 97, 132, 266.
Spectroscopic states, 21, 24, 25.
Spin quantum numbers (*s*), 20, 21, 22.
Stereo-chemistry of free radicals, 139, 175, 179, 274.
Sterols, oxidation of, 255.
Subsidiary quantum numbers ($= l$), 20–2.
Succinic acid, oxidation of, 261, 266, 268, 273, 274.
Sugars, oxidation of, 229, 248, 277.
Sulphite radical ($\cdot SO_3$), 112, 235, 236.
Sulphites, autoxidation, 234–6.
Sulphonation, with sulphuryl chloride, 186–7.
Sulphur compounds, univalent free, 72–3.
Sulphuryl chloride, 175, **185–7.**
Surface catalysis, **214–21**, 224, 225.
Surface hydrides, 216.

Tellurium mirror, 7, 8, 11, 104, 117, 119, 124, 134.
Tetralin, 258; autoxidation of, 241; dehydrogenation of, 283.
Tetralyl radical, 258.
Tetraphenyl diarsine, 78.
Tetraphenyldimethylethane, disproportionation of, 51–2.
Tetraphenyl-hydrazine, **64–7**, 281.
Tetraphenylmethane, 41, 59.

Tetra-*p*-tolyl-hydrazine, 66, 67.
Tetrazanes, 68, 69.
Thermal decomposition, catalysis, and anti-catalysis of, **132–6.**
Thioacetic acid, addition to olefines, 189.
Thiol radicals, 183, 188, 189, 236, 271, 272, 282, 283.
Thiols, addition to olefines, 73, 188, 189; substitution of paraffins by, 180; substitution of quinones by, 236; in enzyme systems, 266, 282–3.
Three-body collisions, 5, 86, 89, 90, 94, 121.
Three-electron bonds, 62, 63.
Tin aryls, synthesis of, 161; radicals from, 7, 78, 169–70.
Tin hydride, 85, 225.
Toluene, nitration of, 63; bromination of, 174–5; chlorination of, 185–6.
Trace elements, 282.
Trans-metallation, 207–8.
Tri-*p*-bromophenylmethyl, 37.
Tri-*p*-fluorophenylmethyl, 37, 38.
Trimethylene radical, 11, 104.
Triphenyl hydrazyl radical, 68.
Triphenylmethane, 41, 43, 49, 50.
Triphenylmethane dyes, radicals from, 42.
Triphenylmethyl, 3, 4, 5, 11, 18, 27, 33, **35–60** (ch. iii), **63–5, 68–70,** 72, 73, 147, 148, 167, 203, 204, 208, 233.
Triphenylmethyl anion, 42–3.
Triphenylmethyl cation, 36–8, 43.
Triphenylmethyl fluoride, 37–8.
Triphenylmethyl hydroperoxide, 46.
Triphenylmethyl iodide, 44.
Triphenylmethyl peroxide, **45–8,** 73; radical, 46–8.
Triphenylmethyl radical: mesomerism of, **35–8,** 41, **57–9**; preparation of, **38–42**; stability of, **57–60**; reactions of, **42–52.**
Tri-*p*-tolylamine, aminium salts from, 67.
Tri-*p*-tolylmethyl, disproportionation of, 51.
Truxillic and truxinic acids, 180.
Tungsten, atomic films on, 215, 217.

Ullmann's reactions, 171–2, 210.
Unpaired electrons, *see* Odd electrons.
Urea, biosynthesis of, 276.

Vanadium pentoxide, catalyst of oxidation, 246, 247.
Vapour-phase chlorination, 99–100.
Vibrational energy of molecules, 106–8.
Vinyl acetate, polymerization of, 196, 200.
Viologens, 76–7.
Vitamin B1, *see* Aneurin.
Vitamin B2, *see* Riboflavin.
Vulcanization, 168–9.

Walden inversion, 92, 175.
Wieland's dehydrogenation theory, 261–3, 275.
Wurster's salts, 75–7.
Wurtz-Fittig reaction, 201, **207–10,** 211.

X-rays, reactions due to, 10.
Xanthyl radicals, 41, 47.

PRINTED IN
GREAT BRITAIN
AT THE
UNIVERSITY PRESS
OXFORD
BY
CHARLES BATEY
PRINTER
TO THE
UNIVERSITY

Date Due

OCT 9 '74			
OCT 17 '74			